NEVER GIVE A
SUCKER AN EVEN
BREAK

NEVER GIVE A SUCKER AN EVEN BREAK

Tricks and Bets You Can't Lose

by John Fisher

PANTHEON BOOKS, NEW YORK

For my nephew, James

First American Edition

Copyright © 1976 by John Fisher

All rights reserved under International and Pan-American Copyright Conventions. Published in the United States by Pantheon Books, a division of Random House, Inc., New York, and simultaneously in Canada by Random House of Canada Limited, Toronto. Originally published in Great Britain by Elm Tree Books/Hamish Hamilton Ltd., London.

Library of Congress Cataloging in Publication Data

Fisher, John, 1945-
   Never Give a Sucker an Even Break.

   1. Cardsharping. I. Title.
GV1247.F57 1976   795   76-50097
ISBN 0-394-73330-4

Manufactured in the United States of America

Dialogue from the following W. C. Fields films is quoted with the permission of Universal City Studios, Inc.:

Million Dollar Legs (1932)
International House (1933)
Tillie and Gus (1933)
The Old Fashioned Way (1934)
It's a Gift (1934)
You're Telling Me (1934)
Mississippi (1935)
The Man on the Flying Trapeze (1935)
Poppy (1936)
Big Broadcast of 1938 (1938)
You Can't Cheat an Honest Man (1939)
My Little Chickadee (1940)
The Bank Dick (1940)
Never Give a Sucker an Even Break (1941)

Contents

Introduction

Ever since Satan beguiled Adam and Eve with his apple trick, charlatans, knaves and confidence tricksters have flourished. None, however, could have been more brazen in his fraud than Meriton Latroon, the hero of an anonymous picaresque novel, *English Rogue*, who flourished in the mid-seventeenth century. Whenever his thirst needed slaking he would saunter into an inn, take a scrap of paper and jot down the following poem:

I saw a peacock with a fiery tail
I saw a blazing star that dropped down hail
I saw a cloud begirt with ivy round
I saw a sturdy oak creep on the ground
I saw a pismire swallow up a whale
I saw a brackish sea brim full of ale
I saw a Venice-glass sixteen yards deep
I saw a well full of men's tears that weep
I saw men's eyes all on a flaming fire
I saw a house big as the moon and higher
I saw the sun all red even at midnight
I saw the man that saw this dreadful sight

Upon completion, he would proceed to bet the price of a tankard that he had in fact set eyes upon these additional Wonders of the World. The bet made, the money collected, he would then, for the first time, recite the couplets, reading in the punctuation he had craftily omitted in writing. And no one now could dispute what he said: "I saw a peacock. With a fiery tail, I saw a blazing star. That dropped down hail, I saw a cloud. Begirt with ivy round, I saw a sturdy oak." He had no need to continue to convince his victim that all was lost and ensure that soon his own tankard would be as brim-full of ale as the Venice-glass in the doggerel itself.

Latroon is only one of a whole covey of cozeners who have, through the ages, capitalised upon the shortcomings of a general public so gullible that it is prepared to bet on almost anything. In recent times no one has turned this

7

failing to greater personal advantage than the scandalous octogenarian Alvin Clarence Thomas, or "Titanic Thompson", to use his nickname. Last heard of alive and well and living in Grapevine, Texas, he has brought the art of cozenage to a degree of Machiavellian ingenuity worthy of the greatest spies, politicians, and stage illusionists. When he was only eleven he bet a stranger that the very stone he threw into a fishing hole would be retrieved by his dog after only one plunge into the water. The sucker agreed, provided that the stone be identifiable in some way. He watched as the young "Titanic" obliged by marking the pebble. What he did not see, however, were the countless other stones the boy had been marking painstakingly in a similar fashion for days before he pulled the ruse. Doubtless, somewhere in Arkansas, they still rest at the bottom of that pond. It would have been hard for *any* dog not to have retrieved a winning pebble.

As he grew up, so the delight to be gained from discomfiting financially those unwary enough to be bilked, informed his whole way of life. The lengths he would go to became legendary. It was nothing for him to pull up a road sign twenty miles outside a town and then re-position it five miles nearer. When he next drove that way with a likely victim he'd swear that it couldn't be twenty miles into town. The gambler would pick up the gauntlet, confident that the highways department was beyond reproach. Of course, his pockets were considerably lighter when they did reach their destination. Sly stage management of this kind behind the scenes of a bet once led him to tether eight white horses at random crossroads passed by the train connecting New York's Pennsylvania Station and the Jamaica racetrack. He then boarded the locomotive himself and subtly inveigled a whole crowd of major league horse betters into jeopardising their cash on the number of pure white steeds they would spot on their journey. Only Titanic dared "guess" high. Working for Titanic Thompson was a haughty boastfulness ingrained in his character which encouraged the most level-headed of men to attempt to outsmart him at his own game. But in trying to teach him a lesson, they were of course playing straight into his hands, flies to his spider in no uncertain way.

The braggadocio was a trait which he shared with the one name which overshadows all others in any rogues' gallery of petty fraud, the great W. C. Fields, whose philosophy gives this volume its title, a philosophy acquired during an adolescent apprenticeship when – if his biographers are to be believed – scarcely a day went by when he was not bilked by some unscrupulous manager, agent, or partner. How much he lived up to it in real life is still a matter of conjecture, possibly because people insist upon looking in the wrong places. Paranoiac at the thought of being taken for a sucker himself, he seldom gambled, and then only on pool and golf, where his own keen manipulative ability gave him a decided advantage and the element of chance was minimised as a result. But even if each round of golf was approached with the psychology of the shell-game operator, one would do better to look at his negotiations with the film companies whose vast corporate sums were as red rag to the bull of his instinct for survival. It gave him immense satisfaction to rail a studio for servicing him with a script which he would promptly dismiss as being full of holes, whereupon he would offer to straighten it out for 15,000 dollars. The rate which he could thus command for a couple of sentences scrawled upon the back of an envelope or a cryptic mark or two on the pages of the original, made him a veritable Picasso of the storyline. The ultimate con, of course, was that, whatever the script, he usually only said what he wanted to say anyway.

In the films themselves, however, there is no debate. For most people the most memorable moments are those which crystallise the image of Fields the charlatan, whether peering suspiciously from behind a fan of five aces, manipulating paper money as he deftly shortchanges the box-office queue, or making the little pea skedaddle invisibly from one walnut shell to another. It does not matter that his bluff would frequently be called. In images like these his whole demeanour spells out fakery in the way Astaire spells out class. And while enhanced by the background of carnival sideshow, sleazy saloon and seedy county fair, he never needed the geographical advantage. One recalls the moment he enlists ventriloquism as a confederate and sells a "talking dog" to yet another sucker. The deal completed, the hound looks at its new owner and, by courtesy of the Fields larynx, declares, "Just for that, I'll never talk again." Fields gets the last laugh as he scampers away from the scene of the transaction prophesying: "Stubborn little fellow, he probably means it, too."

The psychology that makes such ruses work in the first place is not far removed from that called into play by the professional magician. While W.C. would have abhorred the respectability such a label would have given his crafty shenanigans, and been apprehensive of the risk of exposure it courted, there is no doubt that with his flair for showmanship he would have made a great one. Bob Howard, his one time trainer and confidant, quoted by Robert Lewis Taylor, Fields's first and best biographer, once said: "When things were going smoothly, Bill was unhappy. He had to have somebody or something to pit his wits against." But the parallel with the likes of Harbin, Henning and Kaps suggested by that last sentence does not end there. As a juggler – he had, in his own words, a "fatal facility for juggling things" – he could beat the Chinese at their own game. But this went beyond his distrust of Orientals. Without question, he possessed the manipulative dexterity and poise needed in addition to the itch to deceive essential for all great hocus-pocus. So naturally did this come to him that once when he fell down stairs he did not spill one single drop of the martini in the glass in his hand at the time. Sprawled across the bottom step, he lifted it triumphantly: "Look! Not a drop spilled!" That he had broken the base of his spine faded into insignificance beside what was to him the highpoint of his juggling achievement.

One of the greatest and saddest ironies of his entire career is that at the height of his fame he refused an offer of $5000 a day from MGM to play the title role in *The Wizard of Oz*. The reason he gave was pressure of work in writing another film at the same time. One is tempted, however, to surmise that in no way was the patron saint of every knave who ever played upon the ignorance of those forever seeking the elusive pot of gold at the end of an imaginary rainbow, ever going to give substance to their dreams, even if for pot of gold it meant substituting the less desirable courage of a lion, heart of a tin man and brains of a scarecrow.

All of the gambits or "stings" in this book are in the spirit of Fields, most have long since been appropriated by the magical entertainer. As such they can still puzzle, infuriate and deceive, are still capable of winning a near-to-innocent drink at a bar. If the book has one purpose it is to entertain. Studied carefully, however, it can still educate one to the wiles and psychology of the major league swindlers and bunco-men. At the risk of sounding too much like those moralistic treatises by reformed gamblers that proliferated in the 1880s, not one person in the world is totally proof against the ingenuity of the most

10

unscrupulous confidence-trickster. Perhaps none gave wiser advice than the gambler quoted by the hero of Damon Runyon's *Guys and Dolls*:

"Son, no matter how far you travel, or how smart you get, always remember this: someday, somewhere, a guy is going to come to you and show you a nice brand new deck of cards on which the seal is not yet broken, and this guy is going to offer to bet you that the Jack of Spades will jump out of this deck and squirt cider in your ear. But, son, do not bet this man, for as sure as you do, you are going to get an ear full of cider."

In short, never play another man's game or, if you must, make sure that you have done sufficient research to be capable of beating him on his own ground. The actor Thomas Mitchell had a favourite story which told of the visit he paid his friend born William Claude Dukenfield shortly before his death at the age of sixty-six on Christmas Day, 1946. Mitchell got the surprise of his life when he saw Fields, propped up in the sanatorium bed, out of all character thumbing through a copy of the Bible. "What are you doing?" Mitchell enquired. One can hear the reply that came from that velvety nasal drawl even now: "Looking for loopholes." Certainly, if anyone was going to find them, it was the comedy genius and magician-by-proxy whose spirit this book celebrates.

Drawing by Al Hirschfeld from the book *A Flask of Fields*.

Shameless Simplicity

In which the trickster challenges the victim to perform facile-sounding feats, both prosaic and bizarre, which prove themselves impossible upon the attempt.

Samson

"I can lick my weight in wildflowers."

Pick your prey and direct him to hold an ordinary wooden safety match between the fingers of one hand in such a way that it lies across the back of the middle finger, near the tip, and below the index and third fingers. The illustration shows the exact position. Emphasise that he must keep his fingers straight throughout, then challenge him to break the match.

However hard he presses upwards with the middle finger or downwards with the other two, he will amazingly not succeed. The reason is that the fingers lack certain muscles which we take for granted in other parts of the body, like the wrist, more conventionally used for breaking things.

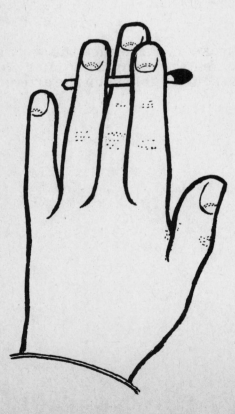

Should the challenge rebound on you, simply hold the match as shown, and keeping your arm and fingers straight, swiftly smack your hand down flat on the table top. That way you can break the match. With practice you can show off by breaking two or even three matches with this method all at the same time.

Molasses

"Molasses – the spreadingest stuff I ever saw in m'life."

Here is another seemingly simple proposition which will prove tantalising to anyone who attempts it without knowledge of the secret which makes it possible. Bet your victim that he cannot set light to a sugar cube with a match so that it burns with a flame. When he tries, he will produce only a brown treacly mess. Taking the cube from him, you ask him to light a match for you. When *you* apply it to the sugar, however, the cube bursts into flame.

What the sucker does not know is that the sugar catches fire only because you have managed, under the misdirection provided by his striking your match, to attach a very small quantity of cigarette ash to the cube. The ash – vegetable carbon – acts as a catalyst, the presence of which causes the sugar to catch fire. Provided that you do have an ashtray that is in use on hand when presenting the item, it is the work of a second to dip the sticky part of the cube into the ash for a small speck to adhere, thus winning the day for yourself once again.

Glacier

"Suffering sciatica – water!"

From hot cubes to cold ones! Present your dupe of the moment with an ice cube afloat in a glass of water and a short length of string; then wager that he will not be able to remove the ice cube from the glass with the string without tying any knots. He can try as much as he likes, but he will not succeed, not even by placing the string beneath the cube and attempting to balance it precariously.

When he finally gives in, take the string, soak it in the water, and then double it into a loop at the centre. Place the loop onto the ice cube and pour salt over them both. Wait a while and you will then be able to lift the ice cube with the string which will have become frozen to it. What actually happens is that the salt causes the ice to melt. Stop pouring the salt, however, and the water that results on the top of the cube will refreeze, but this time with the string embedded in it.

Meniscus

"My best friend died of drinking too much water. His was a case of internal drowning."

You show a glass of water, full almost to the brim, and a cork. You challenge your victim to float the cork on the surface of the water *without* letting it touch the glass. He tries, but whenever he thinks he is on the verge of success, the cork inexorably drifts to one side to bounce against the rim.

It is possible, however, to fulfil your conditions, even if you do cheat slightly. From another glass continue to fill the original one carefully until the surface of the water – or meniscus – is as high as possible without spilling, literally raised convex-fashion a fraction above the rim of the glass. Now float the cork. This time it would move to the centre of its own accord, even if you did not place it there. Of greater importance, however, is the fact that once it is there, it stays there, drawn irresistibly to the point where the water is highest.

Tipsy

On discovering his hip-flask unstoppered on its side:
"Somebody left the cork out of my lunch."

This mock-juggling ruse would have gladdened the heart (or should it be nose?), of the great W.C., whose own instinctive sense of equilibrium was, as we have seen, never impaired by alcoholic uncertainty.

Take the cork from the previous swindle and offer to pay for the next round if the victim can balance it edge to edge on the rim of a bottle full of liquid, and then using only one hand pour a drink from the same bottle without disturbing the balance of the cork. He would have to be a skilled juggler merely to balance the cork in the first place, let alone to embellish the feat by pouring a glass.

The secret is pretty sneaky. Take two forks and stick them into the cork as shown, the prongs almost interlocking. Just ensure, if the cork is not straight-sided, that the handles point downwards away from the wider end of the cork which should be at the top of the arrangement. The cork should now balance quite easily on the rim of the bottle for the scientific reason that the addition of the cutlery shifts the centre of gravity of the entire structure directly below the actual point of balance. Pouring from the bottle will alter the angle of the bottle itself, but will not disturb the cork which will remain perpendicular, as long as you pour from the side of the rim opposite to the point of balance. You will not be able to empty the bottle, but you should be able to pour at least half of the contents without spoiling your success.

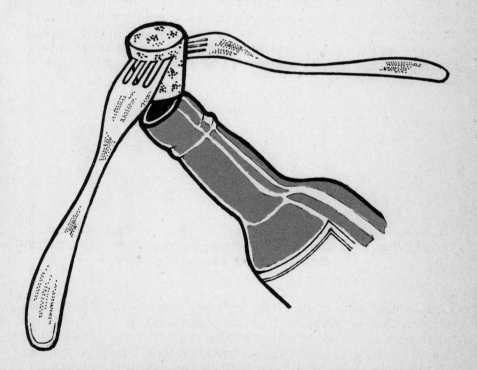

Obviously, practise with caution the first few times. You will soon develop an uncanny knack for handling the props and find that the challenge almost works itself for you.

Mixture

W.C.:   *Bring me a drink.*
Waiter: *Water, sir?*
W.C.:   *A little on the side – very little.*

Still at the bar, find two small jigger glasses, one of which you fill to the brim with whisky, the other with water. Take a visiting card or playing card and place it over the mouth of the glass of water, carefully inverting this and placing both card and glass on top of the glass of whisky. Make sure that the rim of the top glass is in exact alignment with that of the lower. Challenge someone that you can now make the water and whisky change places without altering the positions of the glasses in any way.

Merely pull out the card a fraction of an inch to allow air to enter, leaving a gap between the glasses which allows the liquids supposedly to mix. In fact, that is what they do not do. Gradually the water and whisky will transpose, not through magic, but because of the greater specific gravity of the water.

Cocktail

On awakening to find a full-grown goat in bed beside him: "Right then and there I swore that I would never again poison my system with a maraschino cherry."

The literature of baffledom is overloaded with puzzles which involve the moving of matches. While most of them have become hackneyed over the years, such stunts, ideal for the bar, have caused so many small sums to change hands that this volume would be incomplete without at least one. Moreover, it was not difficult to decide which variation on the theme would have held most attraction for Fields.

Place four matches to form a Martini glass as shown, adding a small coin to denote a cherry. The object is to move two matches in such a way that the cherry will end up outside the glass. You must not move the cherry. The glass must stay the same shape.

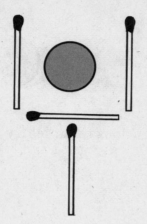

You can, if you wish, mislead the victim upon whom you spring the puzzle by suggesting some solutions that don't quite fit. You could, for example, move matches C and D but that would only turn the glass upside down and technically the cherry would still be inside.

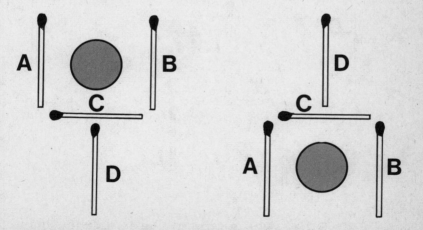

Alternatively, you could make the adjustments depicted in the next illustration, thus achieving your end, but having to move *three* matches, C, D, and A, to do so.

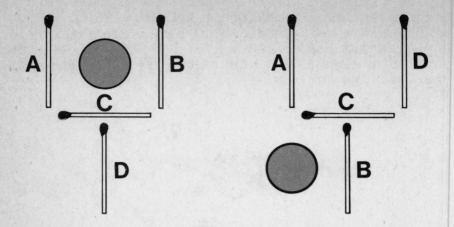

The actual solution does technically require two moves; the catch resides in the fact that they could be interpreted as one and a half.

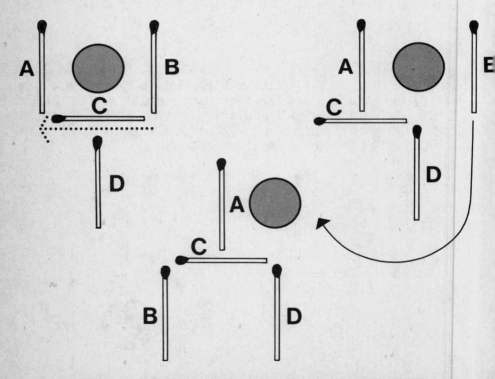

First slide C half-way along to the left. Then bring B down to the end of C, as shown. Now the cherry should be out on its own, the way, no doubt, Fields would have wished!

Exchequer

Disgruntled Man: You're a fraud, a charlatan, and a rogue.
               sir!
      W.C.: Ahhh – is that in my favour?

For originality and effect this occupies the same high position in the hierarchy of coin-sliding problems as the last item holds in the realm of match-moving. You have to arrange ten copper and ten silver coins alternately in four rows of five coins, as shown. The coins should be as near equal in size as possible. British five pence and two pence pieces are ideal.

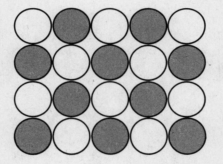

The wager is to arrange the coins into segregated horizontal rows of copper and silver coins. But there is one condition: you can touch only two coins. That's all you say. In actual fact, while you may touch only two, there is nothing to stop you moving more. Extend your right index and second fingers and put them on coins A and B respectively.

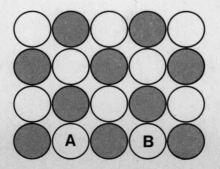

Then, sliding both coins against the table surface, swing them up and around until they occupy these positions:

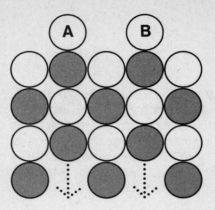

Then slide them down in the direction of the arrows, each one pushing three coins ahead of it. The coins should then arrive in the stipulated position.

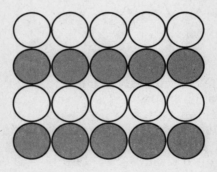

Pick-up

"Me dishonest? Meishack, Shadrack and Abednego!"

You arrange nine coins in three rows of three to make a square. You contribute five or more of the coins yourself; the rest must be contributed by your innocent gull. You then offer him a chance of pocketing both yours and his if he can pick up all nine coins in four continuous straight lines. There is only one stipulation. Each line must start at the end of the previous one. Should he fail, you pocket the coins.

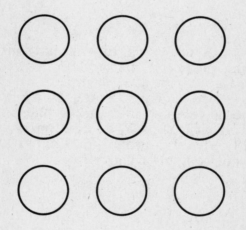

Try as he may, it is not possible to gather the nine in anything less than five lines, *unless* he knows the secret stratagem. The catch is in the wording, which says nothing about extending imaginary lines beyond the coins. The sucker will assume – wrongly – that each line must end on a coin. This is how you prove him wrong:

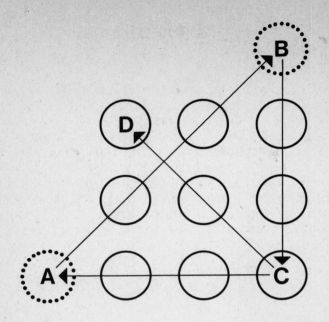

Pick up the three coins in the bottom row in the direction of the arrow, counting "one" as you arrive at A. Proceed from A as shown, picking up the intervening coins and counting "two" as you reach B. Then bend south, picking up the two coins remaining on the right-hand side, and coming to rest, "three", at C. Finally, complete the operation on the final diagonal, ending with "four" at D. And don't forget to pocket the coins.

Hazard

"A man who over-indulges lives in a dream. He becomes conceited. He thinks the whole world revolves around him—and it usually does."

Equip yourself, if possible, with a dice cup or failing that a straight-sided tumbler. Hold the cup, as shown, with a die – a lump of sugar would do – between thumb and forefinger. Balance a second die on top of the first. The challenge is to toss the first die up into the cup, and then to repeat the process with the second, ending with two dice in the cup. It sounds easy, until one tries.

Most people have no difficulty catching the first die, but as soon as they set the second on its upward course, the first flies out. There is a secret, of course. Instead of tossing the second die up into the air like the first one, you hold your hand high, release the die and then suddenly lower the cup to catch it on the downward swing. Don't descend too fast or else the first die will fly out again; just fast enough so that the cup comes beneath the falling die before it reaches the floor.

Untouchable

W.C.:   *Was I in here last night and did I spend a twenty dollar bill?*
Barman: *Yeh!*
W.C.:   *Oh, boy! What a load that is off my mind! I thought I'd lost it.*

The sucker will really think you are out of your mind on this one. You display a crisp, unwrinkled treasury note or bill and explain that when you drop it, his task is to catch it before it falls to the floor. If he succeeds he can pocket the note; if he fails he must pay you ten pence for the attempt. You demonstrate on yourself and it all appears so simple, but whenever the sucker tries, he will be attempting the impossible.

The secret is all a matter of fingers and thumbs. You must hold the note between the finger and thumb at one end, the length of the note pointing downwards; your victim must position his own finger and thumb on either side of the note at the centre, as close as he can get to the paper without actually touching it. In fact you give him every opportunity to place his hand in what would appear to be the most ideal position for grasping it.

Explain again that the object is for him to catch the note when you drop it. When you do release it, however, it will slip right through his fingers before he has had a chance to register his senses. The newer and therefore the flatter your note is, the more impossible it becomes for it to be caught. Just make sure that each time you release the money, you do so suddenly, as a surprise, without giving him the briefest moment of advance warning in which to anticipate your actions. The reason why you can catch the note yourself – when you drop it – is because your own brain is in possession of all the facts needed to synchronise the grab with the release.

Never Play Cards with Strangers

In which the charlatan is introduced to the peculiar properties of the pasteboards when entrusted to digits as dextrous and devious as his own.

Second-deal

To Mae West: Do you play cards? I'll show you a few card tricks. Show you the first one or two for nothing. Then if you wish to make a wager. . . .

S. W. Erdnase, author of *The Expert at the Card Table*, the classic work on gambling technique with playing cards, wrote: "To become an adept at second dealing is as difficult a task as can be given in card handling, but once acquired, like many other arts, it is as easy as habit." If you wish to master this most impressive of sleights, Erdnase's book is where you should look first. If, though, you lack the patience to persist with the genuine gambit until it becomes a habit, the following will prove an admirable routine for simulating the function of the sleight, without at all detracting from the stunned look on the face of the onlooker.

Before the demonstration you will need to make a secret arrangement of cards at the top of the pack. Working face-down from the top place any three jacks, then an indifferent card, then the fourth jack. Begin by casually false shuffling and/or cutting the cards. (See the Appendix for simple methods.) Explain briefly what a second or even third deal is supposed to achieve, namely the secret retention of respectively one or two cards on top of the deck as the card beneath is dealt onto the table. Deal out two hands of three cards to the sucker and yourself. When you deal the sixth card, don't place it down; merely use it to scoop up your other two cards and place all three face-down on top of the pack. Turn over the spectator's hand. It reveals three jacks.

You now explain that by putting those cards back on top of the pack, you can, through using the second and third deals, immediately deal three jacks into that same hand again. Put them back on top of the pack and again deal two hands, scooping yours back again to the top of the pack with the sixth card. Again, turn over the spectator's cards. Again, he gets three jacks. Provided that you deal and pick up the cards at a steady momentum, no one should notice that one of the jacks has changed its suit. It will be assumed that they are the same three cards. At no point, of course, mention the suits of the jacks. As long as you always scoop your hand back as described, thus reinstating the original set-up, you can carry on the demonstration virtually *ad infinitum*. However, three or four times is about enough. Don't go on so long that people begin to suspect that your "recoil" of the top card is not so much "invisible" as non-existent!

Casework

W.C.: *Would you like to engage in a little game of cut – high card wins?*
Gambler: *What stakes?*
W.C.: *Make it easy on yourself.*
Gambler: *A hundred dollars, gold.*
W.C.: *I'll cover that. I'm travelling a little light. The country is fraught with marauders. I'll give you my personal IOU, a thing I seldom give to strangers.*

The ability to memorise cards in and out of sequence is an important weapon in the armoury of the card-sharper. Obviously if one can remember which cards have been played and exposed during the course of a game, one will have an edge over the opponent who just lets them pass by. The technical term here is "casing the deck". The following demonstration, while requiring some memory work of the very simplest order, could win for you the reputation of having developed this ability to super-human dimensions.

Have someone shuffle the pack. Take it and spread the cards face-up on the table. Mention the gambler's ability to memorise the order of complete packs, while you survey the cards as if you were doing just that. In fact, you only remember the top card, say the seven of hearts. Gather the pack and place it face-down on the table. Ask the victim to cut off a packet of cards and place them away from you. Now issue your challenge; namely that by looking at the top card of one heap, you can always assess the card at the top of the other. Openly peek at the value of the top card of the nearer (originally bottom) half, (say the two of clubs), and without showing it replace it saying, "The card on this pile tells me that the card on the far pile is the seven of hearts." He turns it over. It is! Complete the cut, (thus putting the two of clubs at the top of the pack), and have someone cut the cards again. Once more you look at the top card of the bottom pile, replace it and state your case, "The card on this pile tells me that the card on the far pile is the two of clubs."

And so it goes on indefinitely. You're getting all the information you need for the divination right under their noses, but the sheer audacity of the system provides its own misdirection. If anything, you'll be accused of using a marked deck! And that's another story.

Aces

W.C.: *Don't show it to me. The cards are a gentleman's game. I don't want to look at it.*
Gambler: *(cutting to a card) King!*
W.C.: *Oh! (Then cutting his card – a two!) Ace!*
Gambler: *I didn't see it!*
W.C.: *(Fumbling through the pack) Well, well, here you are – here you are, Nosy Parker – ace! I hope that satisfies your morbid curiosity.*

Another legendary demonstration of the card-sharper's expertise is his ability to cut instinctively to the four aces in a shuffled pack. When practised by the high-powered gambler it most probably entails sheer twenty-four carat skill. Alternatively, it could be a simple exercise in hanky-panky like the one that follows.

The feat will naturally be more impressive with a borrowed pack, which you will have to gimmick in a surprising fashion. Politely take your leave of whatever company you are in and pay a supposedly natural visit to the bathroom. No one must know at this point that in your pocket is a pack, the newer the better, which you have secretly waylaid from your host. You need one other thing, a pair of nail-clippers, which you should carry with you. Lock the door behind you and get to work. Take the aces and with the clippers trim a slight crescent from each of their top right and lower left face-up corners. Make the cuts clean and round, and then shuffle the cards back into the pack. If when you now riffle the outer left edge of the face-down pack, you cannot instantly detect the cards, it will be necessary to make the cuts deeper.

Later when you come to demonstrate your skills, produce the pack as one provided by your host. Run through it and take out the four aces. Hand the rest of the pack out for shuffling, then ask the person holding the pack to take any ace and to lose it in the pack. The three other aces are each lost in a similar fashion. Finally the cards are handed back to you. It is now a simple matter merely to riffle the outer left corner of the face-down pack and cut at the desired cards. A slight break in the action will automatically identify an ace for you. Repeat with the other three aces as dramatically as possible while still retaining some vestige of credibility!

If you wish to make the experiment appear even more impressive, you could trim the red and black aces in opposing corners, as shown in the illustration. You would then have no difficulty in cutting to the aces in the order of colours called out by the spectator.

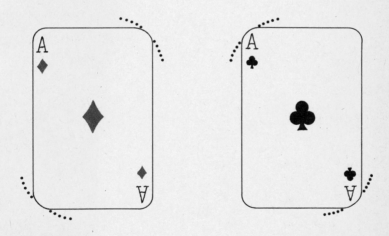

Circus

"Never give a sucker an even break. Why? Most people have a feeling they are going to be reincarnated and come back to this life. Not me. I know I'm going through here only once."

The following swindle has long been known affectionately as the Circus card trick, in recognition of the frequency with which it once appeared alongside the walnut shells and "find-the-lady" in the repertoires of mountebanks who attached themselves to circuses on tour.

Offer the pack for shuffling. Take it back, fan the cards, and have one chosen and noted. While the victim shows his card to the other people in the audience, you are stealthily remembering the card at the bottom of the pack in your hands. This will be your key card. Have the chosen card replaced on top and the cards cut several times, making sure that his card is lost somewhere in the centre of the pack.

Taking the cards yourself you now announce that you will – surprise, surprise – attempt to find his chosen card. You deal the cards singly from the top of the face-down pack into a face-up pile. Keep dealing until you come to your key card. The next card dealt will be the selected one, the identity of which you must remember. Then deal four or five cards more. Take the next card, hesitate and deal it face-down separately onto the table. Now bet the victim that the next card you turn over will be his chosen card. He will have noticed that you missed his card about half-a-dozen ago and will gladly accept the bet, whereupon you do not turn over the face-down card, but go back to the face-up pile, find his card, and turn that over *face-down!*

Shill

W.C.: *During the night, I was awakened. A thief had broken*
      into my tent and tried to roll me for my poke.
Son: *Roll you for your poke – what kind of talk is that?*
W.C.: *He tried to steal my pocketbook, son.*

So far I have deliberately avoided swindles which depend
for their chicanery on the use of a confederate or "shill",
the technical term applied in gambling circles to the
employee of the sideshow or gambling house who bets his
master's money under pretence of being a legitimate
player in order to stimulate extra business. In the following, however, a shill is used in a special way. You can, of
course, appoint him in secret beforehand and divide the
profits between yourselves afterwards. What sets the game
apart, however, is that you can also present it as a
demonstration, openly nominating a spectator to play the
part of the shill. While he'll find himself winning some of
the time, he will still end up as puzzled as the sucker
himself as to why the sucker should lose *all* of the time.

Discard the jokers from the pack beforehand and arrange
the rest of the cards so that the colours are alternated
throughout, namely red, black, red, black, and so on. In the
performance you cut the cards into two halves ensuring
that the bottom card of one half is red, of the other half
black. Now riffle shuffle these halves together. If you can
trust his proficiency with the deck, you can even allow the
sucker to do this for you. He may also cut the cards a few
times as long as he completes the cut each time. Take the
pack from him and deal the cards into four face-down piles
of thirteen cards each.

So far everything must appear transparently fair, but
what neither sucker nor shill will be aware of is the curious
relationship that exists between the first two piles dealt
(we'll call them A and B) and again between the second two
piles (C and D). For every red card in pile A, the card in the
corresponding position in B will be black. Similarly, for
every black card in A, the corresponding card in B will be
red. The same applies to C and D. Deal the cards simultaneously from the tops of two related piles, and you'll deal
red and black pairs each time. None of this you reveal to
the audience.

The sucker is now invited to take a pile. If he chooses A you discard B or vice versa. Then nominate another spectator as your shill and let him take one of the remaining heaps, C or D. You take the last heap. Another example: if the sucker chooses D, C would be discarded, and the shill and yourself would be left with A and B.

At last we come to the object of the game! The three of you are to deal face-up one at a time, together, cards from the top of your pile. Each time the party with the odd-coloured card wins. Thus, if two people turn up red cards, and one a black, the one with the black wins. If you all turn up the same colour (which you can't) then it's a draw. You now proceed with the turning. Not once in his whole sequence of thirteen cards will the sucker win! The reason is easy to deduce. The shill and yourself will always deal a red-black pair between you because you have specially related piles. This means that whenever the sucker deals a red, whichever of you has a black *must* win. Likewise, whenever he deals a black, the one with the red *must* win. The sucker must lose every time. He may even shuffle his cards before he deals, but in no way can he deal a winning card. Think about it. It works!

Kentucky

"Don't forget – Lady Godiva put everything she had on a horse."

If you discard from a full pack of fifty-two cards one heart, one club and one spade, and then deal the remaining forty-nine cards into four piles determined by their suits, you will find, upon exhausting the pack, that one pile, namely the diamond one, will contain one card more than the other piles. That should be obvious. In the early fifties, however, a magician called Tony Koynini, flagrantly defying the obvious, used this knowledge as the basis of a simulated horse-race game in which the operator wins every time. His routine, entitled "Derby", was full of subtleties – enough to throw anyone familiar with the basic principle

36

off the scent – which it would be unethical to disclose here. The following, however, presents the basic bones of the game in simplified form.

In addition to a pack of cards, you will also need sixteen matches and some coins. The matches are arranged in two parallel lines and represent sections of the track along which the horses, the four aces, will race. A move of an ace/horse is determined by dealing a card of the corresponding suit from the top of the pack. Thus the idea of numbers of cards in a pile is subtly translated into one of moves along a track. If the cards of one suit outnumber those of the other three, it can be contrived that the ace/horse of that suit will reach the finishing line, as represented by the last match, first.

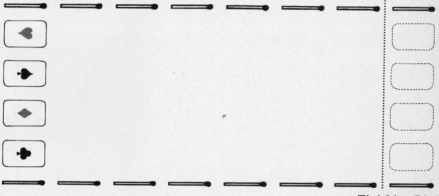

Starting Post

Finishing Line

Since you are not going to exhaust a full pack of forty-nine cards (i.e. fifty-two minus three), you will need to stack the cards first. Make a pile containing in any order any six hearts, six clubs, six diamonds and six spades, but excluding the four aces. Place these cards face-down on top of the remaining cards. Then insert the four aces throughout the bottom half of the pack, ensuring that each face-down ace is above a card of a matching suit. This is all the preparation needed.

When ready to play bring out the pack and have your three opponents each nominate an ace/horse for themselves in turn. As they call them out, you remove them in turn from the face-up pack placing each card as shown at the starting post. You emphasise their absolutely free choice in this respect and that they have left you – without any choice – with the fourth ace. With the cards facing you, fan through them and remove this last ace, say the ace of clubs. In doing so, however, you have to add to the top of the pack an additional card of that suit (here a club) from the bottom part of the deck. This is facilitated by the fact that because of the set-up immediately below the ace as it faces you is just such a card. As you fan through, push the two cards into alignment, and casually break the pack above the ace, taking the ace itself and all the cards beneath it away in the right hand. Then transfer the double card to the back of the pack, immediately returning the rest of the cards in the right hand to the face of the deck. Square up the cards in the hands, and flip the pack over face-down in the left hand, whereupon you deal the ace face-up into the starting position left nearest you.

The situation is now that amongst the top twenty-five cards of the face-down pack, the clubs outnumber the other suits by one card. You could if you wished start playing immediately. It is better, though, to have the cards shuffled at this point. Either false shuffle (see Appendix), or, more impressively, thumb off the top twenty-five cards to one contestant, and divide the rest of the pack between the other two. A slight pencil dot in the top left and bottom right-hand corner of the twenty-fifth or twenty-sixth card will enable you to fan off the correct number without counting. Just make sure that you gather the cards back in the proper order, namely with the larger packet of twenty-five on top. False cut (again, see Appendix), and hand the cards to another party ready for dealing, not however until you have all placed your bets on your ace/horse. The idea is that whoever wins, collects all.

Now the dealing begins. Whenever a spade is dealt from the top of the pack, the ace of spades moves forward one space as marked by a match. Likewise, the other cards. You will *always* reach the finishing line first in spite of what must appear the most impossible conditions.

Jonah

"Boys, this mummy sitting over here inveigled me into a game of chance entitled . . . draw poker. I figured right from the start I'd have to shoot him. It was all I could do to take his money!"

This could be the most astonishing poker challenge of them all. When presented well, it appears as if the operator has absolutely no control over the cards, that the outcome of events is entirely in the hands of the sucker himself. This is as far removed from the truth as Fields himself was from taking holy orders.

Remove from the pack three sets of three of a kind plus one indifferent card, say three aces, three kings, three queens and a jack. The jack is the "Jonah" card, and the secret upon which your prosperity depends. However the cards are dealt between you and your victim, you will always win, provided that the odd Jonah card ends up in *his* hand.

There are several ways of ensuring that this happens. Have the three trios on the top of the face-down pack, the Jonah in the tenth position. Casually thumb off in batches the top nine cards, without counting them out loud. Hand them to the victim for shuffling. Let him now replace them on the pack and deal two hands of five cards. He'll get the Jonah!

If the Jonah card is secretly marked on its back – with gradual use all cards acquire identifying marks, nicks and scratches of some kind – you can play draw poker. Have him shuffle the ten cards and spread them face-down on the table. Both players must now draw cards alternately until each has a hand of five. Just make sure you don't pick up the Jonah card. If you draw first, there is no way he can avoid getting it; if he hasn't taken it beforehand, just make sure that it's the last card he picks up. If he draws first, the odds are still highly in your favour that the Jonah will not be the last card on the table, the only card you *would have* to take. Should this happen, what is one small loss amonst so many gains?

For another variation, have him shuffle and cut the ten. Take them back and fan them slightly, noting whether the Jonah is at an odd or even position from the top. If odd, deal two hands yourself. If even, stress that he did all the mixing himself and hand them back for him to deal. You haven't done anything to the cards except touch them, so he should have no suspicions. Still he gets the Jonah.

Finally, assemble the ten cards with the Jonah at the top. Shuffle the packet, keeping it at the top if you can do so casually and convincingly. Start to deal, the Jonah to the sucker, the next to yourself, then pause as if having a bright idea. To make it even fairer for the victim you will show him the cards as they are dealt, stud poker fashion, and he can keep or reject them accordingly. Whichever four he chooses to complete his hand, it is a foregone conclusion that he is going to lose anyhow.

If you doubt the invincibility of the hand without the Jonah, consider this. Should the sucker get a pair (say two aces), you will beat him with two pairs (two queens and two kings). Should he get two pairs (say two aces and two kings), you'll beat him with three of a kind (three queens). Should he get three of a kind (say, three kings), you'll amaze him with three of a kind (say, three queens), *and* a pair (two aces), thus making a full house!

Martini

"Shades of Bacchus!"

If any gaffed deal ought to have appealed to the great W.C. it was this one, admirably suited as it is to being performed in what passes as a typically Fieldsian alcoholic haze.

You will need a pack with a one-way backs design, the term used to describe cards with backs so designed that some distinguishing mark will differentiate one end of a card from the other. Pictorial backs lend themselves most easily to the idea. Imagine a pack with a dog motif, not that Fields could! Place the cards all the same way with the picture right way up. Have one chosen, secretly reverse the pack end for end, and then offer the pack for the return of the card. If you now look at the backs of the cards you can instantly detect the chosen card. It's the one that is upside-down.

Ideally borrow such a pack and secretly set all the backs one way with the exception of the spades, which go in the opposite direction. You can now demonstrate how Fields would have dealt the cards in one of his more inebriated moments. Shuffle the cards as impressively as you can, making sure that you do not disturb the end for end arrangement. Act the part of the supposedly befuddled charlatan as well as you can, and deal cards haphazardly – in no regular rotation to north, east, south or west – into four hands in any sequence. At least that is how it appears. In actual fact, you contrive to deal the thirteen cards with reversed backs into your own hand and to make sure that each other hand also gets thirteen. Everyone turns over their cards and, such are the powers of alcohol, it's the drunk who gets the grand slam!

Automatic

On being coerced into playing a game:
W.C.:   *Poker? Is that the game where one receives five cards? And if there's two alike that's pretty good, but if there's three alike, that's much better?*
Gambler: *Oh, you'll learn the game in no time.*

Most audiences will be as aware of the device of stacking cards in a pre-arranged sequence whereby they will arrive in the right hands as they are of marked cards and second-dealing. Here, however, you allow the *spectators* to arrange the cards in the sequence *they* desire and prove that beyond all the odds the cards will come out as *you* want them to.

First take the twenty high cards from the pack, the aces, kings, queens, jacks and tens. The spectators nominate amongst themselves three of their number to play. They are each asked in turn to suggest a combination of five cards from the twenty, disregarding the suits at this stage. As the various hands are called, you lay them face-up on the table in front of the person who called them, placing the last five in front of yourself. Your only stipulation is that they should not call high hands. All this enables you to build up the hand you eventually want to receive as you are setting the cards down. Suppose you want a royal flush in spades. In arranging the hands, just make sure that in one hand a spade goes second, in another third, in another fourth, and in the last both first and last. An example layout is shown in the illustration. When you pick up the hands, first take the one with two spades (B), place it face-up on the hand with the spade second (A), place both on the hand with the spade third (C), and finally drop them all on the remaining hand (D).

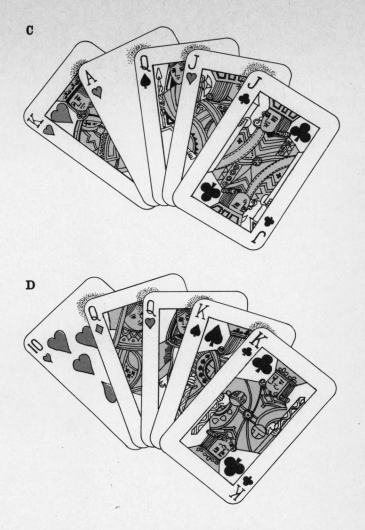

Turn the twenty cards face down and you will have a spade at every fourth card in the pile. False shuffle (for which see the Appendix), if you wish; then keep cutting the packet until a spade appears on the bottom. Deal four hands of five cards and you'll get a royal flush in spades!

Honesty

"Now listen you, gentlemen of the jury. In this game I deal myself four aces, all regular. What is my astonishment when High-Card there lays down five aces, against my four? I'm a broad-minded man, gents. I don't object to nine aces in one deck, but when a man lays down five aces in one hand – ! And besides, I know what I dealt him!"

In the last dodge the cards were set up brazenly under the very noses of the spectators without their being aware of what was happening. Here you rely on a set-up, but leave it to the manufacturer of the playing cards to do the hocus-pocus for you.

Many brands of cards come from the factory with each suit arranged in order from ace through to king. Locate such a source of cards and you'll be able to give the following demonstration of how a crooked gambler works and how honesty always (?) wins! Read the following through with an appropriately set-up pack in hand and you will see that it practically works itself.

Begin by stressing that you use a new pack. Break the seal, and without disturbing the order of the rest of the cards, remove the jokers and any advertising or score cards. Have the cards cut several times, making sure that you end up with a 6, 7, 8, 9, 10, jack, queen, king or ace on the bottom of the pack. Deal seven cards face-down from the top, one to each of seven poker players. Then explain how crooked gamblers often resort to a bottom deal, a device for dealing the card they want from the bottom of the pack, yet making it appear as if it were coming from the top. Show what you mean. Deal the first six cards of the next round to their respective hands, then clumsily take the bottom card and deal it to your hand. Deal seven more cards from the top, making three in each hand, and then repeat the obvious bottom-deal to yourself fourth time around. The fifth card for each hand is then dealt conventionally from the top of the pack.

Now you explain how dishonesty never wins. Turn over each of the six hands in turn and reveal that *each* contains a full house, namely three of a kind and a pair! Then reveal your crooked hand. All you have is three of a kind. You would have lost even by cheating. Had you been really honest, you state, you would have discarded the crooked hand and dealt yourself another five off the top of the pack. This you proceed to do. Turn over your new hand slowly. It will be a straight flush, five cards of the same suit in correct sequence, far superior to any full house.

Getaway

Judge: Have you anything more to say before I find you guilty?

W.C.:   So you're going to deal from a cold deck, eh?

To close this section on a note of dubious hilarity, bet a poker player that he can't beat four aces with a royal straight flush. He will accept enthusiastically, all the while puzzling over where he can lay his hands on the nearest copy of Hoyle or Scarne, from which to quote the rules and prove you wrong. Before he gets there, however, you take the pack, remove your four of a kind and nonchalantly pass him the rest of the cards with the line, "There's my four aces. Where's your royal straight flush?" At which point you run.

Follow Me —
If You Can!

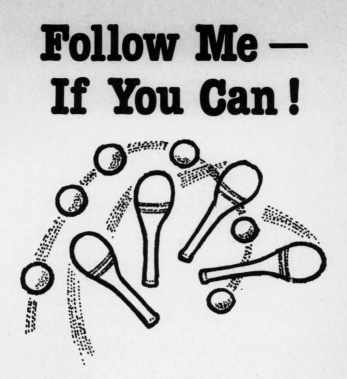

In which the trickster unblushingly inveigles the unsuspecting gull into following the leader – but in less
innocent a fashion than that exercised in infancy.

Edifice

On standing for the Presidency: "It is of interest to note that I have remained true to the hobby of crap-shooting ever since, and on this I rely for a great many votes."

The basic challenge presented here is best summed up by the illustration. You have three straight dice, similar in every respect and ideally about three-quarters of an inch square. Take two of them and wager anyone that he cannot balance them successfully side by side on top of the third at an angle as shown. It's impossible, unless you happen to know the *modus operandi.*

While the dice are falling about all over the place from the sucker's frustrated attempts, discreetly apply a slight amount of saliva to the tip of your right index finger. Transfer the moisture to the "one-spot" side of one of the dice, at the same time as the left hand picks up another die. Bring them together, the two "one-spots" face to face. A gentle squeeze and the dice will adhere as a single unit, making the balancing possible in the process. As you take the two dice down again, separate them between your fingers, remembering to rub off any tell-tale moisture before handing them over to yet another victim to try his luck.

Pyramid

"I'll knock 'em for a row of lib-labs."

This sting would have appealed to Fields the juggler, Fields the pool hustler, and Fields the carnival knave at one and the same time. You take three pool or billiard balls and place them on the table to form a triangle, each ball touching the other two. You then take a fourth ball and carefully rest it on top of the triangle to form a pyramid. The pyramid stays erect. This you achieve time and time again, but each time the sucker attempts to duplicate your result, the balls in the triangle roll away before he can bring the fourth ball to rest.

Your secret gimmick could not be more obvious, namely the chalk. If it is green, draw a line with it around the green ball about one third up, connecting in fact three imaginary points on its circumference where it will make contact with the triangular base of the pyramid. If the chalk is white, use a white ball. You form the triangle with any three other balls, then gently place the gimmicked ball on top, making sure that the chalked line is in position and holding the triangle with your free hand until you feel that the fourth ball has gripped. Carefully take your hands away and the pyramid should stand there.

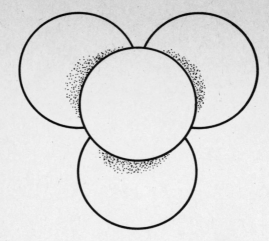

Eventually dismantle the structure and in the process of taking off the top ball rub the chalk off on your hand. Now challenge the sucker to duplicate what you have done. As he is chasing balls all over the table in his attempt, you have ample opportunity to "chalk up" another ball in secret ready to perform the dodge again.

Tumbler

"I was in love with a beautiful blonde once – she drove me to drink – 'tis the one thing I'm indebted to her for."

Line up three tumblers in a row, designating the one at your extreme left 1, the one in the centre 2, the one at the extreme right 3. You can mark the positions with playing cards should you wish. Tumbler 2 is right way up, the two outside tumblers upside down. You now show how with three moves you can leave all three tumblers standing *mouth upward*, ready for filling. Each *move* must consist of turning two tumblers over at the same time, one tumbler in each hand.

50

You demonstrate, making it look absurdly simple. Merely turn:

1 Tumblers 2 and 3
2 Tumblers 1 and 3
3 Tumblers 2 and 3

chanting the positions as you do so. Emphasise the numerical sequence: " 2 and 3, 1 and 3, 2 and 3". Now you challenge the sucker to do the same, at which point you make the one sneaky move upon which your prosperity as a carnival pitchman depends. Nonchalantly turn tumbler 2 upside down. It all seems fair, the tumblers back as they started; but there is, in fact, a subtle difference. The centre glass is still standing the opposite way to the two end tumblers, but now it is mouth downward while the others are mouth upward. However religiously he follows through the "2 and 3, 1 and 3, 2 and 3" ritual, the sucker will not finish with three tumblers mouth upward. His tumblers have to end all mouth downward, ready for emptying!

The mathematics of his starting position are so loaded against him that it is impossible for him to end up with three tumblers right way up ready for filling, *however many* regulation moves he makes.

Transparent

"I may be a liar, but at least I'm a gentleman."

Remove the cellophane tube from a cigar and squeeze it flat by drawing it between the index and second fingers of one hand. At the centre point along one edge tear a minute notch with your thumbnail, and then halfway between this notch and the end of the tube make a second notch. If you have difficulty in making the notches you can get the same effect by pricking the cellophane wrapper with a pin in the appropriate places. This is all done in secret, the device which enables you to bet with certainty that the sucker will not be able to perform the simplest action with the cellophane, while you can.

Hold the cellophane in such a way that the notches face downwards, and tear the flattened tube into two. It should look as if you are tearing from the top, but you will find that with a downward move of one hand you can tear upwards at the centre notch. This is what you do, the fingers and thumb of each hand holding the cellophane about three quarters of an inch away from the notch on each side. Without the notch, however, it requires superhuman strength to tear the tube. Give the un-gimmicked half to the sucker, keeping the notched half for yourself. Challenge him to tear his half as you once again unashamedly summon the aid of the notch in tearing yours apart. The sucker will be struggling with his all the way to Havana and back!

Flopover

"As crooked as a dog's hind leg."

For this, equip yourself with an empty matchbox, the type with a label on both sides. Place the box on the edge of the table, with about a third protruding. Using only one finger, you then slowly lever the box up to an upright position. Perhaps not surprisingly, it stands there. You then pass the box to the sucker and challenge him to do the same. However carefully he lifts the box with his finger, he will fail. The box will topple over every time.

Why should the box stand to attention for you and not for your victim? Merely see to it that when you place the box down for yourself, the bottom of the inner drawer is nearer the table. When you place it over the edge for the victim, make sure that the drawer is upside down. The extra weight on top causes the box to topple. When that weight is shifted underneath, it exerts a stabilising influence. Carnival pitchmen have been known to work the swindle with a full box of matches with a coin hidden between the bottom of the drawer and the sleeve to achieve the additional weight. It works just as well, but this version leaves you clean. Should your empty box not have enough extra weight distributed in the case of the drawer, simply wedge a piece of match where the coin would go.

Twister

"I take no fol-de-rol from any man, much less any fiddle-faddle."

The above title is somewhat ambiguous. It could refer either to you or to the elastic band which enables you to perpetrate the swindle. The band should be at least a quarter inch wide. Hold it as shown in the first illustration, which shows your hands from your point of view. Your right thumb (in the loop) and forefinger (outside) hold it at the top, while your left forefinger (in the loop) and thumb (outside) hold it at the bottom. Then, by sliding your right thumb and forefinger in opposite directions, as indicated by the arrows, impart two twists to each side of the band. The result is shown in the second illustration.

The challenge with which you now present yourself is to remove the twists by changing the positions of the hands, but without altering the grip between both thumbs and

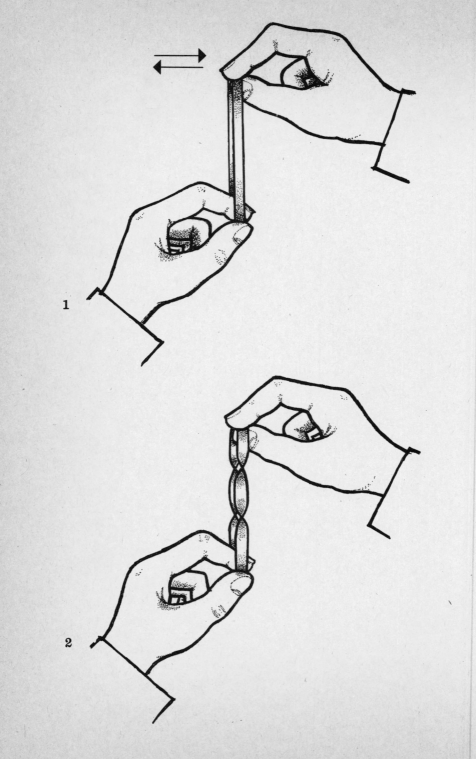

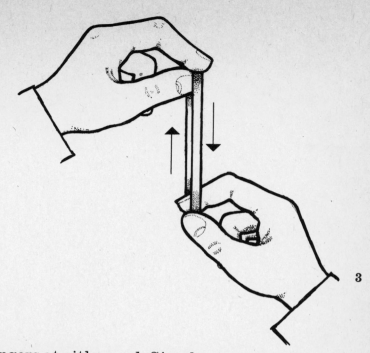

3

forefingers at either end. Simply move your right and left
hands in opposite directions past each other until you
arrive at the position shown in the third illustration. The
twists will melt away. Reverse the positions of the hands
to bring yourself back to the second illustration.

Instruct the victim to take the top of the band from your
right thumb and forefinger between his own right thumb
and forefinger, and the lower end from your left thumb and
forefinger likewise in his left hand. Stress that he is now in
exactly the same position as you were in the second
illustration. At least, that is what he should be led to
think! Topologically his situation, because of the left-
right reversal as he faces you, is far more involved.
Challenge him to get rid of the twists as you did by
reversing his hands, lowering the right hand and raising
the left at the same time. When he does so, however
scrupulously he follows your own moves, the twists, far
from melting, double themselves, four on each side of the
hand. It is impossible for him to rid himself of the twists
without altering his grip. When he gives up, carefully take
the band back from him and show him how easy it is.

Hexagon

"What won't they think of next?"

The following coin puzzle lends itself admirably to the "you-do-as-I-do" motif of this section. You lay out six coins of equal value in two rows of three as shown, openly numbering the coins from 1 to 6. You then show how by moving only three coins, 4, 5 and 1, in that order, you can transform the rows into a near perfect hexagon. You do this several times, each time saying out loud the numbers of the coins moved, namely 4, 5, 1. Make sure that on the completion of the moves 4 touches 5 and 6; 5 touches 1 and 2; and that 1 fits snugly in the gap between 5 and 4, touching them both.

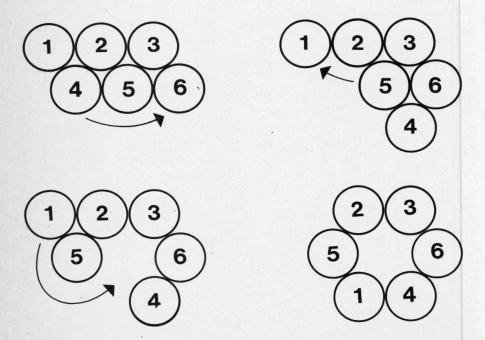

You then challenge the sucker to emulate what you have been showing him. Needless to say, he fails. The reason why he fails is that before he starts you arrange the two rows for him as in the following illustration. As far as he will remember, the lay-out looks the same as before, and you count them from 1 to 6 the same way as before, but he will be unable to make the hexagon unless he imagines the moves in mirror-image.

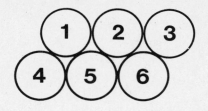

He'll move the coin designated 4 down to touch 5 and 6. Then as he slides out 5 it will gradually dawn upon him – if it hasn't already – that you are cleverer than he thought you were. And that is exactly what you want him to think.

Hydra

"It is impossible to find twelve fair men in all the world."

The confidence trickster who could these days get away with using a double-headed penny in tossing a coin would require the shameless effrontery of a Geller. Disguise the principle, however, and he could well find himself on the scent of even better propositions.

Take ten coins of similar value, one of which must be a double-header. If you are adept at sleight-of-hand, borrow the coins and sneakily switch one for your fake. Hand five to the sucker and keep five, including the double-header, for yourself. You both count your coins, ostensibly to check that you have five each, surreptitiously to ensure that your double-header is second from the top of your pile. You now instruct the victim to "follow your leader"

Everything you do, he is to do in unison with you:

1 Turn all the coins in the pile head upward.
2 Turn the top coin over and place underneath the pile.
3 Take the next coin and without turning it place it underneath.
4 Again turn the next coin over and place it at the bottom of the pile.
5 Again take the next coin and without turning it place it at the bottom.
6 Turn the whole pile over.
7 Turn the top coin over and replace on top.
8 Turn the whole pile over again.
9 Turn the top coin over and replace on top.
10 Turn the whole pile over a last time.
11 Count the coins out in a row on the table and show how all five coins should be back as they were at the start, all heads upward.

At least *yours* will be heads upward! His will come out head, head, tail, head, head, whereupon he scratches *his* head and you cunningly get rid of the incriminating evidence.

Mismatch

"Never mind what I tell you to do – do what I tell you."

This is another adaptation of the principle used in Hydra. The secret is the same, but at the same time less familiar and therefore better. Most people have heard of a double-headed penny, but have you heard of a double-headed matchbox?

The box should resemble the one used in "flopover" in that it should have a label on both sides. Remove the drawer from the sleeve and with a razor blade cut it carefully into two across its centre width. You now re-assemble the matchbox but reverse one half of the drawer in the process. If you now open the box at one end by about a third it will appear the correct way up; open it from the other end and the drawer will appear upside down. Fill this zig-zag drawer with matches and you are ready to bilk the world once more.

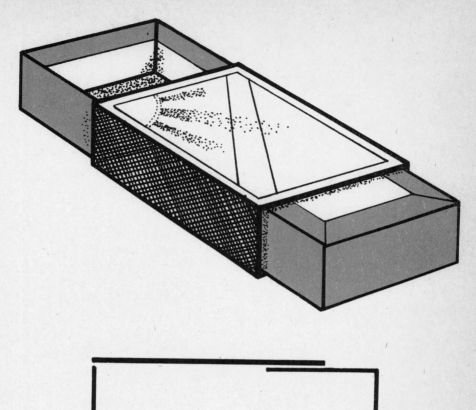

You will also need an ungimmicked matchbox of the same design. This one goes to the sucker. You cling to the "double-header". As in Hydra, he must follow your actions exactly.

1 Open the box so that the matches are showing. (You will have to acquaint yourself with which end of yours is which. Also make sure that the matches in both boxes lie about equally in both directions; you do not want all the striking heads at one end of the box.)
2 Close the box.
3 Turn it over sideways.
4 Turn it over lengthways.
5 Again turn it over sideways.
6 Open the box and take out a match.

This is where the sucker trips up. Your box is the right way up, but his will be upside down, the bottom of his drawer a barrier between him and his matches. Repeat as often as you dare.

Odds That Aren't What They Seem

A compendium of what purport to be – unless otherwise stated – seemingly even-money bets which are in actuality biased remuneratively towards the operator. The latter, when desiring merely to demonstrate their effectiveness, should equip himself with a heap of coins which he distributes evenly between himself and the supposed sucker. If he persists in making sufficient plays, the total amount will soon perforce accrue back to his own person.

Dicey

Singing above the rattle of dice: "Bringing in the sheaves/Bringing in the sheaves/We will come rejoicing ... A hundred and twenty dollars, a hundred and twenty-five, a hundred and thirty ..."

Dice, or the "galloping dominoes" as Fields would have called them, lend themselves especially well to paradoxical proposition bets which appear to offer an even, if not better than even chance, but do in fact give the hustler a marginal edge over his victim. For an encyclopaedic breakdown of the exact percentages of each possible combination of falls one should consult Scarne. Here are just a few such bets that offer you a better than average return as even-money propositions.

Begin with two dice and bet someone that he will roll both a 6 and an 8, before he rolls two 7's. The sucker will reason that since there are six ways to make a 7 and only five ways to make either a 6 or 8, a 7 is obviously easier to roll than either of the other two numbers, and therefore he must be on to a good thing. In fact the bet is far from in his favour, being almost two to one in yours.

Equip yourself with a third die for the next proposition. You keep one and give the other two to your victim. You propose that before he rolls his dice, you will place your die with a specific number showing. If, after his roll, the spots on any two or on all three dice then total seven, you win. If not, you lose. You stress that you can have no idea of how the other two dice will fall when you place your own die down. Regardless of this, however, provided that you make sure your die shows an ace (or 1 spot), your chances of winning will be five out of nine. Repeat this as often as you dare, then hand him the third die. Explain now that when he rolls all three, if a seven shows on any two dice or on all three, *he* will win. In effect you have turned the bet around, but by the end of the day, the sucker will still have lost more than half the total number of throws.

Finally, add two more dice to make five. Declare aces or 1-spots wild, and then bet that if the sucker rolls a pair, he wins. If he rolls three-of-a-kind, he loses. He will reason that since it is more difficult to roll three-of-a-kind than a pair, your offer is more than advantageous. What he will overlook is the fact that it is *easier* to roll three-of-a-kind than a pair with aces wild, incredible as it may sound. *Without* aces wild, the odds against throwing three-of-a-kind amongst five dice are 5·5 to one against, while only 1·2 to one against throwing a pair. On the other hand, *with* aces wild, the odds against three-of-a-kind are 2·2 to one against, while against a pair they are surprisingly 5·5 to one, more than twice as much.

Serial

Man: Would you like to make a few honest dollars for yourself?
W.C.: Do they have to be honest?

On American radio many years ago, the Arthur Murray Dancing School offered twenty-five dollars worth of dancing lessons to anyone who could find in his wallet a bill of which the eight digit serial number contained a 2, a 5 or a 7. It was, in fact, a device to get as many people as possible onto the dance floors of the country since the odds of any one of three specific digits appearing is as high as seventeen to one in your favour.

If you think that's too high for you to offer even money on the proposition, merely specify two digits. The odds will still favour you, at five to one. Alternatively, you can bet the sucker that before he removes the dollar bill or pound, (both carry eight digits), he will not be able to name any three of the digits in his serial number. The odds are still healthily on your side.

You can present all the above propositions as even money bets. In this last one, however, you offer to pay him at two to one in his favour. State that you will pay him, say, ten pence if all eight digits on his note are different, provided that he pays you five if two or more are the same. Don't get dizzy, but the odds here favour you at fifty to one!

Sandwich

W.C.: Ever bet on the races?
Man: No, I never wager.
W.C.: You never wager. It's not a bad idea. It's a good system.

This simple proposition can be used as a prelude to a series of coin bets of the more conventional "heads-or-tails" genre. You challenge the sucker that in guessing the date of a coin, any coin, which you are going to ask him to bring at random from his pocket, you will be closer to accuracy than he will. You explain that he will have one guess, while you have two, but to make up for that slight advantage not only can he call first, but you will bet him at two to one. Only after the calls have been made will he bring the coin into view.

Let us suppose that he calls 1961. This means that you must call the two years that sandwich it in time, namely 1960 and 1962. In spite of your allowing him two to one in his favour, the odds are actually something like twelve to one in yours.

Heads-or-Tails

" 'Tain't a fit night out for man or beast."

The "heads-or-tails" motif is in all probability the oldest in the history of gambling. Archaeologists have deduced that flat pebbles from the Old Stone Age found in the caves of Maz d'Azil, France, with a design painted on one side only, were used for primitive betting purposes bordering on divination; maybe with propositions like this one.

You show eight coins and ask the victim how many heads he thinks are likely to turn up if each coin is tossed individually. Normally he will reason to himself – or you can, in fact, spell it out for him – that since there is a fifty-

fifty chance of either a head or tail falling with each coin, with eight coins it would seem most likely to end up with four heads. You then make your offer, namely that you will give him odds of two to one that he will *not* get four heads. He will, no doubt, question your sanity, especially since four heads will tend to turn up more often than any other single number of heads. What he will overlook, however, is that your own interest rests in *any* of the other combinations, giving odds in your favour of eight to three. Four heads will tend to score more often than, say, three heads, but four heads will not score more often than *either* one, two, three, five, six, seven *or* eight heads!

Another similar play upon odds uses just three coins.

Spectator Wins

(H) (H) (H)

(T) (T) (T)

Performer Wins

(H) (T) (T)

(H) (H) (T)

(H) (T) (H)

(T) (H) (T)

(T) (T) (H)

(T) (H) (H)

Spell out to your victim that there are four ways in which the coins can fall, namely all heads, all tails, two heads and one tail, or two tails and one head. Explain to him that if they fall either all heads or all tails, he wins and you will pay him two coins of whatever value you are using. If they fall the other way, he must pay you, but he need only pay you a single coin. In appearances you are offering him an even chance of winning, but payment which is two to one in his favour. In fact the odds against him are three to one, since on closer inspection you will find that there are actually six ways in which coins can fall in a combination of heads and tails, even though the ratio of two of one symbol to one of the other appears the same in each case.

Spinner

"I'm like Robin Hood – I take from the rich and give to the poor – us poor."

The attraction of the preceding item rests in the fact that the odds favour you without recourse to the standard cliché of coin-tossing, namely the double-headed or double-tailed coin. It would be difficult to get away with the conventional use of such a well-worn gimmick today, although the game Turnover described elsewhere in this volume disguises that principle in your favour. There are, however, other gaffed coins in this area with which the public is far less familiar.

You can purchase from magical supply houses coins with edges which have been bevelled in such a way that when spun on a hard smooth surface they will infallibly fall heads or tails accordingly. If the coin is meant to fall to reveal heads, the bevel will slope towards that side of the coin. The illustration reveals the principle in profile.

Another gimmick, one which you can more easily make for yourself, involves cutting a slight nick with a sharp knife along the edge of a coin on one side. This enables you to challenge anyone that you can tell whether a coin will fall heads or tails when spun behind your back, preferably

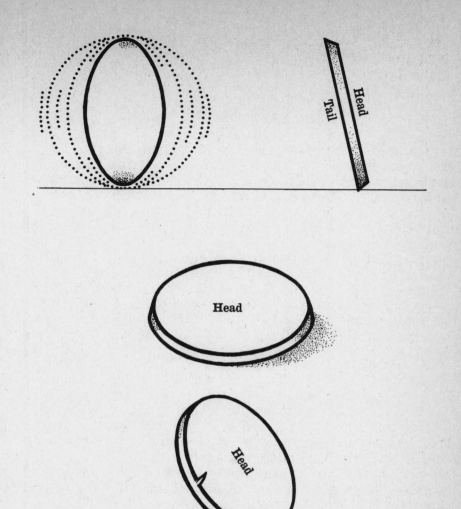

on a wooden surface. You merely listen intently to the way it stops spinning. It it stops abruptly, you know it has fallen onto the side with the notch. If, on the other hand, the spinning subsides more gradually, the nicked side will be uppermost. Experiment will best identify the contrast in sound, as no two "nicked" coins will be exactly alike.

Penney

Prior to meeting legendary gambler, Nick The Greek: "Heads it is. Nicholas Andrea Dandolos, I am ready."

In October 1969, there appeared in the *Journal of Recreational Mathematics*, a problem based on an amazing, but little known fact discovered by the aptly named mathematician, Walter Penney. Given the situation whereby in tossing a coin three times in succession you have one chance in eight of hitting any one of the eight possible sequences, namely, HHH, TTT, HHT, TTH, HTT, THH, HTH, THT, it is possible, whichever combination the sucker himself chooses to bet upon in advance, to choose one for yourself which is more likely to appear first in a random series of tosses. For example, if the chosen combinations were HHT and THH, and the coin fell successively THTHH, THH would win. The odds are always in your favour.

The mathematics of the principle were explained in his usual meticulous detail by Martin Gardner in the October 1974 edition of *Scientific American*, to which the interested reader is referred. For the purposes of play, however, it is sufficient merely to learn the following formula. Whichever combination the sucker calls, to obtain one which will bring the odds into your favour, mentally drop his last symbol, and then put in front of the two symbols left the opposite of the last of that pair. So if he calls HHT, drop the T giving you HH, then add in front of that the opposite of H, namely THH.

The odds in your favour work out as follows:
1 He calls HHH, you call THH, and obtain odds of seven to one in your favour.
2 He calls HHT, you call THH, with odds of three to one.
3 He calls HTH, you call HHT, with odds of two to one.
4 He calls HTT, you call HHT, with odds of two to one.
5 He calls THH, you call TTH, with odds of two to one.
6 He calls THT, you call TTH, with odds of two to one.
7 He calls TTH, you call HTT, with odds of three to one.
8 He calls TTT, you call HTT, with odds of seven to one.

As you can see, the very worst odds you can get are still two to one in your favour! *Whichever* sequence of three the sucker selects, there will always be one left which will give you the winning edge in play.

Payline

Air Hostess: *Are you air sick?*
W.C.: *No. Somebody put too many olives in my martini last night.*

Find seven identical small pay envelopes, the kind that will hold a playing card snugly. In the first five you place a picture card, in the last two a spot card. You then bet the sucker that when the envelopes are shuffled and laid out on the table in a line he will not be able to point to three picture cards in three tries.

Because of the way in which you explain the procedure as a preliminary, the odds do appear to be in his favour. Initially he has five chances in seven of pointing to a picture. Once he has got one, the chances of a second are four in six, and then three in five to secure the third. "In your favour all the way", you spiel. In spite of your reasoning, however, and your offer of even money regardless, he invariably fails to land a lucky trio. In fact, the odds are two and half to one against him.

The same principle coupled with the fallacious reasoning can be adapted in many ways. One novel variation involves the use of a small opaque bottle and seven olives, two of which are green, five black. The green ones are considered the "unlucky" ones. Place all seven olives in the bottle, the neck of which should be of such a size that it will allow only one olive to pass through at a time. Ask the sucker to shake them and then wager that he will not be able to roll out three olives without getting an unlucky green one amongst them. If a green olive shows, he loses. Your explanation of his chances of winning are the same as above: five to two that the first olive will be black, then four to two for the second, finally three to two for the third. Again you bet merely even money, but the odds are still two and a half to one in your favour.

Cartomancy

"I'll bend every effort to win . . . and I come from a long line of effort benders."

More proposition bets have been devised with cards than with any other gambling tool. It might stagger you to learn that some of the following odds favour you so much; but rest assured, they are accurate.

Have the pack shuffled and then cut into three face-down heaps and then offer to bet that there is no picture card on top of any pile. The more astute victim will reason that since there are only twelve picture cards in the pack you are, at even money, giving yourself a considerable advantage. While he hesitates, you declare a change of plan and offer to bet instead on the possibility that a picture card *will* appear. With his mind working backwards, he will now reason that the proposition favours him. In fact you will find the odds approximately six to five in your favour.

You can enlarge them, of course, by increasing the number of piles. With four piles the odds are two to one that a picture card will show. Alternatively, you can include the aces in the same category as the picture cards, in which case the odds are only slightly less than two to one that you will hit a winning card with only three piles.

Have the cards gathered and reshuffled, then spread them face-down on the table. Bet your victim that he won't turn up any four of a kind nominated by himself in any thirty-nine cards. This also works two to one in your favour.

You can secure approximately the same odds with another wager which this time makes use of two shuffled packs. Offer to bet that as you deal cards simultaneously from the top of each pack, two identical cards will appear together at the same position before you have exhausted all 104 cards. In your spiel, you shamelessly "explain" to the sucker that it is "obviously a fifty-fifty proposition since the chance of matching two cards is one in fifty-two and there are fifty-two chances". Usually they fall for it.

A similar "two-together" proposition can be made with a single pack by cutting it into two piles of twenty-six cards, and offering even money that two matching cards of the same colour, say the eight of hearts and the eight of diamonds, will appear simultaneously. The odds remain about the same.

A different kind of "two-together" bet involves asking someone to name two values, disregarding suits, say "ace" and "five" and wagering that in spite of his free choice an ace and a five will arrive together side-by-side in the shuffled pack. He shuffles, then checks by spreading the cards out on the table. Here the odds are three to two in your favour, although you can edge up that advantage by asking instead for a value and a suit, say "three" and "diamond". The odds will then be three to one to your good that on spreading you will find a three adjacent to a diamond. The fact that there are only four cards of one value causes people to overlook the eight chances that exist for any one of the other twelve cards of the specified suit to arrive on either side of a value card. Less favourable, but still giving you odds of five to three, is the bet that two red or two black cards of matching value will find themselves nestling together in the shuffled pack.

Matrimony

"Marriage is a two-way proposition, but never let the woman know she is one of the ways."

Long ago a tradition persisted amongst Soviet peasant girls whereby one would hold six long blades of grass in her fist and extend them to another to tie the six top ends into three pairs, and then the six bottom ends in a similar fashion. If her tying resulted in one continuous loop of grass, the second girl would according to superstition marry within the year.

The odds did in fact favour the prospect of matrimony, the chances of obtaining a single loop being eight in fifteen. If you substitute lengths of string for grass you can easily adapt this principle as a betting stunt. Ask the victim to tie both the upper ends and the lower ends in pairs at random. He loses if he produces the continuous loop. To increase the odds in your favour, discard two strings. With only four in hand, you are likely to win two times out of three.

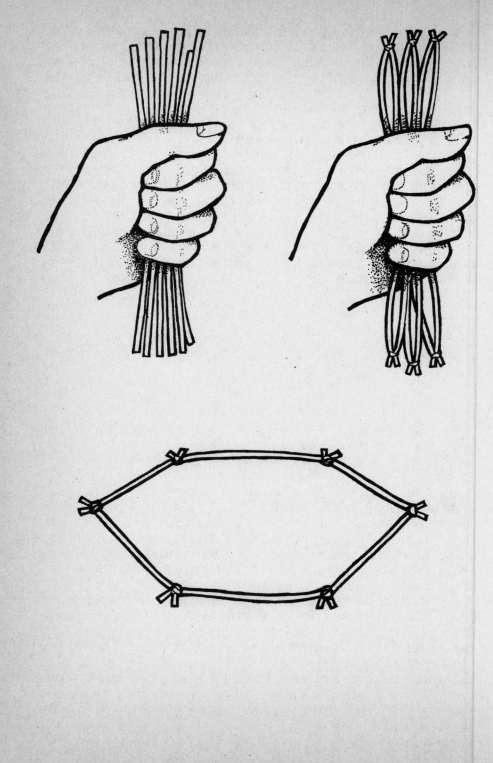

Googol

*"Shall we have another wager?" And then, as the gambler
reaches for his gun – "Probably at some future day!"*

You will need nine slips of paper and a pencil. Hand
everything to your opponent with instructions that on
each slip he write at random a different number. He can go
as low as one, as high as a googol, namely one followed by a
hundred zeros. The only stipulation you make is that he
should not write either two consecutive numbers, or the
same number twice. Also you must not see what he writes.
When he has finished he is to place the slips number sides
down on the table. Then you make your bet. You will start
turning over the slips at random and even though you have
no idea of what numbers he wrote, you wager that you will
stop turning on the highest number.

Simply remember to turn over any three slips without
stopping, then carry on turning until you reach a number
higher than the highest figure in the first three. Stop
there. If you find yourself turning all the slips, you must
stop at, and therefore choose, the last one turned. This
system gives you the maximum odds of winning which are
just over one in three. Obviously to be certain of making an
overall profit the spectator must pay you at odds of two to
one, but since the object is to find one number amongst as
many as nine, most people will suppose that to be fair.

Birthday

*"I'd rather have two girls at twenty-one each than one girl at
forty-two."*

For this you will have to pick the right occasion, ideally a
gathering of no less than thirty people, not including
yourself. Assuming that number is present, bet the sucker
that there will be two people in the room who share the

same birthday (month and day that is, disregarding year). The less well you know the people, the more likely he will be to rise to your bait. Obviously, it must not look as if you have had an opportunity to check dates with everyone beforehand. When one considers that there are as many as 366 possible days to choose from, the probability does seem remote. Yet on an even money basis you have a much better chance of winning than losing.

If you were to attempt this with different groups of thirty people, you would be likely to win approximately seven times out of every ten. The more people, the better your odds, until with about sixty (still few by comparison with 366) individuals, you are bordering close on certainty. To have an absolute 100% guarantee you would need 367 people present, but, of course, the least likely occurrence in all this is that you would ever need them! If you doubt these figures, you only have to check them out with any thirty names picked at random from *Who's Who* or any other biographical dictionary.

Dicing with the Future

In which the mountebank assumes the meretricious mantle of a clairvoyant in determining the successful conclusion of his wager.

Oddity

"Ladies and gentlemen – Brentwood is the smallest giant in the world – whilst his brother Elwood is the largest midget."

The items in this section fall into a special category, the secrets of which are so simple that it would appear utterly impossible for anyone to be hoodwinked by them – until, that is, they are put into practice. This challenge can be performed at the shortest notice with matches, coins, pebbles, even the spots on dice. It all comes down to numbers in the end.

For the purposes of explanation, assume it takes the form of a dice game. You will also need a cup or, failing that, the drawer of a matchbox with which to cover one die. Give that die to the victim, asking him to roll it without your seeing and then to cover it with the cup. When he has done so, you deliver your wager. You claim that you also will put down a die, this time with a number showing, and you guarantee that whatever number he has rolled, the sum of your number added to his will total the opposite of his number. In other words, if he has rolled odd, adding your number to his must make it even for you to win. Alternatively, if he rolled even, that added to yours must produce odd. You always succeed.

How? Because you only ever put down an odd number! If he rolls even, say 4, adding either 1, 3, or 5 to it will give an opposite odd total, either 5, 7, or 9 respectively. But likewise, if he rolls odd, say 5, still adding either your 1, 3, or 5, again produces an opposite, in this case even, total, either 6, 8, or 10.

In explaining the object of the game to your victim, you can throw him off the scent psychologically by quoting false examples. If, you spiel, he puts down a 4, and you then put down a 6, you lose, he wins, because his even number stays even. Similarly, if he puts down a 3 and you put down a 2, he wins again, because his odd number stays odd. Remember that if you do place down an even number he *will* win.

Each time you do win, you can always appear to commiserate with him, by turning your die to a number that would have meant your losing. So, if you put down a 1, converting his, say, 4 successfully to odd, you could then turn your die over to 2 with a line like, "You see how close you came. If I had put down a 2, your number would still be even, and you would have won." You can even set your number down first and cover your die. Make out that it all hinges on whether you put an odd or even number, whether you win or lose. The chances look even, but your dice might as well be loaded, so completely is the ruse in your favour.

Certainty

W.C.: *Son, do you doubt my unimpeachable integrity? Do you think I would resort to a tarradiddle? Do you think I would tell a downright fib?*

Son: *Yes.*

Another twist of the same principle. Take a full pack of cards from their case leaving the joker behind, then ask the sucker to cut the pack into seven piles. You stress that he could arrive at an odd or an even number of cards in any one pile. Before he commences the cuts, however, you bet him that he will end up with an odd number of piles containing an *even* number of cards. He cuts, counts, and checks. You win.

   Gather the cards and start to return them to their case, then as an afterthought offer to repeat the bet. By this time you have secretly added the joker to the pack. That you now have fifty-three cards means that you can adjust the bet, which should now state that when he cuts the pack into seven piles, the number of piles containing an *odd* number of cards will be odd. It works every time.

Milady

W.C.:   Whom have I the honour of addressing, Milady?
Mae West: They call me Flower Belle.
W.C.:   Flower Belle! What a euphonious appellation!

Everyone has heard of the three card trick. In this, however, you attempt something even more remarkable, namely the *seven* card trick. Not only that, but you "find the lady" without even looking at the cards. Moreover, so sure are you of your challenge that you substitute the seventh card, the queen, for a pound note. Should you fail to find the pound you forfeit it; should you succeed, the drinks certainly should not be on you.

Ask the victim to take six spot cards from a pack, and add the pound note to the cards. Turn aside so that you are prevented from getting a glimpse of the action; then give him the following instructions. Tell him to:

1 Mix the cards and the pound note and place them in a straight row on the table in any order.
   He must not tell you where he places the pound.
2 Note the position held by the pound in the row. He may count from either end.
3 He must now rearrange the position of the cards and pound by a series of moves. You must make clear to him the exact definition of a "move". One "move" always consists of changing the position of the pound with one, only one, of the cards on either side of it. Should the pound arrive at the end of the row, there will obviously be only one card with which to arrange it, and therefore only one way in which to "move". First he must make a number of "moves" equal to the position held by the pound in step 2.
4 Make another "move" with the pound, and then another.
5 Now discard the 2 cards at each end of the row.
6 Make three "moves" with the pound
7 Again discard the 2 end cards.
8 Make one "move" with the pound.
9 Now discard the card on the far left.
10 Make one final "move" with the pound.
11 Again discard the card on the far left.

There will be one piece of paper left. The pound note!

Turnover

Man: *There's been a mistake in my change.*
W.C.:   *Ah, at long last, an honest man – you want to return*
      some money?
Man: *No, I'm short.*
W.C.:   *Don't brag about it. I'm only 5 feet 8 inches myself.*

In this challenge the "heads-or-tails" motif is passed through a pseudo-telepathic dimension to your advantage. There is no casual coin-tossing here. Everything appears far more scientifically (?) controlled.

Ask the sucker to reach into his pocket and place a handful of change on the table. While your back is turned, instruct him to turn over at random two coins at a time as many times as he likes, as quietly as possible. Each successive double-turn is completely independent of the others. It doesn't matter if the same coin is included in the double-turning procedure twice, or even more times, in succession. When he is satisfied that he has turned them over enough times, he must cover one coin, any coin, with his hand. Only then do you turn around and immediately declare your interest: "I bet you the value of that coin that, no matter how often you have turned it over, it is now head up." He removes his hand and you pocket the coin.

There is no way you can predict what coins he is going to turn, what coin he is going to cover, points which your pitchman's patter should emphasise to him. What you don't tell him, though, is that before you turn your back on him, you quickly note whether the number of coins showing *heads* is odd or even. An absence of heads showing counts as even. If he then follows your instructions for double-turning the coins, when he stops, if he started with an odd number of heads, he will still have an odd number. Likewise, if there had been an even number of heads showing originally, he will end up with an even number. Without knowing this, he covers one of the coins. You turn back, again secretly count the heads showing, and using simple mental arithmetic, tell him whether he is concealing heads or tails.

Humm-dinger

"For those who are continually embarrassed by the conventional squabble for the restaurant check, I'd advise this: when it comes to the point where, inevitably, the other person says, 'Now let's not fight about this,' just answer 'Very well, old man.' Remember, the complete gentleman never brawls."

This perplexing challenge has undergone many transformations since it emanated from the brain of its inventor, Bob Hummer, a master of the subtle yet intriguing solution. To gain the fullest impact from the principle with a gambling presentation, you will need three tea cups and a pound note or dollar bill.

The cups are turned mouth downwards on the table in a row. Roll the pound into a ball, and balance it on the bottom of one of them. You then make your wager. No matter under which cup the victim places the pound, you will find it first time. Should you fail, he can take the note. Turn aside and only then tell him to place the pound under a cup of his choice. When he has done this he is to switch around the positions of the other two empty cups in order, you say, to confuse you. You turn back and lift one cup. Out rolls the crumpled pound. This you repeat time after time.

Ideally the cups should come from the same set and appear similar. Examine the bottoms of any three such cups carefully and you will find chips, scratches, blemishes, which will act as identifying marks to each one. If you are presented on the spur of the moment with any three cups, a brief glance will single out one blemish as more easily recognisable than the others. The cup with this mark becomes your key cup. This is the principle upon which the whole challenge is based.

Decide quickly upon your key cup before turning aside and remember its position in the row. When you turn back after the pound has been hidden and the cups have been moved, a simple process of deduction will lead you to the pound. If the key cup is still in the same position, then obviously it was not switched around. Therefore it must hide the pound. On the other hand, should it not be in the same position, then it must have been switched. In which case the pound note will neither be under the key cup nor under the cup which is in the position the key cup originally held. That leaves one cup. Lift it and there is the pound.

You don't, of course, have to use a pound note. The next time you are in a restaurant and you arrive at that embarrassing lull in *bonhomie* when it must be decided who is to pay the bill, crumple the latter into a ball and with three cups proceed on the following conditions with the above challenge. If you uncover the bill first time, they pay; if you don't find it, you pay. You'll never go hungry!

Jackpot

"If a thing's worth having, it's worth cheating for!"

Start saving all your odd pennies until you have in excess of one hundred. The exact number is immaterial, although the more you are able to hoard, the more impressive the gamble will eventually appear. Keep them together in a paper bag, metal bowl or some other container which allows of easy access. This is your "jackpot".

When you are ready to bluff the world, choose your unsuspecting victim and explain the jackpot to him. Turn aside, emphasising that you would not cheat by looking, and ask him to reach into the hoard and bring out in his clenched fist any number of coins, provided that they do not exceed, say, twelve pence. He must keep his hand closed for the time being. Turn back and yourself reach into the jackpot and grasp a handful, though make sure that you have, in this example, comfortably more than twelve, the maximum he could have taken. Now, making scrupulously sure that neither of you can *see* or *hear* the other, count your coins to yourselves. You are then ready to make your wager. The challenge is for you to tell him exactly how many coins he has in his hand. If you are right, he must give you, from his own pocket, a sum equal in value to that which he is holding. If you are wrong, he can take the jackpot.

Needless to say, you never forfeit your nest-egg. Your security is locked into the wording of your statement, something like, "I wager that I hold as many coins as you, four more, and enough to make your sum fifteen pence."

You then ask the sucker to name his total. Suppose he says he has eight pence. From your own pile, count off eight – his number; then count off the "four more"; pause, then conclude, "and remember I said I had enough left over to make your sum fifteen pence". Then proceed to count, after reaffirming that he did have eight, "Nine, ten, eleven, twelve, thirteen, fourteen", and then with a triumphant final flourish on the precise final number, "fifteen".

So far, so confusing! But all you have to do is to make sure that you take a larger number of coins than the victim. Hence the specimen number stipulated in the second paragraph. When you first count yours to yourself, the last thing you are thinking of is the number the victim actually took. Merely count off to yourself a small, arbitrary number of coins – say, five – and then count the rest, which we'll suppose to be seventeen. You would then say, on the pattern of the above, "I have as many coins as you, five more, and enough to make yours seventeen." Given that you have made sure that you hold that many *more* coins than he does anyhow, of course you have *as many as* he has, and of course you can make his sum up to seventeen. The dimple throw-off phrase "five more" is total misdirection. So when you count out loud, you count to the spectator's number, the one he has just told you, then deliver the throw-off, and finally continue counting to your main sum of seventeen. So if the victim had nine pence, you would count up to nine, then resume the count on ten.

Once you have grasped the principle, you will realise how simple it is, so simple that you will query whether anyone could possibly be taken in by it. To prove its perplexity, however, you will have to try it out for yourself. The more you repeat it, varying the "throw-off number" each time, the more confusing it becomes to the victim, a situation helped by the endless variations you can play on the theme. Above, the victim takes his coins before you, but there is no reason why you can't go first. You can count yours and announce your wager, before he counts his. You can get him merely to think of a sum, and yet still you win. No less than the late Al Koran, the suave English mentalist/magician, who enjoyed a considerable vogue in the fifties, used to feature a version of this swindle in his stage act. He announced it as "The trick that baffled Einstein." Which only goes to prove that even scientists can be suckers.

The Classic Swindles

Being a self-contained folio of those dodges and wiles which by virtue of their oft repeated success have bestowed greatest distinction upon the noble art of cozenage.

Spot

"If at first you don't succeed, try, try again. Then quit. No use being a damn fool about it."

This piece of hanky-panky is right in the van of the mainstream tradition of carnival swindles, where the easier and fairer it looks, the harder it becomes. The customer is confronted by a red circular spot measuring five inches in diameter painted on the counter. He is given five flat discs each measuring slightly more than three inches in diameter. The object of the game is to cover the red spot completely using nothing more than the five discs. Obviously the spot is the largest possible that can be legitimately covered by the discs, which must be dropped onto the spot one at a time and, once in position, cannot be moved again. The merest speck of red showing means that the game is lost. Needless to say, the customer loses every time.

There are various methods of fleecing the public with this game. They include painting the spot on oilcloth so that its shape can be subtly distorted by stretching and using a key disc that is itself distorted. Most appealing, however, because of its simplicity, is the simple geometrical approach using ungimmicked props. First have the sucker drop the discs as he thinks fit from a height of about six inches. The slightest deviation from a perfect drop with any one of the discs will spell failure on his part. The probability that a skilled player can drop a disc from that height onto the exact position it should occupy is, according to Scarne, about one in three or two to one against. The probability that he will score five perfect drops can then be computed at one in three[5] or 243! Of course the more attempts he makes the more he'll come to reason along exact geometrical lines. The first illustration, as well as indicating the exact relative proportions of discs and spot, shows the arrangement which most people work out in their minds as the ideal to be achieved.

To climax his series of losses allow him to place the discs down carefully without dropping them. The odds are that he will attempt the arrangement shown in the first illustration with the circumferences of all five discs converging at the centre of the spot. Then let him look

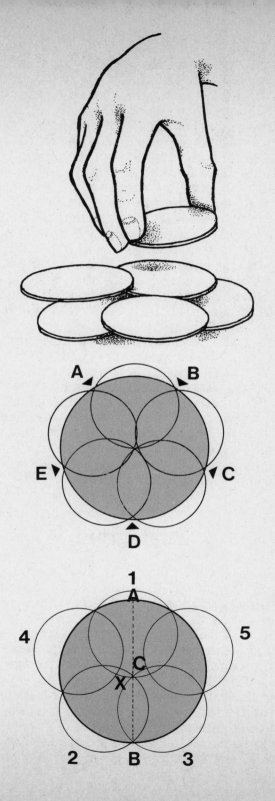

closely and point out – with a magnifying glass if necessary – the minute specks of red around the spot's rim at ABCDE. The second illustration reveals the superior arrangement which you then proceed to show him.

Imagine the diameter AB. First put disc 1 into position, ensuring that its centre rests on AB and that the base of its circumference X is slightly below the centre of the spot, C. Next put down discs 2 and 3 so that their circumferences pass through X and B, whereupon discs 4 and 5 fall obviously into place. The exact measurements for the spot and the discs are respectively 5 inches and 3·045 inches in diameter precisely. The distance CX works out at about 0·07 inch. Nothing less than 3·045 will cover the 5-inch spot as detailed in the winning method. Attempting the first arrangement with discs of this size will automatically result in failure. Using that method you would need discs at least 3·09 inches in diameter to cover the same spot completely.

The goal for which the operator should aim is to be able to effect the second arrangement as rapidly as possible seemingly dropping the discs from a height of six inches, but in fact – by using the misdirection provided by swift up-and-down and back-and-forth movements of the hand – making the drops from no more than about an inch above the spot.

Pentagram

Man: Maybe you're lost.
W.C.: Kansas City is lost; I am here!

This challenge may have originated in Mexico, where it bears the name "Estrella Magica" or "Magic Star". The star in question is the mysterious and legendary five-pointed pentagram which can be drawn in one continuous line without lifting pen from paper. Explain this fact as you draw it and then point out that the star has five points and five intersections, a total of ten spots. The object of the game is to cover all but one of these spots with coins in the following manner. First place a coin on any spot, then move the coin along a line across an intersection and bring it to rest on the next spot. This is repeated with a second coin and a third and so on until nine spots are covered. Each coin must commence at an uncovered spot and finish on an uncovered spot. Each move must jump one intersection, though it does not matter whether this has a coin on it or not. Once a coin comes to rest, it cannot be moved again. You can demonstrate this many times, on each occasion starting your first move from a different spot, yet people are still unable to duplicate your success.

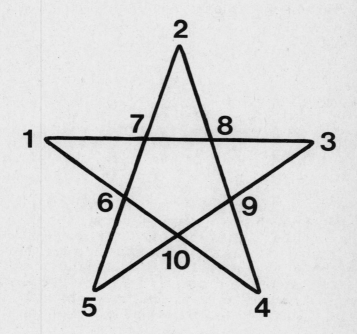

The secret is simple. Your moves follow a basic pattern; each successive coin must end its move on the spot from which you began the preceding move. Assume you place a coin on spot 9 and move it to 2. Your next move is to start at a spot which enables you to move it to 9 itself, namely 5.

The third coin must now end on 5, which means you must start at 7. And so on, until all nine coins are on the star. Here is another example:

First coin	placed on	4,	jumps	10,	ends on	6
Second coin	placed on	8,	jumps	9,	ends on	4
Third coin	placed on	1,	jumps	7,	ends on	8
Fourth coin	placed on	10,	jumps	6,	ends on	1
Fifth coin	placed on	3,	jumps	9,	ends on	10
Sixth coin	placed on	7,	jumps	8,	ends on	3
Seventh coin	placed on	5,	jumps	6,	ends on	7
Eighth coin	placed on	9,	jumps	10,	ends on	5
Ninth coin	placed on	2,	jumps	8,	ends on	9

In demonstrating the moves, do so with a blend of swift actions and indecisiveness. Don't always make the move immediately. Appear to be trying other spots first, then finally come back to the correct one.

Morra

"Mayor, you're okay. I voted for you last election – five times."

This is the ancient game played by most people in childhood in which two players, standing back to back if a third party is available, simultaneously extend either one, two or three fingers as they shout the number they guess their opponent has shown. If both guess right or both guess wrong, that round is drawn. If only one guesses right, however, the other has to pay him as many coins as the combined total of the fingers extended at that point in the game.

So far, so innocent, until the mathematician John Von Neumann worked out a strategy which usually enables those acquainted with it to win, or if not to win, at least to break even. Each time you simply "guess", as the number of fingers your opponent is showing, the difference between the number you are showing and four. You also have to make sure that in any twelve rounds you show one finger five times, two fingers four times, three fingers three times. You must make this more haphazard than it reads

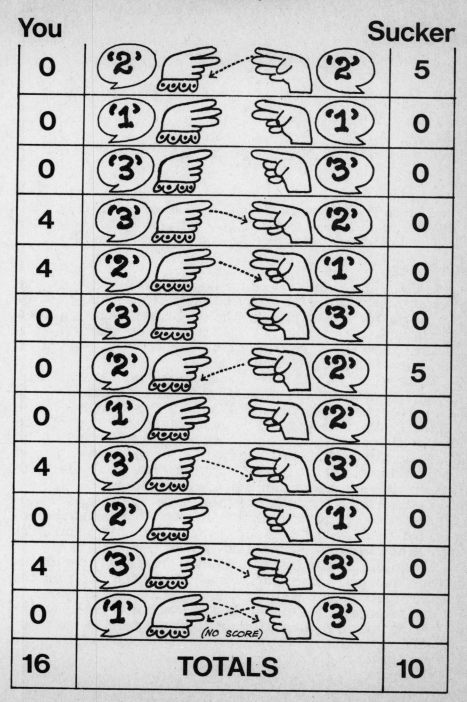

You		Sucker
0		5
0		0
0		0
4		0
4		0
0		0
0		5
0		0
4		0
0		0
4		0
0		0
16	TOTALS	10

so that it doesn't *look* like a system. This will help to disguise the fact that whenever you extend three fingers, you shout "one", two fingers, "two", one finger, "three". The last thing you want is for the sucker to crack the system; otherwise *he* will beat *you*.

Shortchanged

"I know a thief when I see one. When I was young, I was the biggest thief at large. I'd steal golf balls, piggy banks of dear little kiddies, or nozzles off the hoses of the rectory lawn."

That anyone might be duped into paying money for something which rightfully belongs to him only serves to underline the typically Fieldsian philosophy quoted elsewhere in this book, "Suckers have no business with money anyway." If you don't believe the above proposition is likely, try these for size.

Take a five pound note from your pocket and ask the sucker to match it with one of his own. Fold them together and place them both in a glass. Ask him how much is in the glass. He should reply ten pounds, whereupon you offer to sell him both the glass and the notes for six pounds. If he accepts the deal, as he often will, you will make a pound minus the cost of the glass. People *do* forget that one of the five pound notes was theirs in the first place.

You can try the same thing more cheaply this way. Place three coins of equal value in a row and ask the sucker to match them with three similar coins of his own. Let's imagine the coins are tenpenny pieces. Pocket one of your original coins, and have the sucker do likewise from his row. Then push the four coins left on the table in his direction with the words, "Give me thirty pence for the rest of the coins." You will be surprised how many forget that two of the coins they are buying were theirs origi- nally, " originally" meaning only seconds ago. This time you should be ten pence richer.

Inferno

"I'll teach you when you grow up. I never smoked a cigarette until I was nine."

A popular bar game involves securing a drumhead of tissue paper around the mouth of a tumbler with an elastic band. Both players place a small coin on the centre of the stretched tissue. They also need a cigarette, the lighted end of which they take turns in placing against the tissue, burning a small hole in the process. Play proceeds in rotation. Whoever applies the burn that causes the coins to drop into the glass loses and forfeits the cash.

You play legitimately for a while and then warn your opponent that you have at last figured out his strategy. He will probably sound surprised, since the likelihood is that he hasn't got one. Still, you are so confident of your theory, you claim, that you offer to quadruple the bet. You qualify your statement by adding that if he burns the first hole, you are sure that you yourself will win. Win you do, but not through skilled reasoning or logic. This time you make the drumhead, not out of tissue, but out of flash paper. This can be obtained at any joke shop or magical supply house. It looks like real tissue, feels like real tissue, but bring it into contact with the merest spark and it disappears – flash! – in an instant. Say no more!

Corridor

Mae West: *Two rooms – if you don't mind.*
W.C.:   *Yes – The bridal suite. We're married, you know.*
Mae West: *I'll take the suite. Give him the room.*
W.C.:   *But, my dove . . .*

There were ten people seeking separate rooms in a hotel which had only nine vacant rooms in which to accommodate them. For a small wager you offer to demonstrate how the problem was solved *without* people having to double up.

With a pencil sketch a long rectangle which you then divide into nine squares, each space representing a room.

Marking one cross in the first square and another outside, you demonstrate how the first man made his way to the first room, but was overtaken at the door by the second man.

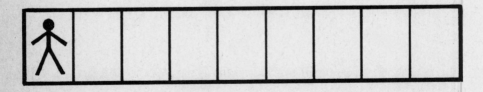

The third man then went into the second room, the fourth into the third and so on until the ninth went into the eighth. Mark each of the seven rooms in the centre with a cross as you count "Third, fourth, fifth, sixth, seventh, eighth, ninth".

At this point there was one vacant room left, whereupon the manager took the extra man still standing outside the first room and led him to the ninth. Circle the cross outside the first room and draw a curve connecting it with the last square, marking the final cross inside as you count "tenth".

Then quickly proceed to *your* room and lock the door!

Dilemma

"Business is an establishment that gives you the legal, even though unethical, right to screw the naïve – right, left, and in the middle."

Have someone place a tenpenny piece of his own on the table and then cover it with any card drawn face-up from the pack. Let's suppose the card is the two of clubs. You bet him five pence that he will *not* answer the value of the card on the table to each of your next three questions.

Begin by asking two completely irrelevant ones. He will be on his guard, expecting a catch, and should answer "the two of clubs" both times. You then ask him what he will take for his coin beneath the card. This places him in a considerable dilemma. He might answer "the two of clubs", in which case you take him at his word, give him the card, pocket the ten pence for yourself and then pay him five pence for winning the bet. You still make five pence out of the transaction. Alternatively, if he refuses to say "two of clubs", he gets his coin back, but has to hand you over five pence for losing the bet. Either way you can't lose. Of course, you can make the stakes higher, if you dare.

Matrix

W.C.:   *May I present my card?*
Mae West: *"Novelties and Notions". What kind of notions you got?*
W.C.:   *You'd be surprised. Some are old and some are new.*

For this game, draw on a piece of paper a five by five grid as shown and then alternate on the squares within the grid thirteen copper coins and twelve silver ones. After the removal of one of the copper coins, you now take turns with an opponent in moving coins of one colour each either up, down, or sideways – but never diagonally – to the one vacant square. The player who eventually finds himself unable to move loses. In fact, provided that you play second, you can always win.

Grant your opponent the courtesy of removing the copper coin of his choice and then to make the first move. He'll have to move a silver coin and this will remain his colour throughout, leaving you with copper. Before you make your first move, however, you have to stretch your imagination. Picture in your mind that the grid – with the exception of the square from which your opponent removed the copper coin – is covered by twelve dominoes. Had the third square in the fifth row been vacated, you might imagine the layout shown in the second illustration. Any arrangement will work, provided that the invisible "dominoes" are not allowed to overlap each other or the original vacant square. Now whenever your opponent moves a silver coin, merely make sure that you move the copper coin that is on the "domino" he has just left. In that way you will always have a move up your sleeve with which to follow his move. In other words, he hasn't a hope of winning.

Columbus

Holding Mae West's arm: "Ah! What symmetrical digits. Soft as the fuzz on a baby's arm."

Although this game is based on a "pairing strategy" similar to that used in Matrix, your imagination can take a rest. Here you use *actual* dominoes.

Two players take it in turns to place dominoes of equal size flat upon a square or rectangle. After one domino is set down it must not be disturbed by the other player. This continues until the square is so crowded that there is no room left for another domino, the winner being the person to place a domino last.

If the first player – you! – places a domino exactly in the centre of the square, all you have to do to ensure eventual victory is to duplicate symmetrically your opponent's play at each successive placing. Refer to the illustration where the numbers indicate the order of play in a sample game. Just make sure that you have enough dominoes, sufficient, in fact, to cover the square completely when they are packed tight edge to edge in conventional lines.

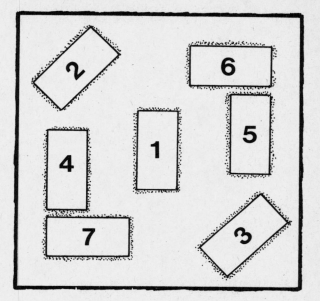

The title? Legend has it that the game was played long ago by Columbus, not with dominoes, but with eggs. In addition to "discovering" America, the explorer was famous for his reputed feat of balancing an egg on end – simply by cracking the wide end slightly, thus flattening the shell into an actual base. Sam Loyd, the American puzzle expert, conjectured that he balanced the egg so that it would stand in the centre of the square (he used a square napkin) in such a game. Only then could he proceed to win the game. By setting it on end he made the egg symmetrical for the purposes of the winning strategy. Unlike the domino, the oval shape of an egg does not retain the same shape when rotated through 180 degrees. Unless the object at the centre can be seen or made to be symmetrical in this fashion you have no guarantee of victory.

Garland

"Somehow, Satan got behind me."

Instruct your opponent to arrange any number of coins in an unbroken circle, each coin touching the two on either side. The object of the game, a sister of Columbus, is to take turns in removing either one coin or an adjoining pair of coins from the circle in such a way that whoever takes the last coin wins.

Provided that you play second – again, as in Matrix, out of courtesy to the sucker who goes first – you can always win. When he makes his first move and thus breaks the circle, just check whether the number of coins left in the arc is odd or even. If odd, for your first move take away the centre coin. If even, take away the two coins at the centre. In either case you will be left with two equal strands of coins. Now whatever move he makes next, you duplicate it from the opposite strand. So if he takes a pair from the strand nearer him, you take a pair from the other. With practice you will be able to make your moves appear less obvious than might sound from this description.

You can vary your strategy by counting from either end of the strand remaining to you, so that in the case of two strands of, say, seven coins, if your opponent removes the second coin from one of them, you could then remove either the second or the sixth from the other. Once again, it's all a question of symmetry.

Buster

"One of my most precious treasures – an exquisite pair of loaded dice, bearing the date of my graduation from high school."

The variety of crooked dice available for illegal gambling purposes is infinite, as the merest glance at *Scarne on Dice*, the definitive work on the subject by America's foremost gambling expert, will show. While it is not easy for the average reader to obtain the elaborately gaffed items detailed in that volume, the dice employed in the following sequence can be constructed by anyone with little trouble.

Special only by virtue of the distribution of their spots, they are known to mechanics variously as "Tops and Bottoms", "Busters", "Ts", and "Mis-Spots". That special distribution is best shown by the illustration which depicts a pair of such dice themselves and their mirror image. One die merely carries the odd numbers, 1, 3, 5, the other the even numbers, 2, 4, 6, in each case with the duplicate numbers on opposite sides to each other.

Hand the dice to the sucker and have him roll them a few times so that he can assure himself they are not loaded. Because he can only see a maximum of three sides on any die at one time, at no point will he be able to see two duplicate sides on any die! He then hands you one die back and depending upon whether this is the odd or the even die, wager that your next roll will produce odd or even accordingly. Repeat, but this time bet the opposite and have *him* roll the other die. Finally hand him the second die back and have him roll both dice together. You wager "odd" – it can only be "odd" – and win again. You've scored your hat trick, stove-pipe of course!

It is advisable to have a pair of straight dice at hand to substitute for the gaffed ones at the conclusion. Should you be challenged, however, you can in fact show that the crooked pair are fair. If they were straight, obviously each pair of opposite sides on each die would total seven. Just put the dice side by side in such a way that they total seven on top and along one of the sides. You can then show that all the other sides, the outer ends, as well as the two sides facing inwards, all total seven. The dice can't be anything but straight! Or can they?

Mosca

On ordering breakfast in the Black Pussy Café: "I don't know why I ever come in here – the flies get the best of everything."

This ancient Spanish game was a great favourite of major-league gambler, Benjamin "Bugsy" Siegel. Legend has it that he would frequently order with his breakfast not only the sugar cubes required, but also a box of the live flies essential for the wager. In this way he would set himself up for sport for the rest of the morning.

All doors and windows in his room would be closed, the air conditioning switched off, then the flies released from their perforated prison. Siegel would unwrap two sugar cubes, position them about six inches apart, and bet his breakfast companion sums to the tune of five thousand dollars that a fly would land on his cube first. He invariably won. One morning in 1947 he had a shrewder opponent in fellow mobster, Willie Moretti. After Siegel had relieved him of five thousand dollars, he only agreed to play again if he could take Siegel's cube. This Siegel agreed and still he won.

Siegel had in fact secretly doctored both cubes beforehand with a drop of DDT on one side. First time around he slyly made sure that the impregnated side of his cube was closest to the table, while that of Moretti's was uppermost. Second time around, under the pretence of moving the cubes further apart, he unobtrusively turned them both over. All so much easier than training flies, the only solution Moretti himself could think of.

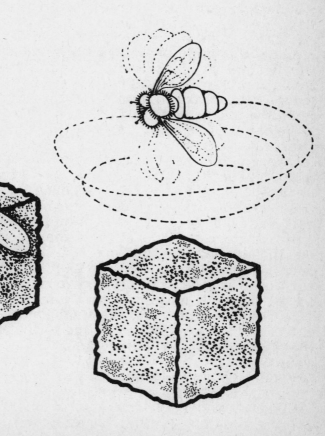

Thirty-one

"I should have gone to night school, then I'd be able to add."

Played extensively in Australia, hence often referred to as the "Australian Gambling Game of 31", this was in fact invented, according to nineteenth-century gambling expert J. H. Green, way back in the dim past by one "Dr Bennett alias Charles James Fox of England" (1749–1806), a statesman and a scholar and notorious as a bad influence on the Prince of Wales!

From a pack of cards remove all the spot cards from ace through to six, twenty-four cards in all, then arrange them on a table as shown in the illustration.

Again the game is for two players. Both take turns in turning one card face-down, adding the values of the cards turned as they do so. Whoever reaches thirty-one first, wins. Once a card is turned face-down it is out of play. Should a player be forced to go over thirty-one, he loses. Have no fear of this, however, because you can win every time, regardless of whoever starts the play, by remembering a simple series of secret key numbers. The sequence is 3, 10, 17, 24, easily remembered as a progression of 7 from 3, i.e. 3, 3+7 or 10, 10+7 or 17, 17+7 or 24.

Should the opponent commence the game by turning over any card higher than 3 in value, turn over a card which will bring the total level with your second key number, which is 10. So, if he turns a 6, you turn a 4. He might then turn a 3, bringing the total to 13, in which case you would turn over another 4 to hit your next key, 17. Suppose he then turns a 1, making a total of 18, you then turn a 6 bringing the sum to 24, the final key. Whatever card he turns next, in no way can he score thirty-one on his next move, whereas you cannot avoid hitting the target on yours.

Should your opponent turn 1 or 2 on his opening move, bring the total to 3, your first key, on yours; should he turn a 3, deliberately play low and strive to hit a key number as soon as possible. For those games where you play first, begin by turning your first key, 3. Whatever your opponent turns second, nothing can prevent you hitting your key numbers in an easy sly stride.

If you persist in playing the game, your opponent will, of course, latch onto the fact that you always start on a 3, or that various numbers, namely your keys, occur with amazing regularity in the totalling. This is where you may, if you wish, explain the whole system to him, how he must always start on a 3, how he must aim to reach the keys. Better still have a "shill" or accomplice take him aside to explain. Now obviously he will feel that with a knowledge of the key numbers, if he turns a 3 first, he must win the game. So he enters another game and this is where the stakes really should climb high. Allow the sucker to being by turning a 3. You follow with another 3 bringing the total to 6. The sucker will now turn 4 to make the first key 10. You follow with another 4, making 14, whereupon he must turn 3 to produce the next key, 17. You then take 3, totalling 20. The sucker adds 4 to this, securing the last key, 24. You follow with another 4, bringing the total to 28, at which the mouth of your opponent should drop to the floor! When he goes to turn a 3 to make 31, he will find that there is no 3 left to turn. He has no choice but to turn a 1 or a 2, playing straight into your hands. Whichever he turns, you then add the other to produce the winning total again of 31. Should he at any point avoid the card you are "forcing" him into turning, don't worry. The path will then be wide open for you to hit a key number yourself.

Nim

"You won't consider me rude if I play with my mitts on, will you?"

Whereas in Garland your winning aim was to pick up the last coin, in the more famous Nim, presumably so called after the Anglo-Saxon verb, *nim,* meaning to take away or steal, it is the picking up of the last object which you must *avoid.*

The game is traditionally played with matches, although coins or any small objects will serve as well. First arrange fifteen matches in three rows of four, five, and six respectively. You now take it in traditional turns to remove one or more matches from any single row or all the matches in any single row. As already explained, whoever is left with only one match to take when it is his turn to play loses the game.

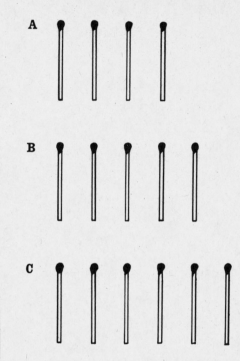

The strategy you have to follow in order to win every time consists of two parts. First, if you open the game, remove either 1 match from Row A, 3 matches from B, or 5 from C. Secondly, when you play again or when you follow your opponent when he plays first, make sure that you leave any one of the following combinations: three rows of matches distributed – in whatever sequence – either 6, 4, 2; 5, 4, 1; 3, 2, 1 or 1, 1, 1; or just two rows with more than one match in a row and the same number in each. A specimen game might go as follows:

1 Your opponent removes two matches from A.
2 You then remove one match from B, leaving 6 in C, 4 in B, 2 in A.
3 He removes 4 matches from C.

4 You then remove all 4 left at B, leaving two rows equal but with more than one match in each row.

5 He can now either take one match from A or C, or both from A or C.

6 If the former, you take the pair that remains and he is left with the last match; if the latter, you take one from the remaining pair, still leaving the last match.

The more you play, the more familiar you will become with the various endings to the game. Play rationally and you should have no problems. Finally, here is one other specimen sequence:

1 You remove one match from A.

2 Your opponent removes 3 matches from B.

3 You remove 5 matches from C, leaving the combination 3, 2, 1.

4 Your opponent removes 1 match from B.

5 You remove 2 from A, leaving 1, 1, 1.

6 He takes one from A.

7 You take one from B.

Once again he has to take the last match. You could almost say "the last straw".

Rattlesneak

On being burgled: "Would you believe it that the rattlesnake to show his appreciation for my hospitality sunk his fangs into the calf of the burglar's leg, stuck his tail out through the flap of the tent and held the intruder fast while he rattled for a policeman."

With little call for dexterity of any kind you can craftily duplicate the classic effects of the three card trick and the three shell game (both to be described later in this book), if you have three small pill boxes that all look the same and a single pill. You place the pill in one of the boxes, then snap all three boxes shut. Moving them around on the table, you defy the sucker to point to the box which he thinks contains the pill. Of course, he never suceeds, a fact made possible by another pill in another pill box held secretly against your wrist by your watch strap or an elastic band.

In explaining the game to the victim, first rattle the pill which he knows about in its box to prove it is there. Make sure, however, that you shake it with your ungimmicked hand. Then, in moving the boxes around, aim at confusing him to the point where he has no alternative but to make a guess at the correct box. If he chooses one of the two empty boxes, pick up the right one and shake it normally. If he points to the box that does hold the pill, pick up instead one of the empty boxes and shake it with the gaffed wrist. He will hear a pill rattling inside a box, but he won't realise that the pill he hears is not the original pill. Your spiel is always the same, "No, *this* one rattles, the other two don't." You can repeat this as often as you wish, as long as you can keep track of the noisy box yourself and don't get your hands confused. Always attempt, however, to finish the sequence when the sucker is legitimately wrong, so that having redirected his attention to the box he should have chosen, he can shake it and, for that matter, take the pill out of the box himself.

If you do not have three similar pill boxes ready to hand, you can achieve the same effect with small match boxes, two empty, one half-full, with a fourth half-full box attached to the wrist. Whatever you use, beware you do not give the game away when you look for the time.

Monte

"Long live the King, but look at the Queen!"

"A little game from Hanky Poo, the black for me, the red for you – all you really have to do is keep your eye on the lady – ten gets you twenty, twenty gets you forty – here we go – keep your eye on the lady." So went the doggerel with which the old-time operators of possibly the most famous swindle of them all commenced their pitch. Today Dai Vernon, the most perfect performer of pure sleight-of-hand in the world, commences his own demonstration with a similar jingle. The Professor, as he is known affectionately to other magicians, has subtly embellished the basic premise of the original game to a point where any of the subterfuges so gained would have made the eyes of the average nineteenth-century Mississippi river boat gambler pop in incredulity. It cannot be the purpose of this book, however, to delve explicitly into what represent the inner secrets of legerdemain as distinct from the dubious wiles of the confidence trickster. More relevant to this volume is an explanation of the basic move on which the standard game, as it is still perpetrated on the streets of London and Manhattan, is based.

The best cards to use are a red queen and two similar black spot cards, say the seven of clubs and the eight of spades. To make them easier to lift from your working surface bend the cards slightly along their length, crimping them – to use the technical term – as shown in the illustration.

With the faces concave, there should be no problem in picking up the face-down cards by their ends. When you bend the cards, place them together so that all will be crimped in the same way.

The key move referred to above and known as "the throw", enables you to pick up two cards in one hand, one of them the queen, then to throw them slowly with their backs face-down on to the table. All seems fair, but as you supposedly throw down the queen, you actually substitute a spot card. Here's how. Place the three crimped cards in a face-down row on the table. You need to known the position of the queen. Now between the pad of the right thumb

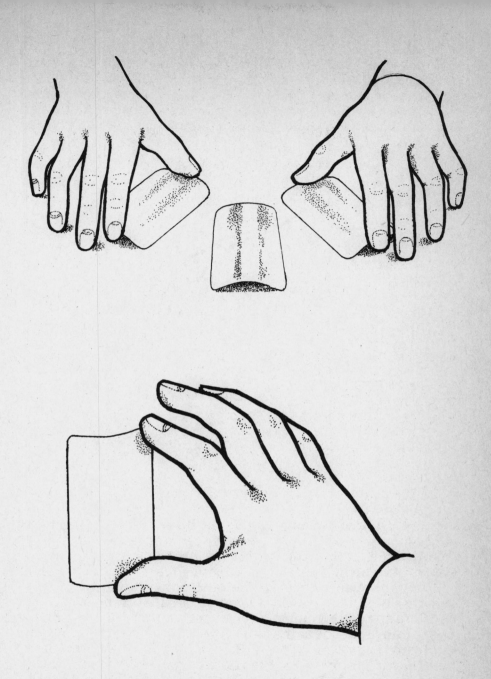

and the tip of the right index finger pick up one of the spot cards by the ends close to the top and bottom right corners. The illustration shows your view at this point.

Raise your hand to show the face to the onlookers. Next pick up the other spot card in a similar fashion in the left hand, again showing its face. Then finally bring your right hand over the queen which you pick up between the tips of the thumb and second finger beneath the first card as shown.

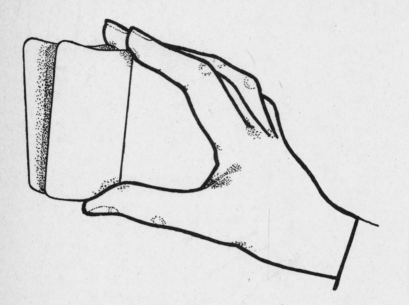

Lift and show the queen to be the bottom card. The hands should be about six to nine inches above the table. In turning the right hand back towards the surface you now appear to throw down the bottom face-down card. What actually happens – with one smooth continuous movement – is that you release the top spot card from between the thumb and index finger and then shift the index finger hold to the queen, at the same time as you release the second finger from the queen. The smaller movement of the fingers is totally hidden by the larger downward sweep of the hand. The spectators now assume that the card on the table is the queen. When they have registered that fact, drop the spot card in the left hand down beside it and finally the remaining "spot" card – in fact, the queen – from your right hand. All this should be done in one easy rhythmic sequence.

Slowly mix the cards around on the table and then offer to pay odds of two to one if the player can find the lady. If you had not allowed the faces of the cards to be seen, the game would be two to one in *your* favour; but since you place the odds in favour of the victim who hopefully has been keeping his eyes open anyhow, logic should dictate to him that he has by far the greater chance of winning. Master the throw, however, and he seldom will. In revealing the sucker's mistake, again pick up the cards as described and you will be all set to play again.

It is advisable to ring the changes on the positions where you throw down the cards and the combinations of moves you make in shifting the cards around on the table prior to inviting the victim to tell you the position of the queen. Always remember to go through the moves and throw legitimately – actually releasing the queen first – at least once before you start accepting bets. The more in fact you study the legitimate movement, so you will gain a clearer indication of the effect the false throw should simulate.

The above move formed the pivot of the routine practised by the most notorious of all monte operators, a character known in sporting circles as "Canada Bill" Jones. Those close to him became so suspicious of the various appearances which he would assume for the world that on the occasion of his funeral, as the coffin was being lowered into the grave, one of the crowd was heard to bet one thousand dollars to five hundred that he was not in the box. That the bystander found no takers is testimony to the longstanding reputation Jones had gained for squeezing through even tighter holes. It was "Canada Bill" who once put into a nutshell the philosophy of his profession: "Suckers have no business with money, anyway." Both the exit and the sentiment are the kind of which Fields would have religiously approved.

Monte-plus

As in the classic three card monte sequence, the success of this swindle depends upon an optical illusion. But, while the object is still to "find the lady", this time no digital dexterity is involved.

In addition to five cards, one of which is a queen, you will need a bulldog clip about two inches in length and an ordinary spring clothes peg. Overlap the cards in a straight row with the queen in the centre. Trap the cards within the bulldog clip as shown.

Stress the position of the queen, then holding the clip turn all the cards over. Ask someone to point to the queen and to mark it by fastening the peg over its end. The cards should then look like this:

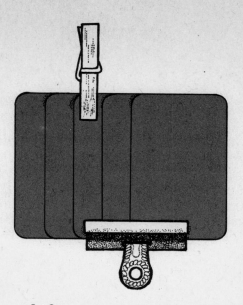

Now turn the cards face-up again and you will be unable to believe your eyes. The peg will never appear to be where it should be, namely on the queen, only on the end card.

The whole ruse depends upon the discrepancy between the ways in which cards overlap when they are face-up and when they are face-down. Make sure that the peg is not too tight so that the sucker can handle it easily, trapping the several layers of card with no problem.

Garter

"The only way I work is cash on the barrel-head!"

In this updated version of the ancient swindle, "Pricking the Garter", a permanent fixture of dock-fronts long ago when the hustlers would use barrel-heads for their working surface, you appear to offer the sucker a fifty-fifty chance of winning. In actual fact, whether he wins or loses is completely under your control. In olden times the operator would use a soft pliable leather thong – hence the title – about four feet in length. You can as easily use a similar length of string or soft rope.

Holding the two ends of the rope together in your left hand and the centre in your right, twirl the latter inwards and lay the rope on the table in this position:

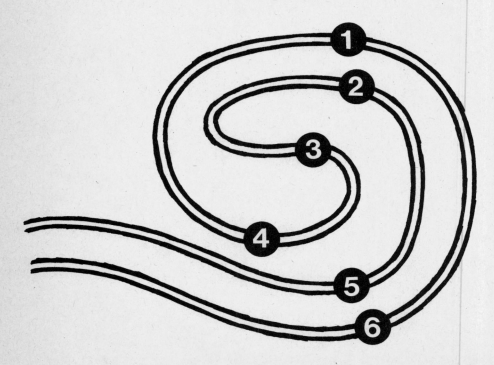

Now pull strand 4 down until it rests alongside 6 and lift 5 alongside 3. This will produce two loops, A and B, in the rope. The result should look as follows:

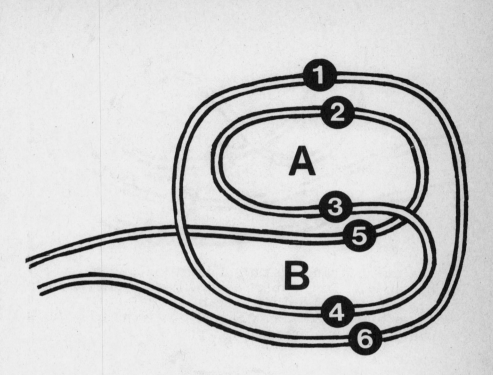

The sucker now has to choose whether to insert his index finger in the centre of either A or B, whereupon the operator will pull at the two ends of the rope. If he puts his finger into the one loop, the rope will come away free. If he inserts it into the other – the correct one – his finger will be caught in the rope when you pull. In order to win, the sucker must trap his finger in such a fashion.

The winning loop is B, a fact that will soon register with the sucker after a few tries. However, at the moment when he thinks he is beginning to grasp the gist of the game, you resort to some subtle hanky-panky. Once again, lay the rope out as in the first illustration, but this time, and without any tell-tale pause, casually put a twist in the final inward twirl as you do so:

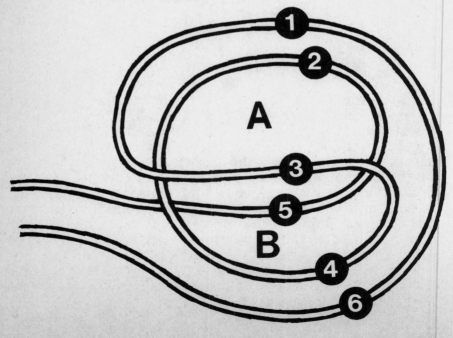

Once again, strand 4 is pulled down to 6 and strand 5 is pushed up to 3. To the most hawk-like pair of eyes there will appear to be no difference in the lay-out, and yet *whichever* loop the sucker attempts to catch with his finger will now come away free when you pull.

Happily, once the rope has been pulled, all the evidence will have evaporated into thin air! Even if you form the correct lay-out some of the time, the odds will still be in your favour (3 to 1, in fact, if you use it as much as half the time). Whenever he places his finger in the free loop you will have an opportunity to lift a strand or two carefully to show he has lost, replace and then demonstrate with your own index finger trapped in the other loop how he could have won.

The Old Army Game

"A little fun, just now and then,
Is relished by the best of men.
If you have nerve, you may have plenty;
Five draws you ten, and ten draws twenty.
Attention giv'n, I'll show to you,
How Umbrella hides the peek-a-boo.
Select your shell, the one you choose;
If right, you win, if not, you lose;
The game itself is lots of fun;
Jim's chances, though, are two to one;
And I tell you your chance is slim
To win a prize from 'Umbrella Jim'."

The Old Army Game

"Who will be the next to outwit me? A little game of chance. Come one and come all. The old Army Game. This is not a game of chance. It is a game of science and skill." Then, on seeing the mayor approach: "Gambling, my dear friends is the root of all evil. For years I was a victim of this awful scourge, gambling, a helpless pawn in the toils of Beelzebub. Beelzebub – Lucifer."

With the doggerel reproduced on the preceding page, "Jim" Miner, alias the "Umbrella Man", one of the most notorious operators of the three shell game in nineteenth-century America, would begin his spiel. It was Fields, however, who really made this swindle his own. He regarded it with such affection that it became a recurring motif in his films – to the extent that one movie which had no connection whatsoever with the swindle was named after it.

The props you require are three half-walnut shells, a pea, and a suitable working surface. For the latter use a felt cloth, a few thicknesses of newspaper, or a rug. The pea, not a real one, should be about 3/10 of an inch in diameter and fashioned from a piece of fine mesh sponge rubber. The amount of "give" provided by the combination of working surface and pea is what makes the swindle possible. For the shells, carefully slice some nuts into halves with a sharp knife. Choose three halves which look approximately the same, scoop out what remains of the kernel, and then with sandpaper smooth down the inside, getting rid of any jagged edges which might impede the movement of the pea.

You also have to learn one basic move. Place the pea on the surface and cover it with a shell held exactly as in the illustration. Now move the shell forward without lifting it from the surface. You will find after a while that you will acquire the knack whereby the pea will travel out of its own accord into your fingers, where it can be grasped secretly between the pads of the thumb and the second finger. The first illustration shows the move forward, the second shows the position of the pea on reaching its destination, as it would appear to someone looking up beneath your hand – if he could see through the table.

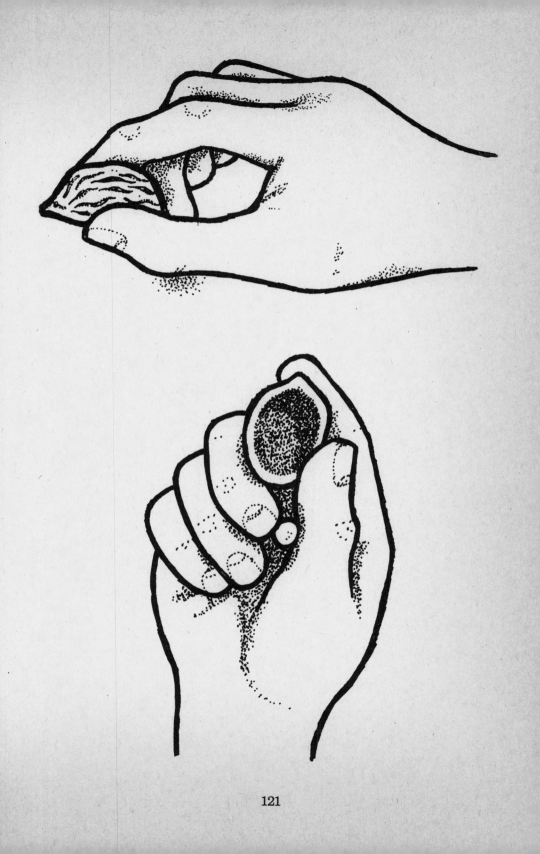

Move the shell back and the pea will automatically ride back beneath its cover. Try it a few times and you will find that the pea and the surface do most of the work for you. Because of the give that exists between them, the shell will not appear to lift at all as the pea leaves.

Once you have mastered the move itself, practise pushing a shell forward, leaving it there, moving your hand – now secretly holding the pea – to another shell and drawing that shell back as the pea rides beneath it. This device enables you to control the exact position of the pea at any moment in the game as you move the shells around. Many combinations are possible in actual performance. Here is a suggested sequence. For clarity in understanding the moves imagine the area on which you'll perform as a rectangular grid divided into 6 squares so:

A	B	C
D	E	F

You start with the shells at D, E and F with the pea in front of E.

1 Cover the pea with shell E and move forward, stealing the pea, to A. Move D to B. Move F to C. Draw A back to E, loading the pea. Draw B back to D. Draw C back to F. Ask the sucker to point to the pea. Nothing in fact has happened so far because the pea, under E, is where it should be. Show the pea at E and tell him how easy it is. He must agree.

2 Again cover the pea with E. Move E to B, stealing the pea. Move D to A and F to C. Draw A back to E, loading the pea, B to D, and C to F. He'll point to D whereupon you show the pea back at E.

3 Once again, cover the pea with E. Move E to A, stealing the pea, F to B, D to C. Draw A back to E, C to F, loading the pea, and B to D. This time he'll point to E and you show him the pea at F.

4 Cover the pea with F. Move F to B, stealing the pea, E to A, and D to C. Draw A back to D, loading the pea, B to F and C to E. He'll point to F and you show the pea at D.

5 Cover the pea with D, move forward to A, stealing the pea. move E to B and F to C. Draw A back to E, B to F, loading the pea, and C to D. He'll point to E. You lift F.

In time you'll develop your own combinations to the point where the movement of the shells will become second nature. As a climax, however, ask the sucker to point to one of the shells. Cover the pea with this shell and ask him then to press his forefinger down on the shell. With his finger in position you push the shell slightly closer to him, but in doing so automatically steal away the pea. You don't do anything differently. Just pretend his finger isn't there. Strangely, he won't feel the pea leave and will swear it is still under his finger. Draw back the other two shells, loading the pea under the one nearer you. Take his bet, then watch his expression when you show him the pea under *your* shell and he lifts his finger to check under his.

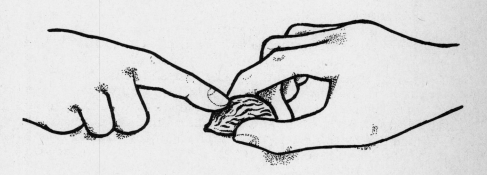

Man: *You cheated us.*
W.C.: *Sir, you impugn my honour. My dear old grandfather said, just before they sprung the trap, you can't cheat an honest man. Never give a sucker an even break or smarten up a chump.*

Appendix

Upon standing for the Presidency:
"When I am elected chief executive of this fair land, amidst thunderous cheering and shouting and throwing of babies out the window, I shall, my fellow citizens, offer no such empty panaceas as a New Deal, or an Old Deal, or even a Re-Deal. No, my friends, the reliable old False Shuffle was good enough for my father and it's good enough for me."

Various items with playing cards have specified the need for false shuffles and false cuts. For complete details the dedicated student should refer either to Scarne or to the classic, *The Expert at the Card Table* by S. W. Erdnase. The following details are merely meant to bridge a technical gap until those books can be consulted.

False shuffle (i): This enables you to keep the order of the entire pack or of an entire packet of cards intact while seemingly mixing them in the sloppiest and therefore the most disarming fashion. Hold the pack face downwards in the left hand. With the left thumb push a few, i.e. about four or five, cards from the top of the pack into the waiting right hand. Now adjust the grip of your left hand and push a few cards this time from the bottom of the pack and receive them on top of those in the right hand. Next push a few cards from the top of the left hand *under* the cards in the right and continue in this fashion, alternating between cards from top and bottom. Remember that the cards that go on top of the right hand cards always come from the bottom of the left hand cards, and that, vice versa, those that go to the bottom of the right hand packet come from the top of the left hand cards. Continue doing this until the left hand cards are exhausted. Repeat the "shuffle" if you wish. The actual effect this has on the cards is that of cutting the pack a number of times. In other words, the essential sequence is not disturbed and it is only necessary to cut the cards at the original top card to bring them back to their original order. The latter may be done openly by fanning the cards with the faces towards you under the pretence of removing the joker or more stealthily by making the top card a key card, a process explained in 'Aces'.

False shuffle (ii): This shuffle enables you to keep one card on top of a pack or packet, while apparently mixing the pack. It should cause you no problem at all if you can do a normal overhand shuffle. Holding the cards in the usual position in the right hand, merely thumb off the top card by itself into the left and then briskly shuffle off all the other cards on top of it. Now take all the cards back into the right hand and shuffle again. Don't worry about the first card this time. It is only necessary to exercise caution as you come to the end of the cards, the last of which should be thumbed singly – back to its starting position.

False cut: This again returns the whole pack to its original sequence. Holding the pack in the right hand from above, fingers at the outer narrow end, thumb at inner, drop about a third of them on the table mentally numbering the pile 1. Drop another similar packet to the right of the pile on the table, numbering this 2. Finally place the rest of the cards to the left of 1, numbering this 3. Now without pausing pick up 2 and place onto 1, and then place 3 onto the pile consisting of 1 and 2. It all seems so disarmingly fair, but the order of the cards has not been disturbed at all. You can vary the ending by picking up 1 and placing it in the left hand, then placing 2 on top, and finally 3 on top of them both. The more you ring this sort of change, the less likely it is that you will be caught.

Acknowledgments

The origins of most of the swindles contained in this book are lost in antiquity. It is sometimes possible, however, to pinpoint an idea to a specific person. With that in mind, I should like to place on record my gratitude to the minds responsible for the following wiles.

Of the items with playing cards, Monte-plus was, I believe, a brainchild of the Canadian comedy conjurer, Joe Stuthard. Kentucky is an adaptation of "Tony Koynini's Derby", a "Magic Wand" publication of George Armstrong from 1952. Likewise Milady can claim kinship with "Strangers from Two Worlds", a mathematical effect described by Stewart James in the magical magazine *Tops* in April 1963. Those interested will find the basic principles used in Second-deal elaborated upon by Harry Lorayne in his book *Close-Up Card Magic*. Look for "Little Fella – Big Fella".

The variation on the classic belt or garter swindle described under Garter was the inspiration of L. Vosburgh Lyons, contributed by him to the 23 July 1943 edition of *The Phoenix*, a prominent magic magazine of that period. Stuart Robson described Inferno, a twist on an old bar game, in the 25 December 1942 issue of the same sheet. Those thwarted in their attempts to "follow the leader" with Twister have the brilliant English magician Alex Elmsley to thank for their frustration. His idea was first published in the 8 January 1955 issue of *Abracadabra*, the world's only magical weekly, which happily – unlike *The Phoenix* – still thrives.

For the introduction to Cocktail, that rarity – an original match puzzle, I am grateful to the delightful *The Pillow-Book Puzzles* by Ivan Morris. The game Matrix was invented by G. W. Lewthwaite and first seen by myself in Martin Gardner's column of "Mathematical Games" in the June 1975 edition of *Scientific American*. Similarly Matrimony is based on the Blades of Grass Game described by the same author in his *Sixth Book of Mathematical Games*.

Anyone seeking more comprehensive information in the fascinating area of probability and proposition bets should consult the excellent quartet of books on gambling by magician Nick Trost or the standard bible on the subject already referred to in these pages, *Scarne's Complete Guide to Gambling*. It was the second volume of Trost's quartet that introduced me to the gambling presentation of the little-known mathematical principle described under Shill. It was Scarne who was the first man to the best of my knowledge who attempted to tear cellophane in print, yet again in *The Phoenix*, 27 November 1942. May that be the only swindle in these pages that *your* sucker ever sees through—literally!

I should also like to thank Darien House Inc. for permission to use the Hirschfeld drawing on page 12. Every effort has been made to trace the copyright holders of quoted material. Should there be any omissions in this respect, I apologise and shall be pleased to make the appropriate acknowledgment in future editions.

Finally my affectionate thanks to those magicians who first introduced me to the delights of deceiving for pleasure and the camaraderie of the magic world. They include Martin Neary—my maternal grandfather, Wizard Edward Beal, Professor Harry Woodley, and Dr. Denis Yetman. I shall be grateful to them always.

About the Author

Born in England in 1945 and educated in classics at Oxford, John Fisher is currently working in an editorial capacity on television production for the BBC. Also an accomplished magician, he is a member of both the Magic Circle and the International Brotherhood of Magicians, and is a regular performer of magic shows on British television.

Among his other books are *John Fisher's Magic Book; The Magic of Lewis and Carroll,* which explores Carroll's interest in conjuring as it relates to his literary work; and *Call Them Irreplaceable,* an appraisal of the style of star quality in the great solo entertainers of the mid-twentieth century.

The Natural History of Big Sur

The Natural History of Big Sur

Paul Henson
and Donald J. Usner

Illustrations by Valerie A. Kells

UNIVERSITY OF CALIFORNIA PRESS
Berkeley · *Los Angeles* · *Oxford*

CALIFORNIA NATURAL HISTORY GUIDES
Arthur C. Smith, *General Editor*

Advisory Editorial Committee:
Rolf Benseler
Ernest Callenbach
Raymond F. Dasman
Don MacNeill
Robert Ornduff

The publisher gratefully acknowledges the contribution provided by the General Endowment Fund of the Associates of the University of California Press.

University of California Press
Berkeley and Los Angeles, California

University of California Press
Oxford, England

Library of Congress Cataloging-in-Publication Data

Henson, Paul.
    The natural history of Big Sur / Paul Henson and Donald J. Usner ; illustrations by Valerie A. Kells.
        p.   cm.—(California natural history guides)
    Includes bibliographical references and index.
    ISBN 0-520-07466-1
    1. Natural history—California—Big Sur.   I. Usner, Donald J.   II. Title.
III. Series.
QH105.C2H46   1993
508.794'76—dc20   92-6938
                                                                                          CIP

Printed in the United States of America

1 2 3 4 5 6 7 8 9

The paper used in this publication meets the minimum requirements of American National Standard for Information Sciences—Permanence of Paper for Printed Library Materials, ANSI Z39.48-1984 ⊗

*For my father, who taught me to walk
quietly in the woods; and my mother, who
was always waiting when we came home.*

Donald J. Usner

*This book is dedicated to my parents,
William and Patricia Henson, without
whose encouragement and gentle prodding
I would never have embarked upon the
path of science and wildlife conservation.*

Paul Henson

Contents

Illustrations

Tables

Maps

Acknowledgments

We would like to thank the many people and organizations that provided support and encouragement during the research and writing of this book. A special thanks goes to the Big Sur Natural History Association for their financial support, for their invaluable advice and guidance, and for giving us access to many of the personal and natural resources we needed to complete this book. Other generous financial contributions were made by the Big Sur Land Trust, the Community Foundation of Monterey County, the Dean Witter Foundation, the Doud Environmental Fund, Esalen Institute, Sam Farr, R. Martin, the Nu Lambda Trust, David and Lucille Packard, Victor Palmeri, Dr. Linus Pauling, Filipa and Boris Veren, and several other donors who wish to remain anonymous.

Technical advice and corrections were contributed by many people. For their time and effort, we want to thank especially Lawrence D. Ford, James Griffin, Terry Jones, Kenneth Norris, Richard Norris, Richard Stanley, Helen Gibbons, Martha Brown, John Smiley, Eric Engles, and Suzanne Shetland. Their attention to detail greatly improved the accuracy of the material. Special thanks are also due to Jenny Wardrip, who created the habitat illustrations in chapters 3 and 4, and Kathy Walker, whose patient and careful copy editing sharpened the text greatly. We also owe thanks to the University of California Press editors who shaped this book into coherence: Art Smith, who edited the nascent manuscript; Ernest Callenbach, who ushered it to its primal book form; and Michelle Nordon, who patiently and cheerfully managed the endless details of the final production of the book.

We would also like to thank, for their enthusiasm and support throughout the process of writing this book, Jeanne LePage, Steven Harper, Alisa Fineman, Evan Goldblatt, Chris Jordan, Brian Hatfield, Colleen Henson, and the Ritchie family. Many other people offered us friendship and welcomed us into the Big Sur community. Foremost among these are Beverly and the late Ernst Ewoldsen, Andrew Gagarin and Odile Segal, the Mayer family, Bob Nash, and the late Boris and Filipa Veren. To these and many other people we owe the completion of this book.

Introduction

When visiting Big Sur for the first time, people often ask, "Just where is Big Sur?" This question is not easy to answer because Big Sur is so many different things to different people. To some, it is the stretch of rugged coastline between Carmel and San Simeon. To others, it is the small collection of roadside businesses and houses in the Big Sur River valley. The wild backcountry of the Ventana Wilderness is included in other visions of "the Big Sur." In her search for a definition, Big Sur writer Lillian Ross concluded that Big Sur is "a state of mind." It seems the area has been poorly defined and little known ever since the Spanish settlers around Monterey vaguely referred to it as *el país grande del sur*—the big country to the south.

Not many would argue, however, that Big Sur's dramatic coastline is the centerpiece of its appeal. Like most visitors, we were overcome with a feeling of awe when we first saw this rocky coast. It moved us as few landscapes ever have and snared us into exploring it further. But the wild mountains behind the coast also attracted us, and after some years of residence, we found that there is much more to Big Sur than its famous mountain-meets-ocean scenery. Looking landward into the heart of the Santa Lucia Range, we realized that the coastline is only the tip of the iceberg, the tempting, titillating edge of Big Sur. We came to identify Big Sur as all of the Santa Lucia Range between the Carmel River and San Carpoforo Creek, including the coastline. This is the area we cover in this book.

Few people suspect the diverse landscapes included within these coastal mountains. Arid, desertlike canyons, jagged mountain peaks, and quiet valleys are tucked away in the range. Verdant river corridors contrast with scorching slopes. A great variety of forest, scrub, and grassland plant communities cover the mountains, from spacious pine forests to impenetrable chaparral to shady redwood groves. The wildlife of the region is equally diverse—ocean creatures such as cormorants and sea otters live in close proximity to arid climate animals such as canyon wrens and whiptail lizards. All of these many pieces add up to create Big Sur.

But what is really known of Big Sur's plants, rocks, and animals? Some people have studied the mountains over the years, most notably students and researchers at Big Creek Reserve on the coast and at Hastings Reserve in Carmel Valley. But almost nothing of this information is available outside of scientific literature. More than 3 million visitors pass through Big Sur each year, and few leave knowing more about the area than when they first came.

This curious lack of natural history material about the area struck us as we began to explore the Santa Lucia Range. While writers, poets, painters, and photographers have long extolled Big Sur's powerful natural beauty, very few looked at the origins of the mountains and the patterns of life in them. The area is world famous for its awe-inspiring scenery and undeveloped mountain coastline. What is less known but equally important is the region's great ecological diversity and its significance as a haven for many species of terrestrial and marine wildlife. We hope *The Natural History of Big Sur* will fill this gap.

The book is divided into two major sections that complement each other. Part I is a narrative overview of Big Sur's natural history, and part II is a detailed description of Big Sur's public lands. While part I focuses on regional patterns and processes, part II describes specific natural features along trails and roads. A prominent rock outcrop or a fire-gutted redwood, a sea cliff exposure or plant succession in a burned forest—in part II, these are discussed in the context of the information presented in part I.

We start off with the foundation of Big Sur's natural history—its geology. Geological features such as topography, soil type, and erosional patterns shape the distribution and evolution of plant and animal species. Big Sur's geology, like that of all of coastal California, has puzzled geologists for decades, and many aspects are still controversial. In chapter 1, we present a summary of the current ideas on this remarkable geology.

A second predominant factor shaping Big Sur's natural history—the weather—is discussed in the next chapter. Many plants and animals are adapted to specific climatic conditions and are thus limited in their distribution. Redwood trees, for example, are restricted to foggy coastal canyons, while chaparral shrubs thrive on hot, dry slopes in the interior of the mountains. The weather, along with the complex topography, creates the wide range of conditions conducive to this diversity.

Starting at the coastline and working upward in elevation, the next several chapters describe the patterns of vegetation on the landscape. The productive edge of the marine world, the rocky shoreline, is treated first. Terrestrial plant life is treated next and is divided into seven major plant communities that serve to simplify Big Sur's complex vegetation.

Many animals tend to live most of the time in one plant community. A meadowlark is typical of the grassland community but would almost never be seen in a redwood forest, and the winter wren is common in the redwood forest but would be a very rare sight in grassland. Thus, we felt it most useful to discuss which species of animals to expect in each plant community. Animals that range over many plant communities, such as bobcats, foxes, and hawks, are described in a more complete overview of Big Sur's fauna in a separate chapter. We include discussions of amphibian, reptile, bird, and mammal species. We also compiled species lists and present discussions of rare, endangered, and unusual species, such as the California condor and the sea otter.

Following the chapters on flora and fauna is a discussion of fire ecology, one of the most important and dynamic influences on Big Sur's natural history. Many of Big Sur's plants and animals have evolved to live with periodic fire. Some species of plants even require fire to reproduce. Although historically viewed as a negative factor, fire is now recognized as an essential element in many ecosystems, including Big Sur's. We found it to be important enough to deserve its own chapter.

No less influential on Big Sur's landscape have been the activities of people. Chapter 7 provides background on the prehistoric people who lived in Big Sur: the Esselen, Ohlone, and Salinan tribes. Arriving about 5000–8000 years ago, these people were an integral part of the area's natural history. They hunted and gathered throughout Big Sur, including the rocky shoreline, and used fire to shape their environment.

The native inhabitants vanished soon after the arrival of Spanish missionaries and white settlers. The changes in the Big Sur environment with this influx of new people are the subject of chapter 8, the final chapter in part I. Big Sur may appear pristine compared to nearby urban areas, but logging, ranching, settlement, and fire management have had a profound impact on the Santa Lucia Range. It is important to recognize these changes, not only to appreciate what Big Sur once was but to be able to anticipate changes in the landscape as development and tourism pressures increase.

Part II builds on the foundation laid in part I. We have broken up Big Sur's public lands into three sections: state parks, coastal lands of the Los Padres National Forest, and interior National Forest lands. We describe natural features along trails and roads in each of these sections with reference to information presented in part I. This will allow the reader to apply the information given in part I to what is encountered in the field. In addition, five maps covering all of the Big Sur area are presented at the back of the book and are cited throughout part II.

The Natural History of Big Sur is not a systematic field guide to the plants and animals of Big Sur. We have, however, generously sprinkled the text with illustrations of common and unusual plants and animals and have provided species lists of plants, birds, reptiles and amphibians, and mammals. Other field guides specific to Monterey County or to the western states are listed at the end of the appropriate chapters under Suggested Reading. In the same way, part II is not a step-by-step physical description of Big Sur trails. The focus is on natural history rather than on trail conditions, mileages, and park regulations. Much of this latter information changes yearly and can be obtained from state park and U.S. Forest Service personnel.

The natural history of the Big Sur area has only just begun to be explored in any detail, and we hope this book will stimulate further research and understanding. Once a thorough appreciation for Big Sur's unique qualities is established, half the battle for preserving the area for future generations will be won. We hope this book is a positive step toward that goal so that Big Sur will always retain its wild and undeveloped character.

PART I

Big Sur Natural History

CHAPTER I

Big Sur Geology

In Big Sur, where the mountains of the Santa Lucia Range rise abruptly from the Pacific Ocean, the two utterly opposed elements of rock and sea contrast more dramatically than anywhere else in the United States. This unique geological circumstance creates both the fantastic scenery that draws thousands of visitors and the rugged maze of mountains that has deterred settlement and sheltered wildlife. A long, tumultuous geological history led to the development of these mountains, and they form the foundation upon which the natural history of Big Sur is built.

The area presents some of the most complicated geology in California, and geologists seeking to understand the origin of the mountains are faced with a formidable task. The range is made of many different kinds of rock, from pieces of seafloor volcanoes and ancient mountain chains, to layers of stream cobbles and sediments from shallow and deep oceans. Diverse rocks that formed under radically varied conditions are now mixed together in jumbled disorder. A complex network of faults fractures the range and blocks of rock have moved great distances along this network, further complicating the picture.

Road cuts along Highway 1 provide clear cross-sections of the diversity of rock types: light gray granitic rock near Garrapata State Park and up to Hurricane Point; steep cliffs of cemented cobbles near Esalen Institute; dark, volcanic rocks near Lucia; and gray, layered sediments near Gorda. Coastal cliffs also vary a great deal, from the contorted rocks of Andrew Molera State Park to the soft layered sandstones at Pacific Valley.

The story of how these rocks formed and came together to make the Santa Lucia Range and the Big Sur coast is still not completely clear, and current ideas seem nearly as extreme as the landscape. Some geologists suggest that much of the rock in the Santa Lucias originated 2900 km (1800 mi) away at the latitude of Acapulco, Mexico, and that some rocks exposed in the mountains were once buried to a depth of 23 km (14 mi) beneath the earth's surface.

This complex geology is reflected in all aspects of Big Sur's natural history. The steep wall of mountains wrings the winter wind of its moisture, providing plentiful rainfall from the coastline to the range's summit, while creating an almost bone-dry rain shadow in its lee. The rugged terrain creates a wide range of environments for plants and animals, from deep, shadowed canyons to sunny, dry slopes. The rocks also weather to a variety of soil types to encourage diversity in terrestrial plants.

TOPOGRAPHY

From Highway 1 the Santa Lucia Mountains appear deceptively simple, as if a single ridge rises from the ocean to a summit ridgeline. But viewed from the air, greater complexity is apparent: the mountains are a chaos of ridges and canyons bordering the Pacific Ocean and extending inland as far as 32 km (20 mi). Deep gorges, jagged mountain peaks, and steep ridges seldom give way to gentle terrain anywhere in the range. It is difficult to make out a clearly defined mountain chain in this rugged land, but patterns do exist. Perhaps most striking is the parallelism of landforms in the range: it is made up of a series of ridges trending northwest–southeast and the coastline follows this same orientation. Narrow, northwest–southeast oriented drainages separate these ridges, and the few valleys in the range also follow this pattern (figs. 1 and 2).

The range stretches for about 161 km (100 mi) from just south of Carmel to a vaguely defined southern limit north of San Luis Obispo. It is only 32 km (20 mi) across at its widest point and gradually decreases in elevation from north to south. Junipero Serra Peak, the highest point in the Santa Lucias at 1787 m (5862 ft), is an isolated mountain mass that sits just eastward of the bulk of the mountains. In the north, a spectacular series of rocky spires—the Ventana Cones—dominates the

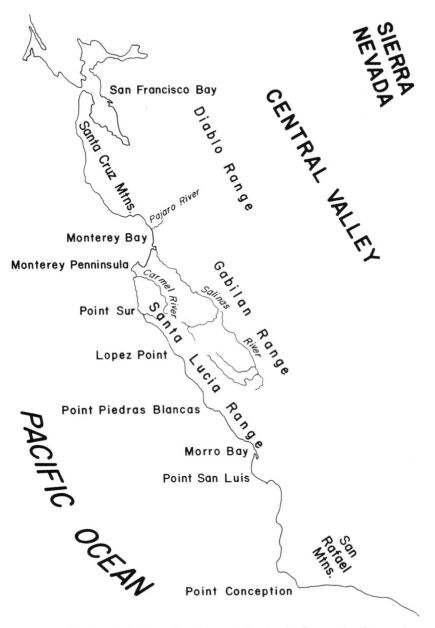

Figure 1. Regional physiography of central California, from Point Conception to San Francisco Bay.

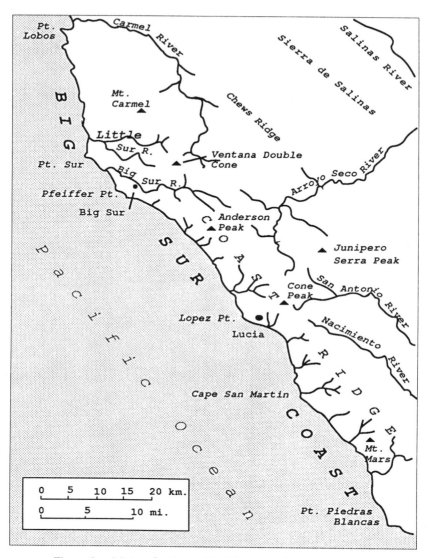

Figure 2.   Major physiographical features of the Big Sur area.

mountains. The southern parts of the range are far more gentle, and few rocky summits protrude (fig. 3).

A single main ridge, the Coast Ridge, fronts much of the immediate coastline. The steep slope of this ridge is cut by numerous deep, narrow canyons that open onto the Pacific Ocean, creating the scenery for

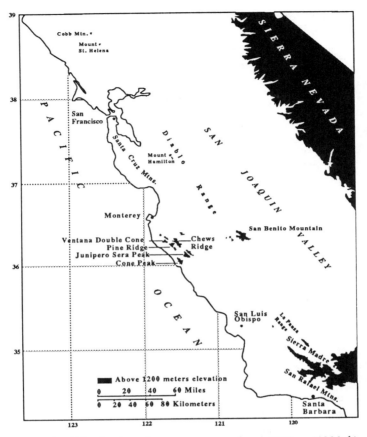

Figure 3.   Distribution of montane areas above 1200 m (4000 ft)
elevation in central California. (After Griffin, J. R., and
Critchfield, W. B., 1976. *The distribution of forest trees
in California.* U.S.D.A. Forest Service Research Paper
PSW-82. Berkeley: Pacific Southwest Forest and Range
Experiment Station.)

which Big Sur is most famous. Like fingers reaching for the ocean, narrow spur ridges perpendicular to the Coast Ridge separate the coastal
canyons.

With its highest elevations at less than 1800 m (6000 ft), the Santa
Lucia Range may not sound impressive. But what it lacks in great elevations, the range more than compensates for in relief. The Coast Ridge
is never more than 11 km (7 mi) from the ocean along its entire length,
and it forms the steepest coastal slope in the contiguous United States,

where it rises from the ocean to Cone Peak (1571 m or 5155 ft) in a distance of just 4.8 km (3 mi).

Here and there the coastal ridges give way to flatlands along the ocean's edge. These coastal terraces are the exception rather than the rule, however. For most of its length, the Coast Ridge and its spur ridges drop abruptly into the Pacific, presenting a vertical wall of rock scalloped irregularly into rocky coves with very few sandy beaches. The steepness continues offshore where a narrow continental shelf drops to the continental slope in only a few kilometers. The ocean reaches a depth of more than 3600 m (12,000 ft) just 80 km (50 mi) offshore. Two deep submarine canyons cut into the shelf near the Big Sur coast: the Sur Submarine Canyon, reaching a depth of 914 m (3000 ft) just 13 km (8 mi) south of Point Sur, and Partington Submarine Canyon, which reaches a similar depth of 11 km (6.8 mi) offshore of Grimes Canyon. These canyons merge and drop into the deep plains of the Pacific Ocean as one of the deepest submarine canyons on earth.

Parallel to the dominant ridges, the Big Sur coastline trends sharply northwest–southeast in a jagged series of rocky points. The most westward of these is Point Sur, a dark, isolated cone of volcanic rock that sits like a pivot point where the coastline turns slightly eastward. Other than this bend, the northwest–southeast trend of the coastline is broken only at Lopez Point, where it takes an abrupt turn to an east–west orientation for a short distance.

The eastern flank of the Santa Lucia Range descends to the Salinas Valley, where the steep, rushing mountain streams level out and join the Salinas River. Fan-shaped piles of sediment have accumulated where the streams spill onto the valley floor. The striking parallelism in the region continues in the long, straight, northwest–southeast trend of the Salinas Valley. The Carmel River Valley parallels the Salinas as it drains the northeastern portion of the range. The Big Sur River also flows northwestward through the north-central mountains. No drainage cuts across the range.

The ruggedness and steepness of the Santa Lucia Range clearly reveal that this landscape is not very old. Ruggedness is testimony to the youth of mountain ranges, as the slow processes of erosion have yet to wear down the recently risen rock. The Santa Lucia Range has been uplifted from near sea level to their present height in only the past 2 million years (which is short in geological time), although the rocks that make up the range are ancient and have a complicated history.

Geologists, puzzled by the juxtaposition of very dissimilar rocks in the Santa Lucias and elsewhere in California, have long suspected that the rocks must have moved into position by movement of the earth's crust after they were formed. But a coherent picture of just how such movement could have occurred did not emerge until the theory of plate tectonics was developed in the mid-1960s.

PLATE TECTONICS

Coastal California occupies a tenuous position at the boundary of two huge, moving pieces of crustal rock—the Pacific and North American plates. These are two of seven large and several small plates that make up the solid outer layer of the earth (fig. 4). About 80 km (50 mi) thick, these crustal plates "float" in constant motion on partially molten rock like ice floating on a viscous sea. Some plates slide past each other laterally along deep fractures in the crust known as *strike-slip faults*. The Pacific and North American plates slip along a network of strike-slip faults in the San Andreas system.

While these two plates are sliding laterally past each other, other plates are colliding and still others are pulling away from one another. Most plates move extremely slowly, comparable to the average growth rate of a human fingernail. At this rate, which varies from 1 to 13 cm (0.4 to 5 in.) per year, a plate could move as much as 1300 km (800 mi) in just 10 million years, a short span of geological time.

The Pacific plate moves northwestward relative to the North American plate at about 3.8 cm (1.5 in.) per year. Coastal central and southern California ride the Pacific plate, while the rest of California is on the North American plate. The sliver of coastline, including the Santa Lucia Range, has moved northwestward several hundred kilometers along the San Andreas fault system in the past 30 million years. Each small movement along the fault creates a tremor of some magnitude, and nearly all of California's earthquakes are caused by periodic movements along the San Andreas fault system.

Many of the rocks of the Santa Lucia Range were formed at a different kind of plate boundary than the strike-slip fault that exists there today, however. Prior to 30 million years ago, a plate under the Pacific Ocean was colliding directly into North America rather than sliding past it. This oceanic plate, called the Farallon plate, slid down under the less dense continental crust in a process known as *subduction* and vanished beneath the continent. As it slipped into a deep undersea trench and down under the continent, a thick wedge of ocean floor rock was

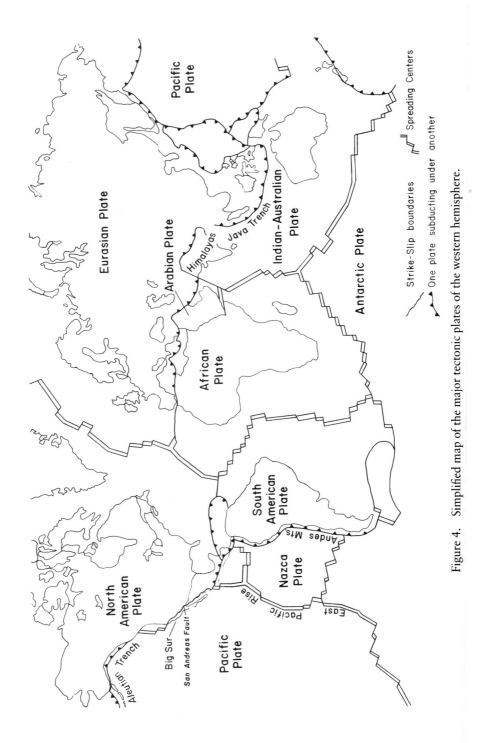

Figure 4. Simplified map of the major tectonic plates of the western hemisphere.

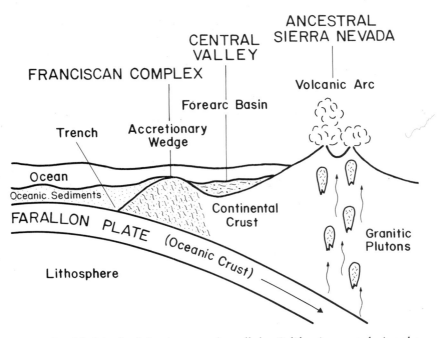

Figure 5. Model of subduction complex off the California coast during the late Mesozoic era.

scraped onto the continental plate. The plates ground past each other, forcing crustal rocks into this so-called *accretionary wedge*. Today this wedge is represented by a crushed and churned mass of rock extending all along the California coast, including much of the Big Sur coast (fig. 5).

Since the late 1960s, most geologists have agreed that the predominant rocks of the Big Sur region formed during this great collision of plates and that movements of the San Andreas fault system later transported the rocks northwestward to their present location. However, more recent studies of the rocks of the Santa Lucia Range suggest they may have an even more distant origin. In fact, new methods for determining the origins of rocks place them much farther to the south, in tropical latitudes, prior to 55 million years ago. A whole new theory of continent building emerged in the early 1980s to explain the origins and movements of these and other far-traveled rocks.

According to the new ideas, each continent is, in part, a patchwork of many smaller pieces of the earth's crust, blocks of rock called *microplates* or *terranes* that most often originate as oceanic plateaus, seamounts, or ocean floor sediments. These blocks move along with the plates but are broken off the oceanic crust and are attached to continents when an oceanic and continental plate collide.

The Santa Lucia Range appears to be partly composed of distinct terranes, and the entire west coast of North America may in fact be made up of many terranes. The new scenarios not only show these terranes moving hundreds of kilometers along the San Andreas fault over the past 30 million years but also suggest that the rocks originated much farther away before entering the San Andreas system.

The concept of wandering terranes colliding into and adding to continents has gained wide acceptance among many geologists, but is still contested by some. More studies are needed, but large parts of the Santa Lucia Range seem to be remnants of far-traveled microplates. This story will no doubt continue to be refined by new data and ideas.

EARLY CENTRAL CALIFORNIA GEOLOGICAL HISTORY

The bulk of the Santa Lucia Range is composed of two large blocks of rock: the Salinian block and the Nacimiento block. These blocks have their origins in the early geological history of California. To tell the story of their formation, it is necessary to go back 130 million years, when the western shoreline of North America lay about where the Sierra Nevada stands today and the Santa Lucia Range did not exist.

About that time, the Farallon plate was sliding under the North American continent in a deep trench offshore, and thick layers of sediments that had accumulated on the ocean floor over millions of years were scraped off the downgoing plate. These sediments slowly piled up in the thick accretionary wedge between the trench and the continent. The leading edge of the Farallon plate melted as it descended into the hot interior of the earth. The molten rock triggered volcanic eruptions at the continent's surface and formed a series of volcanoes inland from the wedge. Deeper in the crust, other masses of magma called *plutons* cooled very slowly over millions of years beneath the volcanic arc and solidified into granitic rock.

The chain of volcanoes formed an ancestral Sierra Nevada range, while the wedge sediments accumulated undersea in a pile that eventually reached sea level to form an offshore chain of islands. A wide basin separated the Sierran volcanic arc from the accretionary wedge. The outlines of the modern topography of California thus began to be defined: the Sierra Nevada granites rose beneath the volcanoes to the east, the wide basin eventually closed and drained to become the Cen-

tral Valley of California, and the great wedge of rock eventually lifted
high above sea level to become the South Coast Ranges, including portions of the modern Santa Lucia Range.

As subduction of the Farallon plate continued into Late Cretaceous
and early Tertiary time, 60–70 million years ago, the granitic plutons
of the Sierra Nevada slowly uplifted above ground and began to erode.
Sand, gravel, mud, and cobbles washed down from the Sierra highlands
and accumulated in the surrounding lowlands. The Central Valley of
California is today underlain by these conglomerates and other sediments piled about 9000 m (30,000 ft) deep. Similar conglomerate formations remain in the Santa Lucia Range and the Sierra Nevada.

According to microplate advocates, two exotic terranes entered the
scene at this point. One, a piece of crustal rock that had formed in
tropical latitudes, collided with the southern portion of the Sierra Nevada chain about 55 million years ago. The rocks of this drifting terrane
were similar in composition to the Sierran granites and were probably
part of a distant volcanic arc. A second terrane made mostly of sea floor
rocks was joined to the accretionary wedge about the same time and
slowly began to be crushed and mixed with ocean floor sediments in the
wedge.

Subduction stopped about 29 million years ago when the Farallon
plate disappeared beneath the continent and the North American and
Pacific plates met. The two plates then began to slip laterally past each
other, and the San Andreas fault system formed, marking their
boundary. As the fault appeared, a piece of the ancestral Sierra Nevada,
including the newly attached exotic terrane, was dragged northwestward along with the Pacific plate. This mass of plutonic and metamorphic rocks, called the Salinian block, now underlies most of central
coastal California, including much of the northern interior part of the
Santa Lucia Range. Another massive piece of crustal rock, the Nacimiento block, was also torn off the North American plate and joined
the Salinian block during its northwestward migration. Composed
mostly of rocks from the accretionary wedge and the associated sea
floor terrane, the Nacimiento block underlies much of the Big Sur coastline and the southern interior part of the range.

BASEMENT ROCK ASSEMBLAGES

These two giant chunks of crustal rock, the Salinian and Nacimiento
blocks, make up the bulk of the Santa Lucia Range (fig. 6). Together

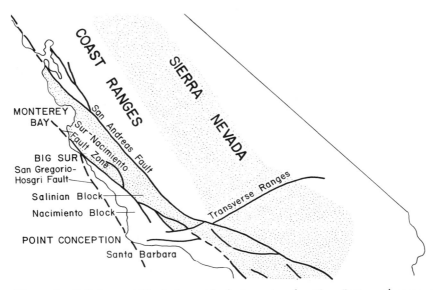

Figure 6.   Salinian and Nacimiento blocks in regional setting. Patterned areas
indicate granitic and metamorphic rocks.

they form the core, or *basement,* of the range and contain its oldest
rocks. Each is a distinct, fault-bounded sliver of the earth's crust. The
juxtaposition of these two blocks has long been a puzzle to geologists,
for the rocks of each block formed under vastly different conditions.

THE SALINIAN BLOCK

The Salinian block is bounded on the east by the San Andreas fault and
on the west by the Sur-Nacimiento fault. It extends for about 480 km
(300 mi) northwestward from the Transverse Ranges north of Santa
Barbara to Bodega Head north of San Francisco on land and continues
from there an undetermined distance offshore (fig. 6).

The Salinian block is made up of hard granitic and metamorphic
rocks. Its granitic rocks cooled slowly deep beneath the earth's surface,
which allowed large crystals to grow that are visible to the naked eye.
Its metamorphic rocks formed by the partial melting of sea floor rocks
that also cooled slowly, forming large crystals. Most of the Salinian
rocks thus have a crystalline structure formed under conditions of very
high temperature and relatively low pressure. The crystalline structure
gives the rocks a coarse, granular appearance, and reflective faces of

crystals sparkle on fresh cuts of rock. The crystalline Salinian block is today surrounded on all sides by very different rocks. This seemingly misplaced island of Salinian rocks has intrigued geologists for decades and led one to label it "a Mesozoic orphan in the California Coast Ranges."

If one imagines moving the Salinian block southeastward along the San Andreas fault—opposite to the direction it is thought to have traveled—it would reach a region between the southern Sierra Nevada and the Peninsular Ranges where rocks similar in composition to the Salinian granites are found. The similarity of the rocks has led geologists to believe that the block was once positioned in the southern Sierras and that later movements of the San Andreas fault brought it northwestward to the central coast.

Some common metamorphic rock types of the Salinian block include marble, which is metamorphosed limestone; amphibolite, formed from greatly heated volcanic or sedimentary rocks; and gneiss, a banded, course-grained rock that forms from the metamorphism of a number of rocks including shale, sandstone, and granite. The most common granitic rocks of the Salinian block are quartz diorite, granodiorite, and tonalite.

The metamorphic rocks of the Salinian block are the oldest known rocks from any of the California Coast Ranges. It is difficult to tell when the original rocks formed because they were drastically altered by heat and pressure during their metamorphism. But they are thought to be much older than adjacent plutonic rocks, which have been dated at about 130 million years old.

The crystalline rocks of the Salinian block are easily recognized where they are exposed. Since they have not been radically mixed, Salinian rocks do not appear as crushed and jumbled as the rocks of the Nacimiento block. Limestone or marble outcrops are white in color and stand out vividly. Because of their light color and granitic appearance, some people have described them as "Sierra-like" in appearance. These and most of the granitic rocks of the Salinian block are relatively hard and erode slowly. As a result, they form many of the high peaks of the range, such as the Ventana Cones and Pico Blanco. In some places, granitic rocks have been weathered and crushed by rock movements to resemble sandstone. These decomposed granites easily crumble into coarse sand as they erode.

Highway 1 cuts through Salinian rocks in several places, most extensively between Grimes Canyon and Julia Pfeiffer-Burns State Park (fig. 7).

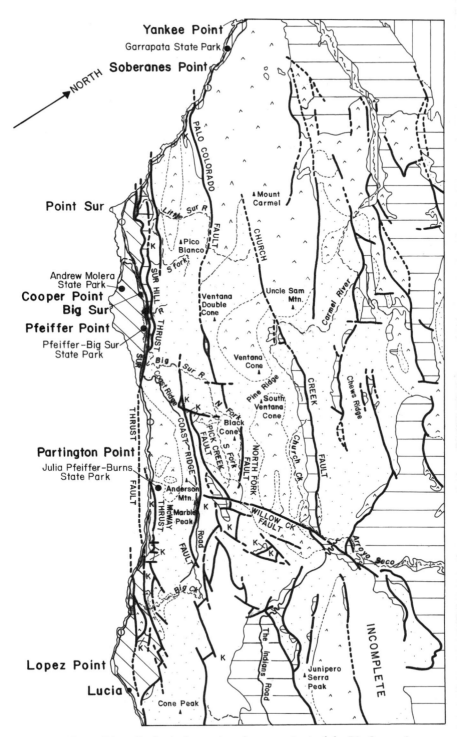

Figure 7A.   Geological map (northern portion) of the Big Sur region.

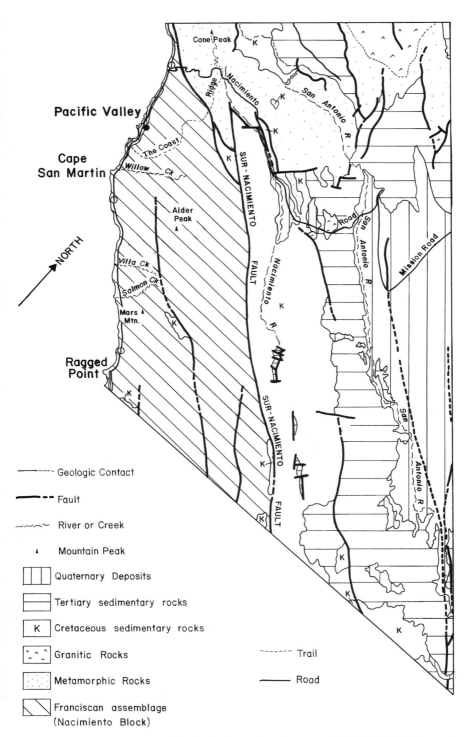

Figure 7B. Continuation of geological map (southern portion) of the Big Sur region.

Salinian granitic rocks also have eroded to form the steep rocky coves south of Carmel to Bixby Creek. They are especially accessible and visible in the coves and coastal cliffs of Garrapata State Park and at Partington Cove in Julia Pfeiffer-Burns State Park.

THE NACIMIENTO BLOCK

The Nacimiento block is the name of a group of rocks that borders the Salinian block along the Sur-Nacimiento fault. It forms the basement rock in the southern half of the Santa Lucia Range and in two broad bands along the coast (fig. 6). It is a fault-bounded piece of a more extensive group of rocks called the Franciscan complex, which is found throughout coastal California.

The Nacimiento block, like the Franciscan complex, is a disorderly mixture of both sedimentary and metamorphic rocks. Most of its metamorphic rocks, in contrast to those in the Salinian block, formed under relatively low temperature and very high pressure. The sediments of the Franciscan complex are rarely in the horizontal layers in which they were deposited. Instead, the layers tilt at all angles and are bent and deformed into undifferentiated masses.

In the Franciscan complex, sandstone and shale (solidified mud) are jumbled into a mixture with metamorphic rocks such as greenstone (metamorphosed lava), chert (a hard, glassy rock formed from the compressed remains of marine microorganisms), and blueschist (a rock formed from sedimentary or volcanic rocks under extreme pressure). In this chaotic mixture, blocks of intact rock "float" in masses of crushed and sheared rock. Highly metamorphosed rock such as blueschist, which forms at burial depths of up to 20–30 km (12–18 mi), is often mixed with unmetamorphosed sandstone or shale.

Many geologists now believe that the mixed-up jumble of the Franciscan complex was created by mixing in the accretionary wedge at the margin of the North American and ancestral Farallon plates. As oceanic crust and overlying rocks were dragged deep into the wedge by the down-thrusting plate, they were metamorphosed under extreme pressures, although temperatures remained moderate. Further mixing in the wedge brought these metamorphosed rocks back to the surface, where they were placed alongside unmetamorphosed surface sediments.

Much of the Franciscan complex, including the Nacimiento block, accumulated slowly in the accretionary wedge between about 130 and

70 million years ago—about the same time that the plutons of the Sa-lian block were cooling deep beneath the earth's surface. The Franciscan rocks were transported northwestward along the San Andreas and Sur-Nacimiento faults to eventually lie in central California alongside the Salinian block. However, recent analysis of Franciscan rocks suggest that, like parts of the Salinian block, some of them formed in tropical latitudes. As pieces of ancient sea floor, they drifted into and collided with North America and were then mixed into the accretionary wedge.

The Franciscan rocks of the Nacimiento block are generally darker in color than the Salinian rocks and range from gray sandstones to dark-green greenstone to black shale. They are coarse to fine-grained, but lack the crystalline structure of the Salinian rocks. Already crushed and sheared in the accretionary wedge, Franciscan rocks erode more easily than the harder Salinian rocks. The lower, gentler landscape of the southern half of the Santa Lucia Range is a consequence of this greater susceptibility to erosion.

Highway 1 cuts through rocks of the Nacimiento block many places between Esalen Institute and San Carpoforo Creek (fig. 7). Franciscan rocks form coastal cliffs and offshore rocks along this same stretch and also between Point Sur and Castro Canyon. They are easily seen in the cliffs at Willow Creek and Sand Dollar beaches, Jade Cove, and Kirk Creek. Some unusual looking Franciscan rocks form the seacliffs at Pfeiffer Beach and Andrew Molera State Park.

OVERLYING FORMATIONS

Both Franciscan and Salinian rocks are often difficult to see outside of road cuts, canyons, and coastal cliffs because they are overlain by younger rock formations and recent deposits of sand and gravel. Since their formation, the Salinian and Nacimiento blocks have been alter-nately submerged and exposed above the ocean. Sediments from the ocean and nearby land slowly accumulated on the basement rocks when they were underwater and became gradually compressed and hardened into sedimentary rocks. These sedimentary rocks and the basement rock itself were worn down again as the range uplifted, although not uni-formly throughout the area. As a result, sedimentary rock formations of many different ages and character overlie the Salinian and Naci-miento blocks.

The oldest of these sedimentary formations was deposited as the

Franciscan was still accumulating 65–70 million years ago, during the Cretaceous period. These rocks are found most extensively in the southern half of the Santa Lucias, but also in patches elsewhere, and consist mostly of sandstones and conglomerates. Studies of some of these rocks on the east side of the range suggest that they accumulated in or near submarine canyons. A few marine invertebrate fossils have been found in these formations. Cretaceous conglomerates are visible in roadcuts along Highway 1 between Julia Pfeiffer-Burns State Park and Esalen Institute (fig. 7); especially good exposures are near the Buck Creek and Lime Creek bridges. These conglomerates resemble a mass of large and small rounded rocks encased in concrete.

The majority of the sedimentary formations lying on the basement rock were laid down more recently than these Cretaceous sediments, that is, during the Tertiary period from 64 to 2 million years ago. Tertiary sediments accumulated on the basement rocks to a thickness of more than 2700 m (9000 ft). They are now found mostly on the eastern and northern flanks of the Santa Lucia Range, while the interior and western slope of the mountains are no longer extensively covered by these sediments. Erosion has removed large sections of the rocks, and nowhere are all of the layers of the many Tertiary deposits exposed in one sequence.

Deposits varying from coarse, terrestrial sandstones and conglomerates of the Church Creek Formation to the fine-grained siltstones and shales of the Monterey Formation are scattered around the mountains. Along the coast, the buff-colored sandstones of the Santa Margarita Formation are exposed in the roadcut along Highway 1 about 1.6 km (1 mi) south of Hurricane Point and in Pfeiffer–Big Sur State Park. Much more extensive and prominent exposures of other Tertiary formations are accessible in the backcountry in Pine Valley, Church Creek, and the Arroyo Seco drainage. The Indians Road also cuts extensively through Tertiary rocks. These wind- and water-carved rocks are some of the most colorful and oddly shaped rocks in the range and lend a distinctive, desertlike quality to the landscape.

The sedimentary formations are a record of events during the Tertiary period. Fine-grained shales reflect periods of submergence beneath deep oceans. Coarse marine sandstones were deposited nearshore or in shallow seas. Conglomeratic rocks indicate the location of ancient stream channels or nearshore submarine canyons where large cobbles washed down in strong currents.

FAULTS

Faults are fractures along which rocks have moved. The Santa Lucia Range is cut by numerous major faults that separate huge blocks of rock. These faults generally run, or strike, northwest–southeast, parallel to the coastline and the general trend of the mountains. Some formed relatively recently as a result of massive rock movements that accompanied the uplift of the mountain range, but the longest and deepest fault in the area, the Sur-Nacimiento fault, is very ancient. It forms the boundary between the two basement rock formations of the range, the Nacimiento and Salinian blocks (fig. 6). Some geologists believe that this fault was most active during the Late Cretaceous period, about 70 million years ago, and that it is the remnant scar of the subduction zone once active off the California coast. The fault originates in the Transverse Ranges north of Santa Barbara and trends out to sea 290 km (180 mi) to the northwest, near Point Sur.

The Sur-Nacimiento fault intersects another major fault, the San Gregorio–Hosgri fault, offshore from Point Sur. The San Gregorio–Hosgri fault lies offshore along much of the Big Sur coast and comes on land north of Monterey Bay at Point Año Nuevo (fig. 6), where it cuts very young (less than 10,000-year-old) sedimentary deposits. This evidence of recent movement classifies it as an active fault. It is part of the San Andreas fault system, relieving some of the stress generated as the North American and Pacific plates slip past each other.

The San Gregorio–Hosgri fault zone was not well-known until the mid-1970s when the construction of the Diablo Canyon nuclear power plant 3 km (2 mi) from the fault sparked interest in its movements. In 1986, researchers found evidence that the fault may be the future site of an earthquake. They believe that a magnitude 7.2 earthquake on the fault may occur during the 1990s and that its location would most likely be in one of two areas: between San Francisco and Santa Cruz or between Monterey Bay and Ragged Point off the Big Sur coast.

The Palo Colorado fault in Big Sur intersects the San Gregorio–Hosgri fault beneath Monterey Bay. Any movement of the San Gregorio–Hosgri fault is likely to cause movement in the Palo Colorado fault, so it is also considered active.

Earthquakes are not new to Big Sur. Small tremors are common, and Big Sur shakes along with the rest of coastal California whenever the great San Andreas system moves. The late old-timer George Harlan,

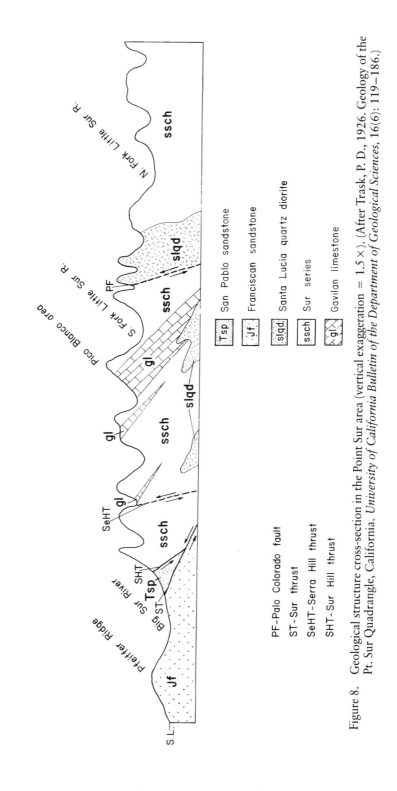

Figure 8. Geological structure cross-section in the Point Sur area (vertical exaggeration = 1.5 ×). (After Trask, P. D., 1926. Geology of the Pt. Sur Quadrangle, California. *University of California Bulletin of the Department of Geological Sciences*, 16(6): 119–186.)

Tsp   San Pablo sandstone

Jf   Franciscan sandstone

slqd   Santa Lucia quartz diorite

ssch   Sur series

gl   Gavilan limestone

PF-Palo Colorado fault

ST-Sur thrust

SeHT-Serra Hill thrust

SHT-Sur Hill thrust

who was living at Lucia, recalled feeling the great earthquake of 1906, which caused widespread devastation in San Francisco. The 1989 Loma Prieta quake was also strongly felt by Big Sur residents.

Faults are often hard to discern in Big Sur because they are obscured by overlying rock formations, landslide deposits, and vegetation. However, they are sometimes marked by wide zones of gouged and crushed rock. A large fault crossing Highway 1 at Hurricane Point leaves such a trail of crushed white limestone fragments. A slice of the same fault crosses the Old Coast Road just 2.5 km (1.5 mi) northeast from Andrew Molera State Park in a narrow zone of crushed rock.

Fault movement can also offset stream courses, forcing them to take conspicuous right-angle turns. Big Creek makes such a turn about 1.6 km (1 mi) upstream from the ocean where a major fault crosses it. In other places, water flows in straight lines along the easily eroded, crushed rock of fault zones. The lower Big Sur River from the gorge to Andrew Molera State Park follows such a course, as does the North Fork of the Big Sur, the South Fork of the Little Sur, the upper Pick Creek, and other streams in the range. The Coast Ridge fault has defined the straight northwest orientation of the Coast Ridge. Conspicuous notches in ridgelines may indicate the presence of faults; Bottchers Gap and Puerto Suelo divide are good examples of such fault-formed notches. Springs can also be indicators of faults, as water percolates through the porous rock of fault zones. Outcrops of serpentine, a slippery, light-green rock, also mark fault lines in many places in Big Sur.

Rock formations in Big Sur have moved along faults into sometimes puzzling configurations. Basement rock has been thrust up on top of younger sedimentary rock in places, and giant slivers of granitic rocks have been moved to lie isolated amid Franciscan sea floor rocks, complicating an already intricate geology (fig. 8).

RECENT EVENTS

Five million years ago, the partially submerged Santa Lucia Range began to rise dramatically. The forces behind this uplift are unexplained. Some geologists believe that because the North American and Pacific plates were not moving exactly parallel to each other, the land west of the San Andreas fault was squeezed between the plates. The compression made the land fold and buckle like wrinkles on a loose carpet. The Coast Ranges represent those wrinkles.

The Santa Lucia Range reached its current height during the Pliocene uplift, when the northern part of the range was at about the present location of Morro Bay. As the mountains rose, streams steepened and erosion accelerated. When the forces behind the uplift began to dwindle, erosion wore the range down, depositing terrestrial (land-derived) sediments in and around the range. These deposits have been largely removed from the range by later erosion, and the range has been through several stages of lesser uplift and erosion since the Pliocene age. The most recent uplift began 1.8 million years ago.

Erosion is constantly removing large quantities of rock from the uplifting range, but sediments have also accumulated in places. Beds of stream gravels, now uplifted to lie as much as 90 m (300 ft) above their stream courses, are examples of recent deposits. Stream terraces are especially noticeable along the Arroyo Seco River on the east side of the range as well as along the Big Sur River and along several smaller streams in the range.

On flat coastal bluffs, beach sands and nearshore sediments 15–30 m (50–100 ft) thick blanket the bedrock. These bluffs, called *marine terraces,* formed as waves cut flat platforms into bedrock and deposited coarse sediments upon them. The platforms have risen above sea level and are further evidence of the range's recent uplift (fig. 9). Narrow marine terraces lie along the coast south of Carmel Highlands to Rocky Creek. Broader marine terraces form the extensive flats from Point Sur to the mouth of the Big Sur River and at Pacific Valley. More subtle traces of ancient marine terraces can be seen in the coastal mountain profile in many places. In cross-section along coastal cliffs or along Highway 1, marine terrace deposits consist of layers of coarse beach sands and cobbles.

Landslides are common phenomena in Big Sur and have also piled into thick accumulations overlying older rocks. Highway 1 cuts through many landslide deposits, recognizable as jumbled accumulations of sand and gravel as thick as 15–32 m (50–100 ft) and often red to orange in color. The red color results from the weathering of iron-rich compounds in the soil and crushed rock fragments.

CONTINUING GEOLOGICAL PROCESSES

Many geologists think the most recent uplift of the Santa Lucia Range is continuing today. When viewed from a high peak or an airplane, remnants of the rolling plain of the last erosional stage are still discern-

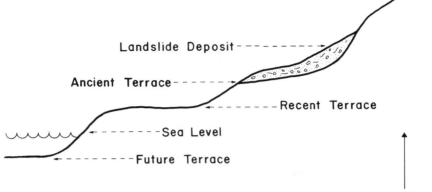

Figure 9.   Profile of wave-cut marine terrace topography.

ible. The mountain range as a whole is seen as a number of rounded
ridges and mountains of relatively equal height surmounted in places by
rugged peaks such as Ventana Double Cone and Marble Cone. This
rolling terrain was once near sea level but has been uplifted; the steep
flanks of the range indicate the extent of the uplift.

The uplift has steepened streams and thereby increased their ability
to cut down into the rock. They continue to incise sharp canyons in the
range, carrying away thousands of tons of ground rock in the process.
Streams in these mountains are remarkably clear in summer, but become muddy torrents during heavy rains. After the extensive Rat Creek
fire in 1985, great plumes of brown water stretched out into the ocean
from all the coastal creeks that drained the burnt area, illustrating the
accelerated erosion taking place.

Sand carried down creeks and landslides is continually moved southward along the coastline by ocean currents. Point Sur intercepts this
movement of sand, which has accumulated in low dunes beside the
point. Sand has also piled up just south of the Little Sur River and in a
few spots near Cooper Point. In all cases, the sand is transported southeastward by the prevailing winds to be blown back into the ocean and
continue its coastal drift. Eventually the sand pours down submarine
canyons to be deposited on the deep ocean floor.

Waves striking the coast also provide a powerful erosive force that
cuts at the rising range. Wave-caused erosion is particularly significant

along the Big Sur coast, where large waves strike directly against the range's bedrock. The periodic landslides that slip down the coastal slopes pile up in irregular mounds in the surf zone. The surf slowly removes the rock and then attacks the cliff again. Clouds of sediment color nearshore waters with a greenish hue in winter when the surf is especially powerful. In winter, the cloudy, greenish water stretches far out to sea after several days of heavy surf action.

The coastal slope is marked with repeated scars, old and new, where large chunks of rock and soil have slipped down. Many of these are caused by the undercutting of the steep slope along Highway 1. Landslides are not exclusively coastal phenomena, however, but are also common on the steep slopes of canyons and ridges. They occur when the ground is saturated with water to the point that layers of soil and rock are lubricated and can slide easily over one another. The majority of landslides occur where small springs or seeps emerge from underground.

These erosive forces have so far been unable to outstrip the pace of the range's recent uplift, but if the uplift slows or stops, the range will gradually be reduced once again to a low, rolling plain.

SUGGESTED READING

Bailey, E. H., ed., 1966. *Geology of northern California.* California Division of Mines and Geology Bulletin 190.

Earnst, W. G., ed., 1981. *The geotectonic development of California.* Englewood Cliffs, N.J.: Prentice Hall.

Fieldler, W. H., 1944. Geology of the Jamesburg quadrangle, Monterey County, California. *California Journal of Mines and Geology,* 40(2): 177–250.

Howard, A. D., 1979. *Geologic history of middle California.* Natural History Guide 43. Berkeley: University of California Press.

Norris, R., 1985. *Geology of the Landels-Hill Big Creek Reserve, Monterey County, California.* Environmental Field Program Publication 16, University of California, Santa Cruz.

Oakeshott, G. B., 1951. *Guide to the Geology of Pfeiffer–Big Sur State Park, Monterey County, California.* California Division of Mines and Geology Special Report 11.

Page, B. M., 1970. Sur-Nacimiento fault zone of California: Continental margin tectonics. *Geological Society of America Bulletin,* 81: 667–690.

Page, B. M., 1982. Migration of Salinian composite block, California, and disappearance of fragments. *American Journal of Science,* 282: 1694–1734.

Pearson, R. C., P. T. Hayes, and P. V. Fillo, 1967. *Mineral Resources of the Ventana Primitive Area, Monterey County, California.* U.S. Geological Survey Bulletin 1261-B.

Reiche, P., 1937. Geology of the Lucia quadrangle, California. *University of*

California Publications, Bulletin of the Department of Geological Sciences, 24(7): 115–168.

Trask, P., 1926. Geology of the Point Sur quadrangle, California. *University of California Publications, Bulletin of the Department of Geological Sciences,* 16(6): 119–186.

Van Andel, T. H., 1985. *New views on an old planet: Continental drift and the history of the earth.* Cambridge: Cambridge University Press.

CHAPTER II

Weather and Climate

Next to geological history, climate is the single most important factor shaping the natural history of the Big Sur region. Diversity, the key word in describing Big Sur's natural history, is largely a consequence of the mild climate and its interaction with the rugged terrain. This climate is often likened to the climate of the Mediterranean coastline. Both regions are extremely dry in summer and rainy in winter, and temperatures are mild year-round. Thus, climatologists classify much of coastal California's climate as a Mediterranean type. But Big Sur's climate is distinct from the climates of the Mediterranean region and the rest of California for many reasons.

The central California coast experiences cooler summers than the Mediterranean basin, due in part to consistent summer fog, which is absent in the Mediterranean basin. Big Sur's climate is also distinct from other Mediterranean climates because of the topography of the Santa Lucia Range. The mountains rise directly from the ocean to elevations greater than 1600 m (1 mi) and lie perpendicular to the prevailing westerly winds. The climate is strongly shaped by the interaction of this steep, wall-like topography with the prevailing weather. Extremes of temperature and humidity can be found in the area on any given day.

REGIONAL CLIMATE

Less than 1% of the earth's land area exhibits a Mediterranean climate: a narrow strip around the Mediterranean basin, the southwestern tip of

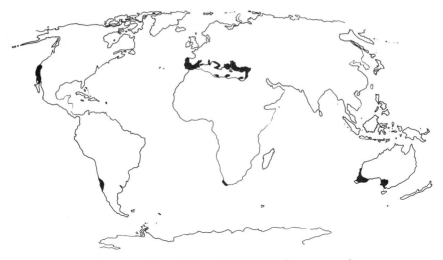

Figure 10.   Regions of the world with Mediterranean climates.

Africa, the coast of Chile, southwestern Australia, and coastal California (fig. 10). All Mediterranean climatic regions occur on the west coast of continents and lie within latitudes of about 32–40° north or south of the equator. Two dominant influences are common to all these areas and cause the Mediterranean climatic patterns: the nearby presence of ocean water and a summer-long flow of dry, westerly air.

THE NORTH PACIFIC HIGH

The North Pacific high is the most dominant influence on the climate of Big Sur. This giant, persistent high pressure cell is responsible for Big Sur's westerly winds and summer drought, as well as its summer fog. The absence of the high in winter allows Big Sur to receive its plentiful rainfall only during this season.

The North Pacific high is part of the global air circulation patterns that arise because of the uneven heating of the earth. Tropical latitudes receive sunlight more directly than temperate regions, and the tropical air expands and rises as it warms. This warm, moist air cools as it rises, and its moisture condenses and falls as rain, resulting in abundant precipitation near the equator. The resulting cool, dry air then moves at high altitudes northward and southward from the tropics. It eventually falls back to earth about 25–40° from the equator in a region of

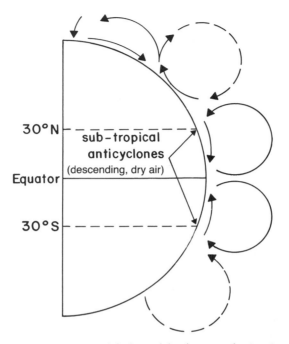

Figure 11.   Simplified model of atmospheric circulation
cells. (After Barry, R. G., and Charles, R. J.,
1982. *Atmosphere, Weather, and Climate.*
New York and London: Methuen.)

high atmospheric pressure known as the *subtropical high pressure belt*
(fig. 11).

The world's great deserts, as well as Mediterranean climatic zones,
lie within this region of dry, descending air. As it spreads out over the
earth's surface, the spinning of the earth causes the downward flow of
air to turn in a clockwise direction in the northern hemisphere. The descending, clockwise-rotating flow of air is known as a *high pressure
system,* or an *anticyclone.* The North Pacific high pressure system is
such an anticyclone centered over the northeastern Pacific Ocean.

The North Pacific high is a very stable phenomenon off the California
coast. On fair days, its cool winds can become strong enough to whip
up whitecaps on the ocean. Winds out of the northwest from the high
are so reliable along the California coast that Richard Henry Dana, in
Two Years Before the Mast, an account of sailing along the California

coast in the 1830s, refers to them as trade winds—winds that can be relied upon for shipping purposes. During his explorations of the California coast, the explorer Sebastian Vizcaino praised the northwesterly wind as "the king and absolute master of this sea and coast."

The consistent windflow out of the North Pacific high pressure system acts as a barrier to storms approaching Big Sur from the North Pacific ocean, pushing them away as they approach. Summer rain is common north of its protective influence along the coasts of Oregon and Washington. Summer storms commonly drift up from tropical latitudes to generate thunderstorms along the coast of Baja California and inland to the Rocky Mountains and the southwest. These, too, are deflected by the North Pacific high so that summer rain from northern or tropical sources is a rarity along the central and southern California coast. Virtually all the rainfall in central coastal California comes when the protecting North Pacific high diminishes and moves southward between October and the end of May.

The North Pacific high is also responsible for bringing the cold ocean water to the California coast in the summer. Its northwesterly winds push surface water toward the coast, and the southeast-bending California coastline steers the surface water southward, offshore. The surface water is further turned by the Coriolis force—an effect of the earth's rotation that turns ocean currents to the right in the northern hemisphere. The result is that the surface water moves away from the coastline. Cold water from the depths of the deep submarine canyons offshore wells up to replace this surface water. The upwelling of cold water, rich in nutrients, fertilizes coastal waters and is largely responsible for central California's abundant marine life. The upwelling reaches its peak from March through July.

When the northwesterly wind contacts the cold, upwelling water nearshore, its moisture condenses and fog forms. The fog piles up along the coast as it encounters the mountains but is often drawn into the Carmel, Big Sur, and Salinas valleys by low pressure over the warm land. It may form a layer anywhere from 100 to 1000 m (330 to 3300 ft) thick. Fog can form during any season in Big Sur, but it is most common in summer when the North Pacific high is strongest and drives the upwelling. The normal pattern of fog movement in California is that the fog moves onshore in the evening and back out to sea by late morning, but this isn't always the case. It oftens lingers all day.

EFFECTS OF THE OCEAN

The cool Pacific Ocean itself is the second major influence on the climate of Big Sur and coastal California. Water temperatures change more slowly than air temperatures, and the Pacific Ocean, a huge mass of water, changes temperature only very slightly throughout the seasons and even less day to day. Its temperature along the Big Sur coast is especially cold in late spring and summer, when the upwelling occurs. Ocean temperatures are also cool because of a southward-moving current, the California Current, that brings cold northern waters to the coast. In the summer, the ocean cools a layer of air, which is then drawn inland to cool the nearby land. Conversely, the landmass cools off in winter, but the ocean temperature remains relatively constant and warms the nearby continent. By acting like an air conditioner in summer and a heater in winter, the ocean thus evens out daily and seasonal air temperatures on nearby land year-round.

These effects of the ocean are familiar to all coastal dwellers. The cold water offshore is what makes California distinct among coastal climates in the United States. The cold, dense air over the ocean promotes stability in the atmosphere, discouraging the mixing and vertical movement of air that cause rain. Furthermore, the cold air cannot hold much moisture, which contributes to the relatively dry climate on the coast. This contrasts with the east coast of the United States, where the Gulf Stream delivers warm, tropical water that causes summer rain and humid weather year-round, and with the Gulf Coast, where the water is warm year-round.

The ocean's influence diminishes with distance from the coast and with elevation. As a result, inland areas and high elevations along the coast experience greater extremes in both daily and seasonal temperatures than low, coastal areas. The mild weather of the coast becomes increasingly variable and "continental" with increasing distance from the ocean. These changes toward a more continental climate take place within a remarkably short distance in the Big Sur area, where steep ridges act as barriers to the ocean's influence. At high elevations or in inland valleys in the Santa Lucias, it often seems as if there is no ocean influence at all. Seasonal and daily temperatures vary much more than they do at sea level on the coast. However, subtle effects of the ocean are felt throughout the range, and Big Sur's climate is overall much more moderate than the climate in mountains located farther inland.

The winter storms that reach the California coast originate and travel over the Pacific Ocean, which, although cool near the coast, is very warm relative to the interior of the continent in winter. Temperatures accompanying even northern winter storms are relatively mild as a result.

Even slight, distant changes in conditions on the Pacific Ocean affect Big Sur's weather. This was vividly illustrated in 1983. In the previous year, for unexplained reasons, the steady equatorial easterly winds on the Pacific died and reversed direction. The net result of this wind shift was a marked warming of surface waters in the eastern equatorial Pacific, including the west coast of the Americas. This weather pattern develops every few years and has been named *El Niño*, "the child," because it usually comes around Christmas time. The warm water warms the air above it, which can then hold more moisture. This normally leads to a moderate increase in rainfall on the Peruvian and Ecuadorian coasts, which is beneficial to local agriculture there. The warm water also causes a die-off of ocean fish and birds that are dependent on cold water.

In 1983, however, El Niño was unusually strong and brought torrential rains to these South American coasts. The warm water and humid atmospheric conditions made winter rainfall in California higher than ever recorded. The resultant landslides closed Highway 1 in the Big Sur area for over a year. Coastal water along California warmed to the point where barracuda and other fish adapted to warm temperature waters appeared. Local commercial fishes, dependent on cool waters and the upwelling nutrients, greatly diminished in number. The warm water replaced the normally cold nearshore water, so that fog rarely formed in the summer of that year. Thus, after the rainiest of winters, Big Sur residents enjoyed hot, sunny summer weather in which even those near the coast could grow sun-dependent crops such as corn and peppers.

WAVES AND SWELLS

Big Sur's coastal cliffs are ideal places to observe the face of the ocean, wrinkled at all seasons with ever-changing patterns of waves. The surface of the ocean is a good place to read much about the weather.

For most of the year, the swell is choppy, irregular, and out of the northwest, driven by storms in the distant north Pacific Ocean. This swell is built up in the spring and summer by the northwesterly winds of the North Pacific high and is often blown into a chaos of whitecaps.

In summer and early fall, a powerful southwesterly swell may reach the Big Sur coast from hurricanes off the west coast of Mexico. These long, even swells are sharply visible on the calm summer sea and are a boon to surfers. Also during summer, large southwesterly swells from storms off New Zealand and Antarctica occasionally reach the California coast.

The winter swells are usually out of the northwest, but a strong southerly wave may develop across this swell during severe storms, when southerly winds make whitecaps on the gray sea. Indeed, the approach of a storm can be foretold by the presence of southerly ripples and waves. The largest swells of winter typically follow in the wake of a storm front and usually strike from the northwest. The slow-rolling giants usually travel slower than the storm itself and arrive just after the front has passed. These spectacular waves roll coastal sediments and kelp beds and significantly erode the coastline. We have observed swells up to 7.6 m (25 ft) high after winter storms.

The glassy surface of the ocean is often marked by large, isolated areas of dark ripples in late summer and fall. These are disturbances caused by schools of bait fish, typically anchovies, that are rising to the surface to escape predators from below. Flocks of sea gulls, pelicans, terns, and other seabirds often gather over these areas to feed on the fish, and sea lions or dolphins join in the melee.

LOCAL WEATHER PATTERNS

As old-timer Hans Ewoldsen says, "When someone asks me what the weather in Big Sur is doing, I ask them, 'Where do you mean?'" Big Sur's weather is indeed marked by great contrasts in both time and place. The high, rugged topography creates these sharp contrasts by breaking up the regional climate into a mosaic of microclimates. High elevations freeze regularly in the winter and receive three or four times as much precipitation as lower elevations along the coast, some of it in the form of snow. Deep coastal canyons stay cool well into the summer season when exposed ridges are parched and hot. It is not uncommon to experience extremes in weather during the span of one day while hiking or driving in Big Sur, and at any given moment, the weather may be substantially different at different places.

As in the rest of central coastal California, the weather in Big Sur is not extremely variable from season to season. Visitors from more inland climates often comment on the lack of seasons on the California coast because of the generally mild temperatures that persist year-round. But the seasons are marked beautifully and clearly in Big Sur, and the steep slopes and high ridges of Big Sur provide balcony seats for the spectacle of sea and sky that each season brings.

SUMMER

On a typical summer day, both valleys and high elevations inland in the Santa Lucia Range may swelter at temperatures above 100°F (37°C) with the air as dry as desert air. At night, the temperature may plummet to the low 40s. But on the coast, the temperature of the cool, damp ocean air may change only 10°F throughout the day, from the low 50s to a high in the mid-60s.

The radical difference in summer high temperatures between interior and coastal sites in the mountain range is reflected in evaporation rates, which may be twice as great in the interior. The relative humidity is usually significantly lower at inland sites as well. But in spite of the interior's dryness, the whole of the range and the inland valleys are still markedly more humid than valleys and deserts farther from the ocean. A slight influence from the ocean even extends far inland to the Sierra Nevada and beyond.

The Big Sur Valley, although open to the ocean at one end, is more continental in climate than the coastline and is much warmer than the coast in summer. Nonetheless, ocean breezes and fog are drawn up the river valley frequently, whereas more isolated valleys are deprived of this ocean air.

The normal temperature gradient with increasing altitude is from warm air to cooler air, but this situation is reversed or inverted in Big Sur on most summer days. Cool ocean air along the coast lies beneath a mass of warmer continental air. In such a temperature inversion, the warm layer of air acts like a lid on the cool ocean air. The cool air often appears as a sharp band of haze along the coast and cannot move up or down freely. Rain is extremely unlikely when the stable summer inversion is in effect since rain is the result of vertical movement and cooling of air.

The temperature may vary 15° to 20°F in a vertical distance of only 100 m (330 ft) across the sharp boundary of the inversion layer. The ocean breeze takes the heat out of most sunny days along the coast, and as cool air continues to flow in from the ocean, the ceiling of warm air may be gradually forced upward. The cool air can reach to a different elevation every day, and the temperature at any given elevation depends on the thickness of the layer. It may reach up to only 60 m (200 ft) above sea level, or it may extend up to 600 m (2000 ft), bringing a cool breeze to the parched ridgetops.

Fog often settles within this inversion layer just along the shoreline in the summer so that any place sheltered from the coast is free of fog. The Big Sur Valley, separated from the ocean by the 600-m- (2000-ft-) high Pfeiffer Ridge, is a good place to see this striking contrast. A thick fog bank may blanket Point Sur and the coastline of Andrew Molera State Park, while it is sunny and hot just 1 km (0.6 mi) up the valley. Entering the valley from the south presents this same contrast as the foggy coastal cliffs are left behind. A drive or walk up a mountainside brings the same dramatic change.

Fog banks typically disperse after 3 to 5 days, and clear skies may prevail for several days until the cycle begins again. But the pattern of fog movement varies from day to day and also from year to year, and several very foggy summers may be followed by a series of relatively clear summers.

The fog does not always stay at low elevations, but sometimes hangs at 300 m (1000 ft) or more, and skies are gray and overcast even from the higher ridgetops. In contrast, sometimes isolated patches of fog cling only on high ridges. This happens when the winds are not damp enough or the ocean temperature is not cool enough to form a thick fog bank. In these instances, the incoming ocean air cools sufficiently only when it reaches high elevations on the mountains. Prominent headlands such as Pfeiffer Point, Soberanes Point, Cape San Martin, and Gamboa Point are frequently wreathed with fog while the rest of the coast is clear.

Although it happens infrequently, rain can fall during the dry summer season if the North Pacific high weakens or moves far enough northward to allow southern tropical storms to move into Big Sur. Tropical storms begin as giant whirlpools in the air over warm oceans. These damp, warm, cyclonic storms commonly drift northward in the summer to bring thunderstorms and rain to the southwestern deserts, southern Baja California, and the southern Rocky Mountains. Occasionally they move up along the California coast.

It's easy to see one of these tropical low pressure systems approaching the Big Sur coast. High, puffy cumulus clouds develop in the sky, which is normally clear or hidden by low fog. A telltale lull in the cool northwesterly wind accompanies the cloud buildup. Warm, humid air moves in, and the cumulus clouds grow slowly larger and darker. Eventually, the cumulus may develop into thunderheads that produce light-ning and rain. Usually, the cumulus clouds stay small and produce some lightning but little rain, which is the ideal condition for starting fire.

For residents of Big Sur, fires in the drought of summer are a dreaded occurrence. Any sign of summer cumulus clouds is a signal to be watch-ful for lightning and smoke. The 73,000-ha[1] (180,000-acre) Marble–Cone fire of 1977 and the 24,000-ha (60,000-acre) Rat Creek fire in 1985 were both caused by lightning.

FALL

The coastal upwelling, periodic fog, and cool, fair weather persist as long as the North Pacific high sits off the California coast. But in the fall, the earth's revolution around the sun causes the northern hemi-sphere to be tilted away from the sun. The North Pacific high pressure sys-tem weakens and moves southward, leaving the coast open to storms. The upwelling stops, fog forms less frequently, and the air takes on a striking clarity. Without fog and the ripples and whitecaps of the north-westerly wind, the ocean becomes flat and mirrorlike.

Fall is a season of beautiful sunsets, when the high cirrus clouds of the first storm systems appear in the clear air and are lit at sunset into an array of colors. Shadows fill the canyons early in the day, and leaves on black oaks, maples, and sycamores begin to change color and fall. The parched land waits for the first rain, which usually arrives in late September or October.

When any storm approaches the California coast, its counterclock-wise rotation brings southerly winds. The first sign of an approaching storm is a calm in the northwestly wind and the appearance of high, thin cirrus clouds overhead, often streaked into mares' tails. A strong, relatively warm southerly wind is a sure sign that a low pressure system is approaching the coast. Thickening clouds, increasing southerly winds, and the appearance of gray curtains of rain over the ocean to the south are the final signs.

The first fall rains are usually light. Sometimes, all the symptoms of a low pressure system appear without bringing any rain, as storms are weak or pass north of the Big Sur area. In fall and winter, it is a game predicting which high cirrus clouds mean rain and which are just bluffs. It becomes safer to predict that they will develop into rainstorms as fall progresses into winter.

1. ha = hectare.

Fall is one of the most beautiful seasons in Big Sur, especially after a
foggy summer. Warm temperatures and clear skies linger into fall. The
humidity is low and the air is calm. Visibility of the mountain ridges
and distant objects on the ocean is at its peak. But Indian summer
weather can sometimes linger into winter and turn from a welcome re-
spite into a drought.

WINTER

Winter rainstorms originate over the Pacific Ocean as systems of air
moving in a counterclockwise, uplifting fashion. The jet stream is a high
altitude current of air circling the globe from west to east that directs
some of these low pressure systems toward California in the winter.

Storms approach the central California coast primarily from the
northwest and the southwest. Northern storms are born in the north
Pacific Ocean and the Bering Sea and are usually cold and bring moderate amounts of rainfall. Winds accompanying these storms blow from
the southwest. In contrast, the southern storms, or "Hawaiian storms,"
form in the south Pacific and are brought northward by the jet stream
when it makes its occasional swing southward. These southern storms
typically bring large amounts of precipitation because they have formed
over warm, wet oceans. They are also very windy because they have
such a long *fetch*, which is the unobstructed distance over which the
wind builds its speed. Winds from southern storms blow from the
southeast. During the 1983 El Niño storms, storm after storm rolled in
on this "pineapple express" and drenched Big Sur's mountain summits
with nearly 500 cm (200 in.) of rain.

When winter storms hit the Big Sur coast, the damp southerly winds-
of the cyclonic storms meet head-on with the steep terrain and are
forced quickly upward. As the air rises, it cools and its moisture condenses and falls out as rain or snow.

The Santa Lucias rise to more than 1760 m (5800 ft), and rainfall
amounts increase dramatically along the gradient from sea level as the
uplifting air becomes progressively cooler. Near the coast, at Pfeiffer–Big Sur State Park, rainfall averaged about 109 cm (43 in.) annually
from 1914 through the spring of 1987. It is estimated that about 230
cm (90 in.) falls near the crest of the mountains. But averages are deceiving. On Mining Ridge at 1200 m (4000 ft) elevation, for example,
where Monterey County maintains a remote gauge for flood prediction,
it rained only 122 cm (48 in.) in the winter of 1980–1981. But in

1982–1983, it rained more than 452 cm (178 in.). No one is sure exactly how much fell because the rain gauge stopped functioning after recording that amount. Similarly, it rained only 39 cm (15 in.) in 1975–1976 at Pfeiffer–Big Sur State Park, while 216 cm (85 in.) fell in 1982–1983 (tables 1 and 2).

Rainfall amounts decrease sharply inland from the coast. The southerly winds, wrung of much of their moisture, warm as they descend the eastern side of the range. King City, located in the Salinas Valley, receives only 27 cm (11 in.) of rain annually on the average. The mountains impose a rain-shadow effect by intercepting prevailing storm patterns.

Winter storms in Big Sur can be violent and bring the strongest winds of the year to the coast. Facing directly into the ocean winds, the Big Sur coast breaks winds that have traveled uninterrupted over thousands of kilometers of open ocean. Winds often blow at velocities of more than 80 km/hr (50 mi/hr) on exposed points and headlands, and winds in excess of 161 km/hr (100 mi/hr) have been recorded at Point Sur and on ridgetops. The wind sometimes drives the rain in horizontal sheets. Branches and whole trees blow down frequently. The steep slopes become saturated and often slump and slide. Large blocks of rock break off cliffs and hillsides, and roads are often blocked or washed out by landslides in severe storms.

According to Richard Dana, a sailor and writer who wrote about his travels along California in the 1830s, these winter storms struck fear into the hearts of sailors. Many ships driven by southerly winter winds wrecked on prominent points of the California coast, including Point Sur. At the first sign of a winter storm, ships would pull up their anchors and head out to sea so that the south wind would blow them clear of the westward-reaching landmass.

Virtually all of Big Sur's precipitation falls between October and May. Stored in underground reservoirs, winter rain alone feeds the creeks and springs of the region. Winter rainfall can vary extremely from year to year, and summer water supplies can be correspondingly plentiful or scarce. When the North Pacific high persists into winter, it prevents storms from reaching the coast and causes severe winter droughts.

The peaks of the Santa Lucia Range receive snow regularly in the winter, sometimes in excess of 250 cm (100 in.) in a season. It stays on the ground for weeks or even months on the highest peaks. Snowflakes have been seen descending nearly to sea level, but they seldom stick below 600 m (2000 ft). Overall, snow is an insignificant part of the

TABLE I.   PRECIPITATION AT SELECTED SITES IN THE
SANTA LUCIA RANGE

Station	Eleva-tion (ft)	Average Precip. (in.)	High (Year) (in.)	Low (Year) (in.)	Years of Data
Willow Springs	250	30.38	63.34 (1940–1941)	11.41 (1975–1976)	47 (1940–1987)
Pfeiffer–Big Sur	300	41.24	85.20 (1982–1983)	15.48 (1975–1976)	73 (1914–1987)
Anderson Peak	3800	69.59	133.91 (1982–1983)	40.28 (1986–1987)	9 (1978–1987)
Mining Ridge	4760	77.53	173.37 (1982–1983)	43.78 (1986–1987)	9 (1978–1987)

region's total precipitation. When snow does fall in the Santa Lucias, it is usually wet and heavy. During a great snowfall in 1974, the weight of the snow on trees broke off thousands of branches.

Because of the warming effect of the ocean, frost is uncommon below 600 m (2000 ft) on exposed coastal slopes of the range and almost unheard of along the immediate coast. Also, the Big Sur coast is walled off from cold, continental air by the Santa Lucia Range so that very cold temperatures are extremely uncommon here. Frosts do occur near sea level in areas that are sheltered from the ocean's influence, and they are not unusual in the Big Sur Valley. Coastal canyons are similarly insulated from the ocean, and frost can occur at low elevations away from the canyon mouths.

Cold air at higher elevations in the mountains is denser than coastal air and thus flows down canyons, especially in winter. Canyons can be noticeably colder than open slopes and ridgetops and are usually breezy because of this cold air flow. The down-canyon winds ruffle the surface of the ocean near coastal creek mouths. These breezes create tongues of dark ripples at each canyon mouth when the ocean is calm and glassy.

A diurnal cycle of wind shifts is noticeable on calm winter days. A gentle breeze normally blows from the land toward the sea in the morning; this is a land breeze or an offshore wind. The wind shifts direction by late morning as the land warms more than the ocean and creates onshore updrafts of warm air. This gentle breeze, called a *sea breeze* or onshore wind, is drawn off the ocean and wafts up the coastal slopes. Hawks, eagles, and vultures take advantage of these updrafts to gain altitude and soar in the mornings. The landmass cools quickly after

TABLE 2. MONTHLY PRECIPITATION (IN INCHES) FROM 1914 TO 1987
AT PFEIFFER–BIG SUR STATE PARK[a]

	July	Aug.	Sept.	Oct.	Nov.	Dec.	Jan.	Feb.	Mar.	Apr.	May	June
Average	0.02	0.05	0.49	1.71	4.66	7.55	7.99	7.63	6.00	3.13	0.84	0.33
Extreme (Year)	0.87 (1980)	2.6 (1976)	8.72 (1959)	8.15 (1962)	14.97 (1965)	27.21 (1955)	23.50 (1969)	22.39 (1940)	19.73 (1983)	12.41 (1967)	7.58 (1957)	2.53 (1934)

[a]Compiled from records on file at Pfeiffer–Big Sur State Park.

sunset, and the cold, dense air flows down slope once again. This is mainly a winter phenomenon. The strong northwesterly winds often overpower these more subtle currents during the summer.

Occasional snow on the peaks notwithstanding, winter in Big Sur is more like the spring of most climates. California peonies and red-flowering currants normally begin flowering in winter, and many other flowers may bloom in mild winter weather. Dormant shrubs in the coastal scrub, as well as herbs and annual grasses, come to life with the winter rains, slowly transforming the land from brown to bright green. Mushrooms, including chanterelles, morels, meadow mushrooms, boletes, and other edible delights, spring up from leaf mulch and needle litter. Mosses in the forest perk up and turn vibrant green. Moisture-dependent newts and salamanders crawl out from their shelter under leaf mulch and logs to make their breeding appearance and make mass migrations toward water. Winter's moisture brings out vivid fragrances from herbs, shrubs, and mulch in the forests and grasslands.

SPRING

Spring brings its own marvelous burst of life to Big Sur. The grasses, which have grown slowly all winter, suddenly shoot up in the increasing sunlight. The bare limbs of maple trees fan out their leaves, and the broad leaves of elk clover and coltsfoot appear along the bare, winter-flooded banks of creeks. Then the real bloom begins: blue lupines carpet the ridgetops, poppies flood the grasslands, and wild lilacs are hung with blue blossoms. Migrant song birds arrive and begin singing and nesting. Lizards and snakes become active, and the gray whales return, heading north on their way to the Arctic with newborn calves.

The North Pacific high pressure system reforms and moves northward as the earth's revolution around the sun causes the northern hemisphere to be tilted more toward the sun in the spring. Storms are forced along a more northern route. The damp winter winds are replaced by brisk northwesterly winds, and the cold upwelling of water begins again. The grasses start producing seeds as the rains diminish, and the ridges turn golden as they dry.

The timing of the arrival of spring varies from year to year. Sometimes the rains stop in March and the hills are gold by May. Other years, the rains continue and maintain a lush growth of deep, green grass through April and into May. Fog begins to form by late spring and establishes its irregular rhythm of drifting in and out to sea and filling coastal ravines. The dry season begins and moisture-dependent plants become dormant until the fall rains, a remarkable contrast to the winter dormancy of plants in more inland climates. Some newts and salamanders also become inactive as the weather dries, while warm climate reptiles come out of hibernation with the advent of warmer spring temperatures. California fuchsia, buckwheat, lizardtail, and others begin to flower in summer as the carpets of color made by lupines, poppies, owl's clover, and other spring flowers fade from the grasslands.

SUGGESTED READING

Barry, R. G., and R. J. Chorley, 1982. *Atmosphere, weather, and climate.* New York and London: Methuen.

Gilliam, H., 1962. *Weather of the San Francisco Bay region.* Natural History Guide 6. Berkeley: University of California Press.

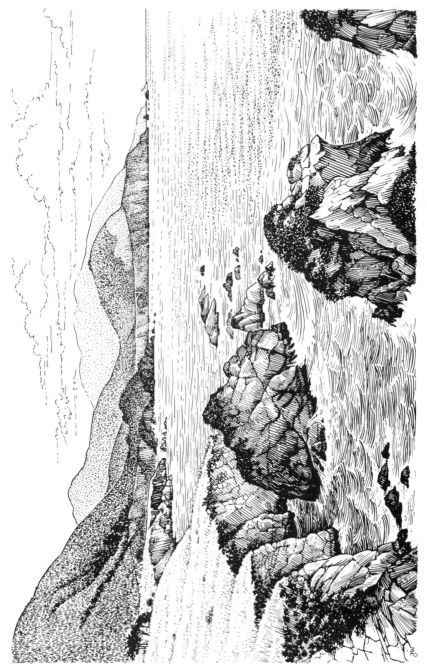

Big Sur's Rocky Shoreline

CHAPTER III

Big Sur Shoreline

INTRODUCTION

Many visitors driving Highway 1 along the Big Sur coast are content to stop their car for a few minutes at a viewpoint and look down at the jagged rocks and booming surf, perhaps spotting a whale or some otters at a distance. But by taking a little more time, it is possible to get quite close to an otter that is pulling mussels off the rocks, or to a cormorant that speeds like a torpedo after small fish. Those that do make the effort to explore the areas where the Big Sur coast is accessible, such as at Pfeiffer Beach, Soberanes Point, and Jade Cove, will be rewarded with some of the most beautiful beaches and interesting wildlife that California has to offer.

Big Sur's shoreline and intertidal areas are full of diversity and richness. The *intertidal area* is that narrow strip of wave-battered rock lying between the high and low tide lines. Hundreds of plant and animal species crowd one another here and compete for living space. Much of the northern Pacific coast from Alaska to Point Conception displays such lushness, and it is due in part to several factors: the upwelling of nutrient-rich bottom waters just offshore, the stable climate and common summer fogs that cool the shore, and the presence of abundant rocky headlands that provide space and anchorage for intertidal organisms.

Overall, Big Sur's intertidal life is characteristic of the exposed coasts of central and northern California. But one factor that makes the Big Sur coast especially interesting is its location along the western coast of North America. According to biologist John Pearse, Big Sur is considered to be within a broad biotic boundary that separates two ecological ocean provinces. At Point Conception, located 200 km (125 mi) to the south, the cool Oregonian Province from the north meets the warmer Californian Province from the south. It is believed that many plant and animal species reach their northern or southern distributional limits near this boundary, and Big Sur is part of the transition zone between the two provinces. Due to overlap from each province, intertidal transition zones can be especially rich in species and can often contain additional species restricted to the transition zones themselves.

The great variety of rock types found here is yet another noteworthy feature of Big Sur's shoreline (see chap. 1). Hard granitic rock, crumbly greenstone, grainy sandstone—these and many other rock types crop out along the shore and help shape the makeup of the intertidal community. Some rocks, such as granite, provide good stable substrate, while others erode easily. Still others contain compounds in their chemical makeup that may discourage certain organisms from settling there. These conditions vary from one beach or cove to another, making no two exactly the same.

But for all its apparent richness, the intertidal zone in Big Sur can be an extremely rigorous environment. All organisms must overcome three major limitations to survive here: wave shock, tidal exposure to air or water, and intense competition for space. Depending on the intensity of these and other forces, an area may be rich in marine life, such as the tidal flats near Point Sur, or they may be almost completely devoid of animals and plants, such as at the wave-battered cliffs near Cape San Martin.

WAVE SHOCK

Wave shock is severe on Big Sur's open coast. About 8000 waves strike the shore on an average day, tumbling boulders and crumbling cliffs. To resist the surf, most plants and animals simply hold on tight. Sea algae anchor with rootlike holdfasts, and their rubbery bodies flow with the waves rather than resist them. Barnacles glue themselves to rocks with a natural cement, while mussels grip with secreted byssal threads. Seastars use their powerful tube feet. If the animal is pried off a rock with a knife, several of its tiny feet may rip off and remain clinging to the rock for days.

Creatures that cannot hold on to the substrate hide beneath rocks or other clusters of animals. Some, such as sea urchins, chitons, and rock clams, even dig pits and burrows in the solid rock. Many inhabitants, especially the limpets, have appropriate shapes to offer the least resistance to the surf. These shapes and anchoring abilities attest to the importance of holding on. Those that let go are quickly swept out to sea or cast up on the beach.

Waves are also beneficial to most intertidal animals. The agitated water keeps tiny food particles in suspension. Filter feeders such as barnacles and mussels grab this food as the waves wash over them. The wave motion also keeps the water well aerated.

TIDAL EXPOSURE

The second factor organisms must contend with is tidal fluctuation. Exposed above water for extended periods of time when the tide falls, plants and animals are in constant danger of desiccation and asphyxiation. An organism's ability to tolerate this exposure usually predicts the upward extension of its range. Most intertidal creatures are unable to extract oxygen from the air, and those exposed above the water must hold their breath. Limpets, periwinkles, barnacles, and mussels lock themselves in their airtight shells, keeping moisture in and air out. Sea anemones contract and hold moisture in their bodies to escape drying out in the hot sun. The more mobile animals slip beneath wet piles of seaweed or into tidepools and wait for the tide to return.

The tides are controlled by a complex interplay of several factors. The gravitational pull of the moon exerts the greatest influence on the oceans, but the gravitational pull of the sun, the rotation of the earth, the shape and depth of coastal shorelines, and the physical properties of water all play major roles as well. The sun exerts a gravitational force on the oceans that is about half that of the moon's. When the sun and moon line up relative to the earth, their forces work in conjunction to create *spring tides*. These consist of higher high tides and lower low tides than average and occur every 14 days on the new and full moons. When the sun and moon are at a right angle to one another relative to earth, the sun's pull is obscured by that of the moon and total tidal displacement is much less. These are the *neap tides,* and they occur on the moon's first and third quarter phases. Low spring tides are thus the best tides to explore the intertidal zone since the entire habitat is laid bare by the ocean for a few rare hours.

COMPETITION FOR SPACE

Water along the Big Sur shoreline is displaced vertically a maximum of about 2.6 m (8.5 ft) during the tidal cycle, and most intertidal plants and animals are restricted in their range to this thin strip. Since many of the animals are immobile or slow moving, acquiring and maintaining territory is a prerequisite to survival. The territorial owl limpet, for example, protects its precious feeding grounds by slowly ramming and dislodging intruders. This algae-grazing snail has been observed bulldozing barnacles, mussels, and even large plants off the rocks.

Those that cannot find or fight for space often live on the bodies of larger plants and animals. Algae, sponges, limpets, and barnacles find suitable property on the backs of crabs or the shells of mussels. This solution has both positive and negative effects depending on the survivability of the host, but it is better than no space at all.

TIDAL ZONATION

Intertidal plants and animals are not randomly distributed along the shore, but instead inhabit distinct bands or *zones* within the intertidal area. There are four major zones in Big Sur's rocky shore: the spray zone (I), the high zone (II), the middle zone (III), and the low zone (IV) (table 3). Below zone IV is the subtidal region. These zones overlap and blend into one another, and certain creatures, such as free-ranging scavengers (hermit crabs) and predators (seastars), are common to more than one zone.

But other organisms are almost entirely restricted to one or two zones based on their specific preferences and tolerances. Periwinkle snails, for example, are mostly terrestrial and are usually only sprayed by waves. Sea urchins, in contrast, live at the lower edge of the intertidal zone and are rarely exposed by the lowest of tides. These preferences create a visible pattern of zonation on the rocks. Differently colored algae grow in dense layers, one above the other, and beds of mussels form dark lateral bands along the surf line.

This description of the intertidal zone applies to most temperate rocky shorelines, but the Big Sur coast differs in several ways. First, there is a relative lack of the tidal flats common to neighboring areas such as Morro, Carmel, and Monterey bays. A few excellent tidal exposures do occur on some of the major points, such as Point Sur, but on

TABLE 3.   CHARACTERISTICS OF EACH INTERTIDAL ZONE

Zone	Exposure	Plants	Animals
I. Splash	Covered only 2–3 hours twice a month	*Prasiola* *Pelvetiopsis*	Rock lice Periwinkles Acorn barnacles Fingered limpets Beach hoppers
II. High	Covered during high tide 2–3 hours twice each day	*Fucus* *Pelvetia* *Ulva* *Endocladia* *Gigartina*	Checkered periwinkles Black turban snails Limpets Striped shore crabs Chitons Acorn barnacles
III. Middle	Exposed during low tides 2–3 hours twice each day	*Iridaea* *Egregia*	Hermit crabs Purple shore crabs Mussels Goose barnacles Sea anemones Black abalone Ochre seastars
IV. Low	Exposed only 2–3 hours twice each month	Surf grass *Laminaria* *Alaria* (brown kelps)	Purple sea urchins Red abalone Octopus Solitary green anemone
Permanent tidepools	Found in low and middle zones	*Corallina* and many of the above seaweeds	Many of the above animals Wooly sculpin Opaleye fish

the whole, the region is simply too steep and wave battered to support such conditions. Second, wave impact inhibits the development of complex intertidal communities, especially where rocks of all sizes are tossed and rolled. A large rock the size of a car may be covered with mussels and algae during the summer, but strong winter waves can roll it around and scrape it clean, eliminating the community that had developed there. Entire boulder fields are likewise affected, and one often hears the thunderlike rumble of rolling rocks in receding waves. Big Sur's high waves, however, do extend the splash zone up cliff faces, thus enabling certain plants and animals to settle at higher levels than they could in more sheltered areas.

The remainder of this chapter gives a brief introduction to Big Sur's more common intertidal plants and animals. Individual site descriptions in part II include more specific treatments of coastal areas and their intertidal inhabitants.

SEAWEEDS

The cool, temperate waters of the Pacific coast support a diverse and abundant seaweed flora. Seaweeds are not flowering plants; all species are some type of marine algae. Like green land plants, they use the green pigment chlorophyll to absorb sunlight for the sugar-producing process of photosynthesis. But seaweeds lack the woody cells used by land plants for support and for transport of water. Rigid supporting tissue is not needed in a world of floating leaves and rubbery stems buoyed up by water. A water-conducting system is likewise unnecessary because most of the algae are continuously splashed and bathed. Unlike the roots of a tree, the rootlike holdfasts of seaweeds serve only as anchorage in the rough surf. Minerals used for plant growth are absorbed directly from the water.

Seaweeds take hold only on secure, stable substrates. Sandy beaches are seaweed deserts since shifting sand and loose rocks offer no stability in the tumult of the sea. But algae do take a firm hold on Big Sur's resistant submerged rocks. The intertidal rocks are coated with layer upon layer of different colored plants, and offshore forests of kelp grow to more than 40 m (130 ft) tall.

The marine algae are divided into three major groups: green, red, and brown. This simple classification scheme is the best way to differentiate common seaweeds. Although the color variation and overlap among the groups is tremendous, most marine algae can be quickly relegated to their respective groups for easier identification. The following seaweeds are just a few of the hundreds of species found in Big Sur. Some coastal sites have a well-balanced mix of many of these species, while others are dominated by just a few.

The green algae are the most closely related to the green land plants. Most species are relatively small in size, and most are a grass green color while others are quite dark. The bright green *Ulva taeniata*, known commonly as sea lettuce (fig. 12), stands out from its drabber surroundings in the high intertidal zone (II). *Prasiola meridionalis*, in contrast, is much darker green and quite short. Soft patches about 1–2 cm (0.4–0.8 in.) tall carpet the rocks of the splash zone (I). Species of *Clado-*

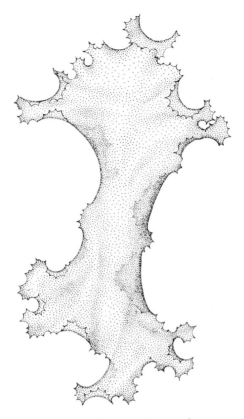

Figure 12. *Ulva taeniata,* sea lettuce

phora are slightly larger and also form green tufts. The tufts are many branched filaments and are often found lining rocky tidepools.

The brown algae are more numerous and conspicuous than the greens. The browns also contain green chlorophyll, but the green color is obscured by an abundance of gold and brown pigments. Thus, the colors in this group range from light olive-green to dark black-brown.

Although not an intertidal species, the large kelps of the offshore forests are usually the first brown algae noticed by visitors. Wide brown patches stretch hundreds of meters out to sea. These colonies consist primarily of two species: bullwhip kelp (*Nereocystis luetkeana*) (fig. 13) and giant kelp (*Macrocystis pyrifera*) (fig. 14). A forest at sea is difficult to imagine, but the bullwhip kelp can grow as tall as 40 m (130 ft). The

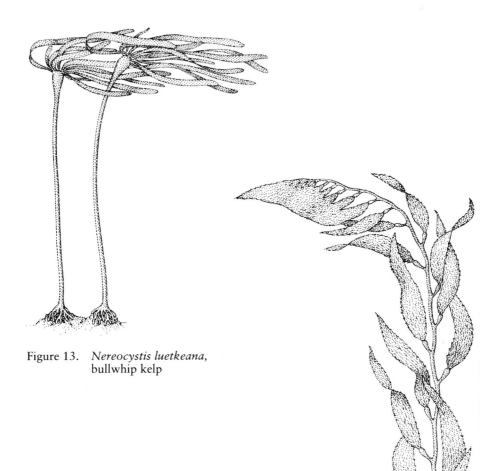

Figure 13. *Nereocystis luetkeana,*
bullwhip kelp

Figure 14. *Macrocystis pyrifera,* giant kelp

Figure 15.   *Postelsia palmaeformis,* sea palm

tops of the plants are kept afloat by gas-filled floats or bladders, while
the bottoms are anchored to rocks with holdfasts. Kelp forests teem
with life and are best compared to a tropical rain forest in their diversity
and lush canopy. Schools of fish find food and shelter beneath the canopy, herds of sea urchins graze the plants' stems, and kelp crabs cling
to the fronds. Otters, seals, and many birds depend on this productive
ecosystem to supply them with prey.

The sea palm (*Postelsia palmaeformis*) forms another, quite different
forest on the wave-battered rocks of the low intertidal zone (IV). Groves
of this brown alga (fig. 15) resemble miniature palm trees a few feet tall.
With their pliant yet durable stems and stubborn holdfasts, the sea
palms are not only adapted to severe wave stress but they are restricted
to it—they cannot grow in sheltered waters. The exposed rocks of Pfeiffer Point near Pfeiffer Beach support a dense colony of the palms.

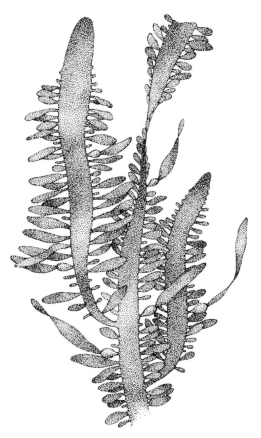

Figure 16.   *Egregia menziesii,* feather boa kelp

Feather boa kelp (*Egregia menziesii*) (fig. 16) has its holdfast on the same rocks in the low intertidal zone as the sea palm, but its long strap-like body floats up to the higher zones. Oblong floats grow on each edge of its flattened stalk, which is gold or olive-green in color. *Fucus distichus* (fig. 17) and *Pelvetia fastigiata,* small brown rockweeds occurring in the high and middle zones, are often covered by these ropey strands. *Pelvetiopsis limitata* (fig. 18) is a similar but smaller rockweed that grows on the highest rocks of the splash zone. The rockweeds are tan to olive-brown algae with distinctive branches that fork in pairs. They are extremely common along Big Sur's rocky shore.

Red algae are often confused with brown algae. The red algae mask their green chlorophyll with blue and red pigments. Such a mix of colors gives rise to a variety of hues, some brilliantly iridescent, but others that

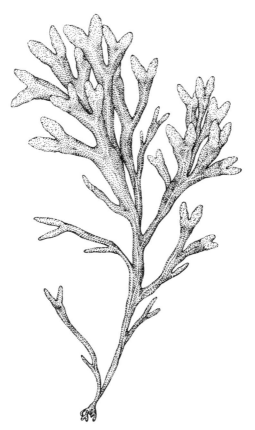

Figure 17. *Fucus distichus,* rockweed

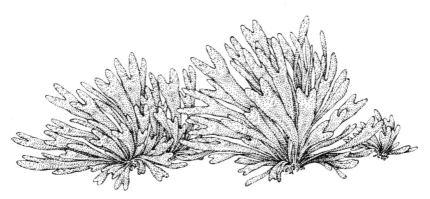

Figure 18. *Pelvetiopsis limitata,* little rockweed

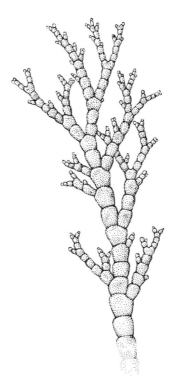

Figure 19. *Corallina vancouveriensis,*
coralline algae

are olive, brown, or black. The reds tend to be smaller than the browns,
and few exceed 1 m (3 ft) in length. In well-shaded and deeper areas of
the intertidal zone, the red, pink, or purple colors of these plants are
more easily seen.

Endocladia muricata, a wiry, upright plant with many branches, is
one of the more conspicuous red algae. Small red and purple clumps
about 4–8 cm (2–3 in.) tall grow near the brown rockweeds and barnacles of the high zone. By contrast, *Gigartina exasperata* and *Iridaea
cordata* are broad, leafy plants of the middle and low zones. The blades
of both plants are red to purple or blue and sometimes resemble an oil
slick in their iridescence.

Another red alga, *Corallina vancouveriensis* (fig. 19), is usually seen
in and around tidepools. Its bright pink branches are jointed and grow
in a flattened pattern 4–10 cm (2–4 in.) high. The coralline algae were

once thought to be animals rather than plants because their tough, calcium-laden stems resemble coral, a colonial animal. Bleached fragments of this plant are often found washed ashore.

COMMON INTERTIDAL ANIMALS

The intertidal region is one of the most rewarding natural areas to explore due to its abundance of readily observed animals. Crabs, chitons, seastars, mussels—every lifted rock and overturned seaweed clump usually reveals a number of fascinating creatures. Even the most mundane intertidal organisms exhibit a complex array of adaptations to their rigorous environment. (By the way, be sure to replace all rocks that you move, and *never* collect any plants or animals along the Big Sur coast. Some of our neighboring intertidal areas, such as the Monterey Peninsula, have been stripped bare by collectors and foragers.)

Snails, for example, are at first glance not very impressive. These *gastropods* (from the Latin word for "stomach feet") are dull, slow-moving creatures. They retreat into their shells at the slightest provocation. But a little more insight into their life history reveals a highly diverse and successful group of organisms. About 65,000 species of snails have been recognized worldwide, including the limpets, periwinkles, turbans, and abalones of the intertidal region.

Periwinkles are the most terrestrial of the four. This snail's Latin genus name *Littorina* translates to "shore dweller," an apt description of the animal's tendency to remain above the high tide line. It needs the ocean only to wet its gills occasionally, and some biologists feel it is an evolutionary intermediate between marine and terrestrial animals. Like other marine snails, *Littorina* is equipped with a radula, which is an efficient, all-purpose tongue. It is actually a hard ribbon studded with rows of teeth, like a rasp or file, and it is used to scrape food off the rocks. Periwinkles can erode coarse sandstone as much as 1 cm (0.4 in.) every 16 years with their constant grazing. They graze the dry rocks of Big Sur's splash zone for microscopic plants and detritus, where their dingy gray shells are inconspicuous.

Other snails, such as the rock snail (*Thais emarginata*) have developed their radula to the deadly extent of using it to drill holes in the hard shells of barnacles and mussels. Unlike the vegetarian periwinkle, the rock snail is carnivorous and even cannibalistic. Adults sometimes eat snail eggs—their own or a neighbor's—and the larvae devour each other while still in their egg capsules until only one youngster remains.

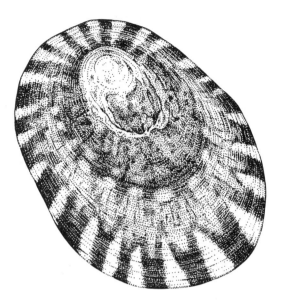

Figure 20.   *Lottia gigantea,* owl limpet

The young snail will soon grow a 2.5-cm (1-in.) shell that is gray or greenish brown with dark bandings, and it will choose comparably sized barnacles and mussels as prey.

Most snails, however, are strictly herbivorous, but such an eating preference does not mean they are passive animals. Limpets are particularly aggressive snails. They graze in the shaded portions of the middle and upper intertidal zones and are snaillike in every way except their shells. The shell has an elliptical perimeter and is either flattened, conical with a peak, or conical with a hole at the apex, like a miniature volcano.

Feeding space for grazers is at a premium in the intertidal area, and the owl limpet (*Lottia gigantea*) (fig. 20) has evolved a stubborn disposition to deal with this limitation. This animal is inactive by day or when uncovered, but at night it searches its mid-zone rock for food and intruders. The latter are unceremoniously bulldozed off the territory, be they mussels, snails, or other limpets. Smaller limpets, such as the gray

Figure 21. *Tegula funebralis,* black turban snail

fingered limpet (*Acmaea digitalis*), are seen clustered by the thousands onto the sides of surf-swept rocks. Their drab shells are about 2.5 cm (1 in.) in diameter with 15 to 25 ribs radiating from the center.

The black turban snails (*Tegula funebralis*) (fig. 21) are even more numerous than the limpets in Big Sur's upper intertidal zones. They blanket the sides of rocks and fill the cracks in between. The tops of their blue shells often wear away to reveal the pearly, iridescent peaks of the spirals. These shells are common homes for hermit crabs (*Pagurus samuelis*) (fig. 22) which are often seen dragging them about in the tidepools. It once believed that a hermit crab, desirous of a new and larger snail shell home, would attack a snail and attempt to evict it. But such interactions are rarely observed, even under forced laboratory conditions, and the hermits undoubtedly move into empty shells. Turban snails are quite capable of protecting themselves with their operculum, a tough hatchlike door that clamps shut over the shell opening. It is an air-tight, water-tight, and crab-tight seal.

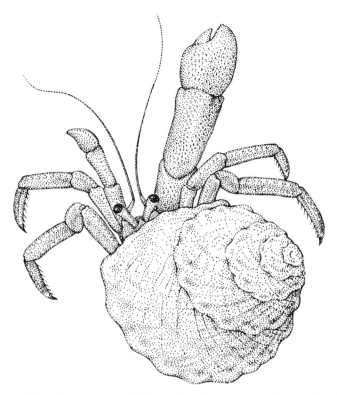

Figure 22. *Pagurus samuelis,* hermit crab in wavy turban snail shell

The abalone is also a snail and a very large one, although it is quite unlike the turban and other snails in appearance. Its shell reveals the characteristic spiral snail design, but with the flattened, more elliptical shape of the limpets. *Haliotis rufescens,* the famous red abalone (fig. 23), grows up to 28 cm (11 in.) long. Its tremendous muscular foot is a prized food, a distinction that has rendered the animal rare. Most legal-sized specimens over 16 cm (6.5 in.) in length are found far offshore or in the lowest low zone. The animal is strictly herbivorous, gorging itself on the plentiful sea lettuce and certain kelps. The smaller black abalone (*Haliotis cracherodii*) is more common on the wave-exposed rocks of Big Sur. It can tolerate the barren rocks here because it is primarily a plankton feeder rather than a grazer like its red cousin. Its black shell is kept clean of small seaweeds and other hitchhikers, unlike that of the red abalone, which often carries a mosaic of plants and animals encrusted on its shell.

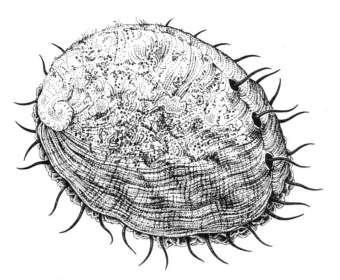

Figure 23. *Haliotis rufescens,* red abalone

The dark blue California mussel (*Mytilus californianus*) (fig. 24) is one of the more obvious tidal markers. It flourishes where good surf and waves shower it with tiny food particles that it filters from the water. It can tolerate the continual pounding of the surf with its heavily ribbed shell and byssal threads. Secreted by a gland in the foot, the threads anchor each individual to a rock. Many of the mussels are also wedged between their neighbors in dense clusters, providing even more staying power. These beds create their own intriguing microhabitat—a mussel forest—and a surprising number of worms, sponges, snails, and crabs live beneath this mussel canopy.

The hard, chalk-colored beds of goose barnacles (*Pollicipes polymerus*) (fig. 25) are distinct from the blue mussel beds. Although these barnacles are often found in close proximity to the mussels, they have a very different set of habitat requirements. They grow atop fleshy stalks that are attached to the sides of rocks, whereas mussels are generally found on horizontal rock faces. The latter feed as a wave washes over them, but goose barnacles wait until a wave passes and water is flowing down the rocks. With their bodies aligned in the direction of this runoff,

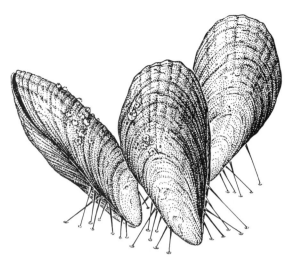

Figure 24. *Mytilus californianus*, California mussel

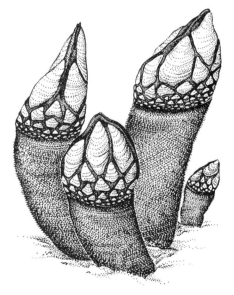

Figure 25. *Pollicipes polymerus*, goose barnacle

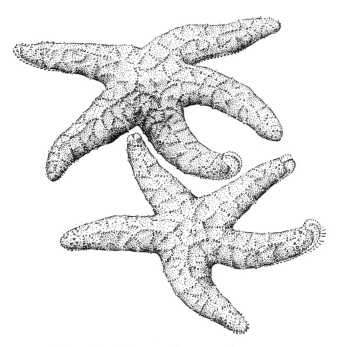

Figure 26. *Pisaster ochraceus,* ochre seastar

they snare insectlike amphipods that float by, taking in creatures and other bits of food as large as houseflies.

Goose barnacles and mussels are favored food items of the ochre seastar (*Pisaster ochraceus*) (fig. 26). The seastar crawls up from the low zone to feed on these shellfish at the lower portions of their beds. This formidable animal has few predators and hence requires no protective coloration. It ranges in color from dull yellow to orange, maroon, and even dark brown. During low tides, it can be found in moist cracks or feeding atop a mussel bed.

The seastar's method of feeding is one of the most bizarre processes in the intertidal arena. Straddling a mussel and prying its shell open as little as 1/100th of an inch, the seastar distends its stomach out of its body and slides it through the crack between the mussel's paired shells.

Once inside the mussel's shell, the predator's stomach digests the unprotected mussel flesh. Other animals justifiably avoid the seastar, according to Ed Ricketts. Limpets and snails will "flee" from a nearby seastar, apparently alarmed to its presence by some unknown substance that the predator emits.

Sea anemones rival the seastars for predatory prowess. The large green solitary anemone (*Anthopleura xanthogrammica*) lives in the middle and low intertidal zones, while groups of the smaller aggregate anemone (*A. elegantissima*) form dense, spongy mats in the upper middle zone. Anemones attach to rocks and are almost completely immobile. Nonetheless, they are quite successful in capturing snails, crabs, and other unfortunate creatures that wander in reach of their stinging tentacles. Once the prey is immobilized by these tentacles, microscopic hairs slowly move the victim toward the center of the anemone where it falls into the creature's mouth. Indigestible shells and other body parts are soon expelled from the mouth.

Several common species of crabs crawl around and beneath the anemones, most giving wide berth to the tentacles. Hermit crabs are the most noticeable, dragging around as living quarters the discarded shells of turban and olivella snails. It is practically impossible to pull a hermit out of its shell because its body has a natural twist that corresponds with the shell's spiral shape. The shell protects the crab's soft, vulnerable abdomen, while the exposed upper body is heavily armored. These animals are scavengers, picking their way across the tidepools and eating practically anything.

Most other shore crabs are scavengers as well. The lined shore or rock crab (*Pachygrapsus crassipes*) (fig. 27) is most active at night, but by day it can be found in the narrow crevices of Big Sur's upper intertidal zones and boulder fields. It has red claws with distinctive purple veining, and its back, or carapace, is 5 cm (2 in.) in diameter with a transverse series of bands. According to Ricketts and others in *Between Pacific Tides,* "To see a group of them attack a discarded apple core is to understand one method by which the rock pools are kept clear of any foreign matter that is to any degree edible." Their chief food, however, is algae, which they shove into their mouths with both claws in a speedy, alternating method.

The purple shore crab (*Hemigrapsus nudus*) outnumbers *Pachygrapsus* in the pools and rockweeds of the middle zone. The two are similar in size and overlap to some extent in habitat, but the large red spots on its claws and the absence of bands distinguish *Hemigrapsus*.

Another crab common to the middle zone is the porcelain crab (*Pet-*

Figure 27. *Pachygrapsus crassipes,* lined shore crab

rolisthes cinctipes). It is flat and small, about 1.3 cm (0.5 in.) across the body. Turn over a rock and they scurry madly for another shelter. These crabs are famous for their ability to throw off, or *autotomize,* a claw or leg at the slightest sign of danger. Unlike the lizards that lose their tails when pulled, these crabs cast off limbs voluntarily. Muscles and tendons are adapted to facilitate the breakage, and an automatic reaction instantly closes broken blood vessels. A new limb soon grows back. Autotomizing also enables the porcelain crab to escape when a leg is pinned beneath a wave-tossed rock, which is a constant danger on the rocky coast. Other many limbed intertidal creatures, such as brittle stars, have also developed this ability.

While crabs hide beneath and between rocks to escape waves, sea urchins (*Strongylocentrotus* spp.) burrow shelters directly into the stone. In surf-swept areas such as Big Sur, up to half the animal's spiny body is buried in these pits. Sea urchins live near the base of kelp beds and forests and feed extensively on these algae. Often present in large numbers, they can effectively defoliate a kelp forest and thus greatly influence the habitat of many other creatures. Undeterred by the urchin's porcupinelike spines, sea otters prey upon them and are an effective check on the urchin population.

Like the urchins, chitons also excavate small pits to escape the surf. Shallow depressions or pits in the rocks of the middle and high intertidal zones are often occupied by *Nuttalina californica,* a gray chiton

5 cm (2 in.) long. A total of twenty-nine species of chitons occur near Monterey and many of these are found in Big Sur. Chitons resemble giant legless pillbugs, and like pillbugs they curl up if pried out of their pits. The pits are slowly gouged out by successive generations, and an individual may inhabit one for over twenty years. They seldom stray except to feed on bits of seaweed. The bright orange gumboot chiton (*Cryptochiton stelleri*) is the largest in the world. An inhabitant of low tidepools, it is often cast up dead on the beach. Its tough leathery flesh conceals the eight shell plates common to all chitons, and after the animals decompose, these plates form the white butterfly-shaped shells seen scattered on the sand.

There are hundreds of other creatures in Big Sur's intertidal habitat in addition to the few mentioned here, including many fish, worms, sponges, corals, clams, octopi, and so on. Several books listed at the end of this chapter give a thorough treatment of this rich and complex habitat.

SEABIRDS AND SHOREBIRDS

Just about anywhere along the Big Sur coast is a good place to sit and watch birds. Processions of pelicans glide along the shore. Cormorants and gulls roost on the guano-stained rocks. Sea ducks, grebes, and loons float in the kelp forests offshore and dive for fish and mollusks. On land, shorebirds probe the sand and seaweed-covered rocks for small invertebrates and scraps. Only a select few of these birds are well-adapted to feed directly in the rocky intertidal on a regular basis. Potential food sources are abundant here, but they are also well protected. Crabs and other small invertebrates escape to crevices, beneath rocks, or within algal growth and are out of reach of most birds. Others are protected by their tough shells, inconspicuous coloration, or repugnant taste. The dangerous surf also discourages birds from foraging here.

A few birds, though, are adapted to these conditions and are considered intertidal specialists. The black oystercatcher (*Haematopus bachmani*) (fig. 28) uses its heavy red bill to crack open mussels and pry limpets off the rocks. Calklike structures on the bird's feet enable it to grip slippery rocks while it feeds. The black turnstone (*Arenaria melanocephala*) (fig. 29) is unable to pop open the large mollusks and instead uses its small, upturned bill to flip over pebbles and seaweed fronds in search of pill bugs and small snails. These stocky, short-legged birds breed on the Alaskan tundra, but some can usually be seen year-round in Big Sur since many nonbreeders remain here during the summer.

Figure 28. *Haematopus bachmani*, black oystercatcher

Figure 29. *Arenaria melanocephala*, black turnstone

The surfbird (*Aphriza virgata*) is similar in appearance to the black turnstone and is one of the few birds found right at the rocky surfline. It frequents mussel beds, flying up as a wave hits and then settling down to quickly feed as the wave retreats. Wandering tattlers (*Heteroscelus incanum*) and western gulls (*Larus occidentalis*) also feed here during low tide. The omnivorous gulls eat stranded crabs, small seastars, mussels, barnacles, and just about anything else they can swallow.

Willets (*Catoptrophorus semipalmatus*), whimbrels (*Numenius phaeopus*), sanderlings (*Calidris alba*) (fig. 30), plovers, and sandpipers are less common visitors to the rocky coast of Big Sur. They sometimes poke around in the seaweed, but are better suited to the sandy beaches and mudflats where they congregate in large flocks.

Figure 30.   *Calidris alba,* sanderlings

Tight-knit groups of sanderlings are common on the stretches of sand between the rocky exposures. They chase the edge of a retreating wave in unison, picking up sand crabs, fleas, and small clams. Willets, whimbrels, and marbled godwits (*Limosa fedoa*) use their long bills to probe deep in the sand, also taking sand crabs. Many birds converge on piles of seaweed cast upon the beach, where large numbers of shellfish, flies, and other morsels are trapped within the decaying algae. Even landbirds such as the black phoebe (*Sayornis nigricans*) come down here to feast on the flies.

Large marsh birds such as the great blue heron (*Ardea herodias*) (fig. 31), the great egret (*Casmerodius albus*), and the snowy egret (*Egretta thula*) have learned to fish the tidepools and kelp forests. Common in coastal lagoons, these tall birds are an odd sight when perched on floating kelp or driftwood. Bobbing with the swells like a buoy, a great blue heron will stand motionless for many minutes as it waits for a fish or crab to come within reach. Between feeding bouts, these birds sometimes roost on offshore rocks.

For landlubbers not willing to embark upon an offshore birding cruise, Big Sur is a good terrestrial base from which to scan for seabirds. The high cliffs offer excellent vantage points for viewing the nearshore kelp beds and large rock islands, and the deep waters close to shore sometimes attract open ocean birds closer to land.

The seabirds frequenting these areas can be divided into two general groups: the pelagic species and the inshore species (see Davis and Baldridge, 1980). Pelagic birds spend most of their lives beyond the edge of

Figure 31. *Ardea herodias,* great blue heron

the continental shelf, feeding in the open ocean and breeding on remote oceanic islands. This group includes the albatrosses, shearwaters, and storm-petrels. It is not common to find such birds close to shore elsewhere in California, but nearby Monterey Bay is a famous exception due to the presence of the Monterey Submarine Canyon. This canyon reaches depths of 1800 m (6000 ft), and the upwelling of its nutrient-laden waters provides food for many seabirds. The Big Sur coast has several smaller submarine canyons, such as Partington Canyon and Mill Creek Canyon, that provide similar conditions.

The inshore species are more frequently observed. These birds spend most of their time closer to shore foraging in waters less than 50 m (160 ft) deep. Three species of cormorants frequent the coast year-round, and several types of loons, scoters, and grebes are seen here in

Figure 32.   *Pelecanus occidentalis,* brown pelican

winter. Other birds, such as the brown pelicans (*Pelecanus occidentalis*)
(fig. 32), arrive in early summer. Several thousand common murres
(*Uria aalge*) nest on the large rocks off Hurricane Point, and pigeon
guillemots (*Cepphus columba*) breed along the entire Big Sur coast.

Big Sur's rocky islands, sea stacks, and steep cliffs provide valuable
roosting and nesting territory for several marine birds. Western gulls, as
well as Brandt's (fig. 33), double-crested, and pelagic cormorants (*Phalacrocorax penicillatus, P. auritus,* and *P. pelagicus*), all nest on such sites.
Each species has slightly different nesting preferences. The Brandt's cormorant, for example, chooses the level or slightly sloped tops of rocky
islets, while the pelagic cormorant chooses narrow ledges on cliffs. Such
behavior lessens the competition for extremely limited space.

The brown pelicans roost alongside the cormorants on these rocks.
They are still common visitors to Big Sur, although they no longer nest

Figure 33.   *Phalacrocorax penicillatus,* Brandt's cormorant

here. The species had its northernmost breeding colony on the Pacific coast at Point Lobos until 1959. An endangered species, the bird's initial decline was thought to be related to DDT residues in coastal waters. The pesticide, ingested by pelicans through the fish they eat, causes them to lay thin-shelled eggs that fail to hatch or are crushed during incubation. The banning of DDT has led to a slow recovery of pelican colonies in southern California, and more are seen in Big Sur each year. They are a spectacular sight as they tuck their meter-long wings and plunge into the water head first, snaring fish in their beak and pouch.

Other seabirds, such as the grebes, loons, and scoters, are seen near shore, but are rarely seen roosting on the rocks. They float in small groups near the kelp forests. Loons and grebes are divers and capture

fish in underwater pursuit. Scoters, which are sea ducks, are more passive feeders and eat small mollusks, crustaceans, and marine plants.
Flocks of these seabirds float beyond the breakers and can be seen from
shore with binoculars.

MARINE MAMMALS

SOUTHERN SEA OTTER

Recovering from near extinction just a century ago, the southern sea
otter (*Enhydra lutris nereis*) is today a common sight along the Big Sur
coast. This carnivorous mammal lives in the nearshore kelp beds within
easy view from the cliffs. Its high visibility, playful habits, and encouraging recovery have made it the animal species most often identified
with the Big Sur coast.

Sea otters (fig. 34) are well adapted to a life spent almost entirely at
sea. They grow much larger than their terrestrial cousins, the river otters. Adult males measure up to 1.5 m (5 ft) long and weigh up to
36 kg (80 lbs); the females are shorter and weigh up to 20 kg (45 lbs).
Their hind legs are short and flipperlike, and their toes are webbed by
hair-covered membranes. The forepaws are much shorter and have bare
palms, and the toes have short, arched claws that are used to manipulate
food. Their flattened tails, about 25–30 cm (10–12 in.) long, are stiff
and serve as rudders when the animals swim. Thick necks, round heads,
and flattened ears give them a streamlined shape for moving quickly
through the water.

The sea otter's thick, lustrous coat is perhaps the animal's greatest
adaptation to a life in the chilly Pacific. Unlike other marine mammals,
the sea otter has no insulating layer of blubber and instead must rely on
its dense fur to maintain its body heat. Densely packed hairs trap tiny
air bubbles that increase the fur's insulative quality. When grooming,
the animals often roll in the water and blow into the fur, refilling it with
air bubbles.

The pelt is a golden brown to blackish color when wet, enabling the
animals to blend inconspicuously with their kelp habitat. Although otters sometimes swim far offshore, most float on their backs atop the
expansive forests of giant and bullwhip kelp. They scour the kelp trees
and rocky bottom, grabbing urchins, crabs, clams, abalones, mussels,
and snails in dives that last up to 3 or 4 minutes. Some otters eat so
many purple sea urchins that their bones and teeth take on a purplish

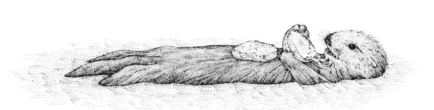

Figure 34. *Enhydra lutris nereis,* southern sea otter

tint due to the absorption of a purple pigment found in the urchins' bodies.

Sea otters use small rocks to crack open their shellfish prey and are thus one of the few animals that have developed tool-using abilities. An otter places the rock on its chest and pounds the shellfish on it until the shell cracks. The loud rapping noise of a feeding otter can sometimes be heard from Highway 1, and abalone shells with large circular holes cracked in them are often found on beaches near where the animals feed. There have been several reports of otters preying upon seabirds in the Cannery Row and Point Lobos areas, but such behavior is probably atypical. Northern sea otters found in Alaska eat fish, while it is believed that southern sea otters do not.

The otters sleep where they feed, wrapping strands of kelp around their bodies as anchors to prevent them from drifting out to sea or onto the beach. They sometimes drape a kelp frond across their eyes on sunny days. Such entanglement in the algae conceals them from the killer whales and sharks that hunt along the Big Sur coast. The kelp forest also serves as a wave inhibitor, deadening the swells and keeping the surface relatively smooth. Feeding, sleeping, and nursing of pups are all easier in such protected places.

Pups are born at sea, and only one is born per pregnancy. Twins are rare, and in such cases the mother usually ends up losing or abandoning one of the pups. A mother cares for its pup for about five to eight months, eventually deserting it and forcing the young otter to fend for itself. It is unclear whether sea otters at one time gave birth on land or if they have always given birth at sea. Some biologists think they may have developed this ability as a response to being hunted. It is known that they often hauled out on land prior to the nineteenth century and were even considered tame and approachable. The northern sea otters in Alaska do haul out, but southern sea otters rarely come onto shore today and are extremely wary and suspicious of any approaching humans.

Before the great hunting period of 1786 to 1848, the sea otters ranged over an area nearly 9700 km (6000 mi) long. They were found on the northern coast of Japan, along the Aleutian chain to the Alaskan Peninsula, and down the North American Pacific coast to central Baja California. San Francisco Bay abounded with otters, and the animals not only swam throughout the bay but also hauled up on shore near the estuaries of San Mateo, San Bruno, and San Jose. Monterey Bay and the Big Sur coast were also well populated with otters, as were the Channel Islands near Santa Barbara and the numerous islands and bays of northern Baja.

The sea otter was systematically hunted throughout this entire range by Spanish, Russian, and American fur traders. To satisfy the great demand for otter skins in China and Europe, Russian and American traders brought native hunters from the Aleutian islands of Alaska down to California. These Aleuts were extremely effective hunters. Using their swift, seal-skin canoes or kayaks and handmade spears and arrows, the Aleuts approached sleeping otters with ease.

The southern sea otter population was noticeably declining after 1815. By the 1830s American and Mexican hunters armed with rifles replaced the Aleuts. Hunting dwindled along the Big Sur coast and elsewhere in California as the animals grew scarce. From the early 1890s until 1917, occasional otters were seen and shot between San Luis Obispo and Monterey. In 1911, a treaty was signed by the United States, Russia, Canada, and Japan protecting sea otters from commercial exploitation. Many people felt this protection came too late and that the southern sea otter was headed for certain extinction.

The subspecies was assumed extinct, but in 1938 a small herd of sea otters was found living just 15 miles south of Monterey near Bixby Bridge. The animals were apparently protected by Big Sur's inaccessibility and undeveloped coastline. Local people and some biologists had been well aware of the animals' existence for years, but the opening of Highway 1 brought it to the attention of the rest of the world. A sea otter game refuge was established along the Big Sur coast, and through careful protection, the population has today increased to more than 1500 animals.

Southern sea otters now range from the coast of northern Santa Barbara County to Pigeon Point, 48 km (30 mi) north of Santa Cruz. They are not migratory animals like the sea lions and whales, but they do move around quite a bit within their home range. Recent studies have shown that it is not uncommon for an otter to move from Big Sur up to

Carmel in a day or two and then return to Big Sur a few days later. Occasionally, an otter wanders as far south as San Diego or as far north as Humboldt County, and there are some isolated populations even farther north that were transplanted by wildlife biologists. It appears that southern sea otters are expanding steadily on both the northern and southern fronts of the range since females with pups are being observed at the perimeters, both north of Santa Cruz and south of Morro Bay.

The Big Sur coast remains a main stronghold of the population. Although this recovery is encouraging, the sea otter is still considered a threatened species for two major reasons. First, a large oil spill could wipe out the population, and second, sea otters suffer a high rate of mortality due to natural causes, poaching, and gill net fishing methods.

To alleviate these threats, the U.S. Fish and Wildlife Service began fieldwork in 1986 on a plan to capture up to 70 otters and translocate them to San Nicolas Island. Located 62 miles off the southern California coast, this island is well within the species' historical range, although no otters are currently found there. The primary goal of the plan is to establish a second population that is located far enough away from the Big Sur population to not be affected by a major oil spill. Thus, this secondary group of otters would provide some measure of assurance that the species would survive an oil spill disaster.

The plan has received stubborn opposition from fishermen and abalone divers. These people feel that the sea otters are overharvesting certain prey items, such as clams, abalone, and crabs. They blame the otter for shortages of these animals and for upsetting the "natural balance" of the nearshore ecosystem.

There is no doubt that the sea otter is a voracious and efficient predator. Otters have an extremely high metabolism and are believed to consume food equaling 20 percent to 30 percent of their body weight every day. We have observed a female otter catch and consume five large *Cancer* crabs in about 70 minutes. However, since otter numbers are still so much lower than they once were within this range, it is difficult to believe that they are actually upsetting the natural balance. A more accurate interpretation, perhaps, is that they are returning the nearshore ecosystem to a structure more closely resembling what it once was prior to the species' near extinction. Abalone, urchins, and other otter prey probably experienced unprecedented population growth when their primary predator was eliminated during the previous century.

Otters may do more than any other single species to increase the productivity of the nearshore ecosystem. One of their favorite prey is sea urchins. Urchins are grazers, feeding on the kelps that make up the kelp forests that line the Big Sur coast. Large populations of urchins have been known to destroy or severely denude kelp forests. Otters act as a natural control on the urchin populations, increasing the size and productivity of the kelp forests by limiting the urchins' herbivorous activities. This in turn provides enhanced food and shelter for hundreds of other species that live within this kelp forest ecosystem.

SEA LIONS AND SEALS

The low rock islands and unapproachable beaches that line the Big Sur coast are frequented by several species of sea lions and seals. These marine mammals are known as *pinnipeds*. Like the sea otters, pinnipeds are well adapted to a life at sea. Somewhat clumsy and slow moving on land, they are remarkably graceful and swift in the water. Their torpedo-shaped bodies offer little resistance to passage through water. Their external ears are greatly reduced or absent, their tails are short, their limbs are modified to flippers, and their large eyes can see through dark waters.

Pinnipeds also have an insulating layer of fat beneath their skin, maintaining an internal temperature that is roughly the same as that of human beings. They can dive to great depths and for extended periods of time in their search for food because they have a modified circulatory system. During a dive, they conserve oxygen by reducing their heartbeat to about one-tenth of its normal rate and shunting blood. This ensures adequate oxygen for the heart and brain.

Two species of sea lion are common along the Big Sur coast: the California sea lion (*Zalophus californianus*) and the Steller's sea lion (*Eumetopias jubata*). The Steller's sea lion is the larger of the two, with males weighing over a ton and reaching 3 m (10 ft) in length; females are much smaller, weighing 270 kg (600 lbs) and reaching 2.3 m (7 ft) in length. Small groups of this yellow-brown animal are seen on offshore rocks, especially near Point Lobos, for much of the year. They do not breed in Big Sur, but have a large breeding colony at Año Nuevo Island north of Santa Cruz.

The California sea lions (fig. 35) are often seen along with the Steller's, hauling out on rocks to sleep or lay in the sun. They are smaller and darker in color, and they make the familiar houndlike bark that is often heard from the highway. California sea lions spend early summer breeding on islands off southern California, Baja California, and main-

Figure 35. *Zalophus californianus*, California sea lion

land Mexico, after which time they return to Big Sur and other areas
off central California. Several inaccessible beaches are favorite resting
spots for these animals, such as the one south of Grimes Point. Herds
are sometimes seen far offshore, swimming rapidly, with individuals
leaping out of the water as they move along.

Sea lions were hunted commercially after the sea otter and elephant
seal populations were depleted. In the mid-1800s, they were harvested
for their oil and hides, the latter being used to make glue. In 1909, they
received protection and today are fairly numerous along central California's coast.

The harbor seal (*Phoca vitulina*) (fig. 36) is much smaller and less
conspicuous than the sea lions. It lacks external ears, is more quiet and
shy, and has an extremely variable skin color that ranges from black to
spotted gray. Groups of harbor seals haul out during low tide, their
mottled colors and quiet manner rendering them almost invisible on the
offshore rocks. They often swim near the surf and sometimes float in
the kelp like the otters. They feed on fish, octopus, shellfish, and squid
and usually forage in or near the kelp forests, rarely venturing out to
sea like the migratory sea lions. These seals give birth in April and May
to a single pup, a process that lucky observers have occasionally wit-
nessed. The cliffs around Dolan Rock and Point Sur are good areas to
view them.

The elephant seal (*Mirounga angustirostris*) is the largest of Big Sur's

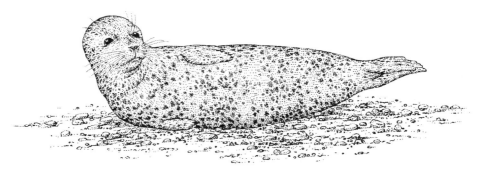

Figure 36. *Phoca vitulina*, harbor seal

pinnipeds. The males can weigh up to 3600 kg (8000 lbs) and reach
6 m (20 ft) in length; the females reach 900 kg (2000 lbs) and 3.3 m
(11 ft) in length. The older males have a hanging proboscislike snout
that gives the species its common name, and their necks and chests are
often scarred from sparring with fellow bulls. Females lack the hanging
snouts, but have faces that are less tapered or pointed than other seals.
They feed on sharks, squids, rays, and other fish.

Elephant seals are rarely seen in Big Sur and do not breed there. Their
main northern breeding ground is at Año Nuevo State Reserve, located
north of Santa Cruz. Young, nonbreeding animals are sometimes seen
along several inaccessible beaches in south Big Sur, where they congregate with California sea lions. These seals are not very shy and will
tolerate some degree of human presence, but they should not be unnec-
essarily disturbed. Like sea otters, elephant seals were nearly exterminated during the nineteenth century. Their recovery has been even more
remarkable than that of the sea otter; from a population low of no more
than 100 at the turn of the century, numbers in 1977 were estimated at
60,000.

GRAY WHALE

The gray whale (*Eschrichtius robustus*) (fig. 37) is a regular and highly
visible visitor to the Big Sur coast. Swimming nearshore on their annual
migration, the whales spout plumes of spray into the air as they breathe.
Individuals sometimes breach, propelling two-thirds of their 14-m- (45-
ft-) long bodies above the surface and then crashing back into the water.

Their migration starts in the Bering and Chukchi seas in the Arctic.
The animals spend the summer there building up their thick layer of

Figure 37. *Eschrichtius robustus,* gray whale

blubber by feeding on amphipods, which are tiny shrimplike creatures. The blubber insulates them from the frigid Arctic seas and serves as an energy reserve. They may not eat for the next 6 months until they return to the rich Arctic waters. They leave the Arctic in October, and most follow the North American shoreline southward. The pregnant females migrate first, followed by the nonpregnant females and males. They pass Big Sur in mid-December and January on their way to the sheltered lagoons of Baja California and mainland Mexico. They give birth to their young in these shallow, protected waters. They swim quite close to land during this southward trek, which is one of the longest migrations of any mammal.

After the calves are born, the whales return north in March and April. Many mother–calf pairs are seen on this return trip. Mating behavior, which usually involves the interaction of a female and two males, is sometimes observed as the whales move north. Prominent cliffs and headlands, especially Gamboa, Lopez, Partington, and Hurricane points, offer unsurpassed vantage points to such events, and whale watching from shore has become a popular Big Sur pastime.

One hundred years ago, whalers used points north of Big Sur to observe their prey before setting off for the hunt. Known as "shore whaling," this European method of whaling was introduced into the Monterey area about 1854. Small whaling villages were established at various beaches. Whales were sighted from the headlands and their locations were signaled to offshore boats. The whales were then pursued, harpooned, and towed back to the beach for processing. Gray whales and humpback whales (*Megaptera novaeangliae*) were easy victims since both are slow-moving species that spend much time nearshore. In just a few years, Monterey became known as a great whaling port. But in just a few more years, by 1888, the whales had virtually disappeared from the California coast. Today, the gray whale is protected by international treaties, and the population appears to be doing well.

There are several other marine mammals occasionally seen off the Big Sur coast, including blue whales (*Balaenoptera musculus*), porpoises and dolphins, and killer whales (*Orcinus orca*). In the spring of 1982, for example, a group of killer whales was observed attacking and killing a gray whale calf near Big Creek. In the summer of 1986, a blue whale 20-m (69-ft) long washed ashore just south of Point Sur.

SUGGESTED READING

Davis, J. and A. Baldridge, 1980. *The bird year: A book for birders.* Pacific Grove, Calif.: Boxwood Press.

Dawson, E. Y., and M. S. Foster, 1982. *Seashore plants of California.* California Natural History Guide 47. Berkeley: University of California Press.

Ferguson, A., ed. 1984. *Intertidal plants and animals of the Landels-Hill Big Creek Reserve, Monterey County, California.* Environmental Field Program Publication 14, University of California, Santa Cruz.

Fitch, J. E., and R. J. Lavenberg, 1975. *Tidepool and nearshore fishes of California.* California Natural History Guide 38. Berkeley: University of California Press.

Hedgpeth, J. W., 1962. *Introduction to seashore life of the San Francisco Bay region and the coast of northern California.* California Natural History Guide 9. Berkeley: University of California Press.

Ricketts, E. F., J. Calvin, and J. W. Hedgpeth, 1985. *Between Pacific tides.* Stanford, Calif.: Stanford University Press.

CHAPTER IV

Big Sur Plant Communities

INTRODUCTION

The great variety of plants that inhabit the Big Sur region is obvious even from the narrow confines of Highway 1. As it follows the Big Sur coastline, the highway enters dark redwood-forested canyons, passes out into sunny grasslands and through woodlands of oaks, and winds along slopes covered with brush. The collage of various plant communities continues up the mountainsides where tall pines look down to the coast from the highest ridges. A closer look reveals even greater diversity; a survey of only 1600 ha (4000 acres) at Big Creek Reserve found 344 species of plants representing 42 percent of all California plant families. This is an astounding number of plant species for such a small area.

The vegetation is exceptional in other ways as well. A number of plants found in Big Sur are unique, or *endemic,* to the region; the Santa Lucia fir is the most significant and well-known example. Many other plants in the range, such as the sugar pine and the ponderosa pine, are distantly isolated, or *disjunct,* from their main populations in the state. Others plants reach their northern or southern limits of distribution here. For example, nowhere else do redwood trees, which are virtually synonymous with fog and the northern California coast, grow in the same ravines with yucca, plants common to the arid climate of southern California.

This combination of endemic and disjunct plants and the mixing of northern and southern floras have interested botanists since the early 1800s. Many were initially attracted to the Santa Lucia Range because of the Santa Lucia fir, which is endemic to these mountains and had become famous in botanical circles by the mid-1800s. The Scottish botanist David Douglas (for whom the Douglas fir is named) first described the Santa Lucia fir near Cone Peak in 1831. The first sugar pines to be described in California were also found in the Santa Lucias, and the Coulter pine was discovered by Thomas Coulter in 1832 in the vicinity of Cone Peak. Another well-known botanist, Theodore Hartweg, collected here in 1850. A number of eminent botanists and ecologists have continued this tradition, including Alice Eastwood in the early part of this century and, more recently, Beatrice Howitt and James Griffin of Hastings Natural History Reservation.

CLIMATE AND VEGETATION

The rugged topography and special climate of the region are the most important reasons for the diversity of plant life in the Santa Lucias. All plants that live in Big Sur are adapted to the Mediterranean climatic cycle of winter rain and summer drought. One of the most striking and obvious effects of this climate is that most of the perennial plants in the area are evergreen. Winters are so mild that plants do not need to become dormant. In fact, winter is the growing season for most plants here. A second consequence of the climate is that a large proportion of the plants here are annuals that germinate, set seed, and die before the onset of the summer drought. As many as 50 percent of the plant species in Mediterranean climatic areas are annuals, whereas 10 percent is typical in other climates.

But as pointed out in chapter 2, the climate is far from uniform over the entire Big Sur area. The rugged, varied terrain of these steep mountains creates a wide range of environments. Microclimatic areas that vary in size from whole watersheds to the shade of a fallen log break up the regional climate. Plant diversity is primarily a reflection of this climatic diversity.

The summer drought is the crucial and most stressful period of the year, and the availability of summer moisture is probably the most influential factor in the distribution of plants in the Big Sur area. Moisture change associated with slope aspect is particularly important. The plants on the two slope aspects—north facing and south facing—are conspicuously different all along the Big Sur coast, changing sharply at ridge crests from forests on north slopes to grasslands and scrub on south slopes. Redwoods can only survive the drought in Big Sur in cool canyons and on north-facing slopes within reach of the fog. Few trees of any kind grow on the sunny ridge crests below 450 m (1500 ft), but annual grasses survive there by setting seed and dying before the summer drought. Scrub plants are specially adapted to withstand drought and thrive on south-facing slopes. Alder trees and willows, in contrast, are not at all drought tolerant and must have their roots near flowing water in canyon bottoms.

The Santa Lucia Range lies mid-way along the California coast in a broad zone of transition between northern and southern California climatic patterns. This climatic transition zone is analogous to the maritime zones described earlier in chapter 3. The area where these climatic zones meet is not a sharp line but rather a broad zone of transition. The Big Sur area falls within this zone and includes plants common to both northern and southern California. Whole plant communities reach their northern or southern limits in the area as well, and this mixture adds greatly to the variety of plants here. The coast redwood is a striking example of a plant that reaches its southern distributional limit in the area. It does not grow south of the Salmon Creek drainage in Big Sur. A number of plants associated with redwoods, such as redwood sorrel, also reach their southernmost distribution in Big Sur. Conversely, the arid climate yucca reaches its northern distributional limit in the area, as do many other southern California plants.

Climate is not static, however, and plant and animal communities must respond to climatic changes by following the climate they need or through evolutionary change. For example, when the northern ice sheet made its most recent advance during the Pleistocene age, the resulting cool, humid conditions along the California coast allowed redwoods to survive as far south as to where the Los Angeles basin is today and inland into much of the western United States. Subsequent warming and drying has forced the redwoods to retreat northward and coastward where the conditions they need persist. Their southern range limit is now 400 km (250 mi) north of Los Angeles.

Other plants have responded to changes in the weather by changing themselves. Many chaparral plants, for example, evolved drought-tolerant characteristics in response to drying trends in the earth's climate. During the Ice Age, some of these plants began to adapt to the summer droughts and periodic fires that are characteristic of Mediterranean climatic regions. Chaparral plants have moved into the Big Sur region relatively recently (in geological terms), expanding into the area as dry conditions have developed over the past 10,000 years.

DISJUNCT AND ENDEMIC PLANTS

The Santa Lucia Range is isolated from other mountain ranges in the state like an island is isolated from other islands. Many of the disjunct plants in the Big Sur region are restricted to high elevations in the range. In following the climate they need, disjunct species have become stranded on the "island" of the Santa Lucias (see fig. 3, p. 11). During a time of warmer temperatures and greater moisture, these plants grew continuously across lowland valleys. But as the climate cooled and dried, the plants were restricted to the higher elevations that remained moist.

The sugar pine is an outstanding example of this type of disjunct plant. It grows only on the north-facing slopes of two Santa Lucia peaks. The main populations of this pine are in the Sierra Nevadas, and the nearest stands are about 220 km (136 mi) to the south in the San Rafael Mountains. Isolated plant populations such as these cannot exchange pollen—or genetic information—with their main populations, and such a cutoff may eventually cause them to evolve into separate species. Such new species would then be considered endemic to the mountains. Sugar pines in the Santa Lucias are already genetically distinct from others in the state, although they are more closely related to southern California sugar pines than to those from the Sierra Nevada. These Santa Lucia trees are also much more resistant to sugar pine blister rust than are sugar pines from other areas, further illustrating their genetic uniqueness.

The Mediterranean climate of California has influenced the abundance of endemic plants in the state and in Big Sur. Plants that were accustomed to the damp, mild climate that dominated much of North America 60 million years ago found refuge in the mild, frost-free coastal climate of California as conditions became colder elsewhere. At the same time, many plants evolved characteristics to cope with the newly evolving Mediterranean climate, with its humid winters and dry summers. Because of these two kinds of plants—relicts from past climates and newly evolved species—many plants in California are unique to the state.

Endemic plants exist in most parts of the state, but the Big Sur region is especially rich in them. Some of these are listed along with other special plants in table 4. The Santa Lucia fir, found only in the Santa Lucia Range, is an example of a relict endemic with a very restricted distribution. Fossil evidence indicates that it once grew widely over western North America.

TABLE 4. SPECIAL PLANTS OF THE SANTA LUCIA RANGE

Common Name	Genus/Species	Status[a]
Santa Lucia fir	*Abies bracteata*	E, R
Little Sur manzanita	*Arctostaphylos edmundsii*	E, R
Hickman's onion	*Allium hickmanii*	E, R
Hoover's manzanita	*Arctostaphylos hooverii*	E
Arroyo de la Cruz manzanita	*Arctostaphylos cruzensis*	E, R
Phantom orchid	*Cephalanthera austinae*	D
Douglas's spineflower	*Chorizanthe douglasii*	E
Hill clarkia	*Clarkia lewisii*	E
Spotted coral root	*Corallorhiza maculata*	D
Cycladenia	*Cycladenia humilis*	D
Hutchinson's delphinium	*Delphinium hutchinsonae*	R
Butterworth eriogonum	*Eriogonum butterworthianum*	E, R
California bedstraw	*Galium californicum* ssp. *luciense*	E, R
Santa Lucia bedstraw	*Galium clementis*	E
Hardham bedstraw	*Galium hardhamiae*	R, E
Incense cedar	*Calocedrus decurrens*	D
Abram's lupine	*Lupinus abramsii*	E
Santa Lucia lupine	*Lupinus cervinus*	E
Arroyo Seco bush mallow	*Malacothamnus palmeri* var. *lucianus*	E, Eg
Palmer bush mallow	*Malacothamnus palmeri* var. *palmeri*	E
One-sided monkey flower	*Mimulus subsecundus*	E
Sugar pine	*Pinus lambertiana*	D
Ponderosa pine	*Pinus ponderosa*	D
Raillardella	*Raillardella muirii*	R, D, Eg
Porcupine gooseberry	*Ribes menziesii* var. *hystrix*	E
Santa Lucia gooseberry	*Ribes sericeum*	E
Hickman sidalcea	*Sidalcea hickmanii* ssp. *hickmanii*	E, Eg

[a]R = rare; E = endemic; Eg = endangered; D = disjunct.

RARE AND ENDANGERED PLANTS

Some plants in the Big Sur area are apparently so limited in their distribution that their whole population could easily be eliminated. Some of these are classified as *endangered*. We list these species in table 4. We used the California Native Plant Society's *Inventory of Rare and Endangered Vascular Plants*, 4th edition, as our guide. The status of these plants may change in the future as new populations are discovered.

The Hutchinson's delphinium (*Delphinium hutchinsonae*) is a rare plant that has been found in only a few places in the Big Sur area: in Pfeiffer–Big Sur State Park, in Laffler and Torre canyons along the coast, and most recently, on the Gamboa Point properties near Vicente Creek. The butterworth eriogonum (*Eriogonum butterworthianum*) is known to grow only in one small area in the vicinity of the Indians Ranger Station. The California Native Plant Society (CNPS) does not consider this buckwheat to be endangered, however, since its population seems to be stable or increasing. It apparently grows only on outcrops of Vaqueros Sandstone. The Arroyo Seco bush mallow is considered rare and endangered. The only known populations of this plant are above the Indians Ranger Station and in Andrew Molera and Pfeiffer–Big Sur state parks. *Raillardella muirii*, a rare and endangered species in the southern Sierra Nevada, has been found on the summit of Ventana Double Cone. This is a very restricted montane disjunct species. Ecologist James Griffin believes that this plant should "receive the highest priority for administrative protection."

Three bedstraws found in the Santa Lucias are considered rare. California bedstraw (*Galium californicum* ssp. *luciense*) has been found only on Ventana Double Cone, on Cone Peak, in the Villa Creek drainage, along Alder Creek, and along the Cruikshank trail. It is classified as rare but not endangered. Hardham bedstraw (*Galium hardhamiae*) is also classified as rare but not endangered. It is confined in the Big Sur area to serpentine soils in the Villa and Salmon creeks area. The Santa Lucia bedstraw (*Galium clementis*) is known from several high peaks in the range and along the Cruikshank trail and in the Los Burros area.

PLANT COMMUNITIES

It is possible to see a great variety of plants in a single short walk in Big Sur. The plants are not distributed randomly, but tend to grow in patterns that reflect varied environmental conditions. Water-loving plants grow along creeks, dry climate plants are found on arid slopes, and cool climate plants stay in canyons and ravines. To understand such patterns of vegetation growth, botanists have devised the idea of *plant communities*. A plant community is a group of plants that tend to grow together in a particular area. One or more plants are typically the most abundant or prominent within a plant community and are said to be *dominants* of the community. Thus, redwood trees are the dominant plant of the redwood forest, chamise is dominant in the chamise chaparral, and so on.

It is important to keep in mind that plant communities are theoretical constructs that are used to simplify the complex patterns of vegetation on land. The boundaries between communities are not clear, sharp lines, and it is not unusual to find a typical plant of one community growing in another community. The patterns of plant distribution reflect very complex biological and physical factors that cannot be precisely described in simple terms. Furthermore, the boundaries of these plant communities can change over time.

Nevertheless, the concept of plant communities is very helpful in describing the vegetation of an area as complex as Big Sur. By recognizing communities, it is easier to identify individual plants. Also, since plant communities reflect environmental conditions, it is possible to predict what kind of microclimate an area experiences by looking at the plant communities that grow there. Different soil types often support different plant communities, such that the geology of an area is sometimes discernible by the plant communities there. Describing plant communities is a way of beginning to understand the entire living landscape.

To give you a feeling for patterns of vegetation on the landscape, we describe where the various plant communities occur: at what elevations and slope aspects, whether they are inland or coastal, whether they are in canyon bottoms or on ridgetops, and so on. But it is difficult to recognize these patterns simply from reading words on a page. You must look carefully at the landscape, which at first appears to be a chaotic jumble of colors and textures, and gradually begin to recognize the patterns that emerge. After a time, one comes to recognize the various communities, as well as the specific plant and animal inhabitants within them, without giving it much thought. "Brush" becomes "chamise chaparral" or "ceanothus scrub," and "woods" become "ponderosa pine woodland" or "tanoak forest." With this enhanced awareness comes an

Coastal Scrub

increased understanding and appreciation of the processes that are at work shaping the natural environment.

In this chapter, we also describe many of the animals most commonly associated with each plant community. Most animals are restricted to a narrow range of habitats. The California ground squirrel, for example, is seen most often in the grassland, and the wrentit is usually found in the coastal scrub or chaparral. We felt that it would be best to present this wildlife in the context of the plant communities in which they live.

We settled on the following seven general plant communities as sufficient to describe the vegetation of the Santa Lucia Range. It is possible to break these down into finer and finer divisions, but for simplicity we used these general types.

COASTAL SCRUB

Highway 1 winds through coastal scrub for most of the road's length in Big Sur. The scents of the fragrant shrubs and herbs of this plant community mingle with the smells of kelp and ocean air, and an intoxicating aroma wafts up the coastal slopes on warm updrafts. On warm days, these smells and the sight of the deep blue ocean lend a distinctly Mediterranean air to the Big Sur coast. Volatile oils in California sagebrush (*Artemisia californica*) (fig. 38) and black sage (*Salvia mellifera*) (fig. 39) are largely responsible for the fragrance of the coastal scrub, but California hedge nettle (*Stachys bullata*) (fig. 40), California mugwort (*Artemisia douglasiana*) (fig. 41), and yerba buena (*Satureja douglasii*) add a minty fragrance as well.

Coastal scrub extends all along the California coast from north to south and continues down along the coast to central Baja California. It grows on coastal slopes and covers more than 800,000 ha (2 million acres) in California, differing in character from region to region. Botanists have divided coastal scrub in California into two major types: northern coastal scrub and southern coastal scrub. Point Sur is usually mapped as the boundary between the two types, but there is no sharp boundary between them. Rather, the Big Sur coast is within a broad overlapping zone between northern and southern coastal scrub and includes plants from both. While many botanists have studied the southern coastal scrub to some depth, few have studied the northern scrub and even fewer have attempted to describe the complex mixing of the two along the central California coast.

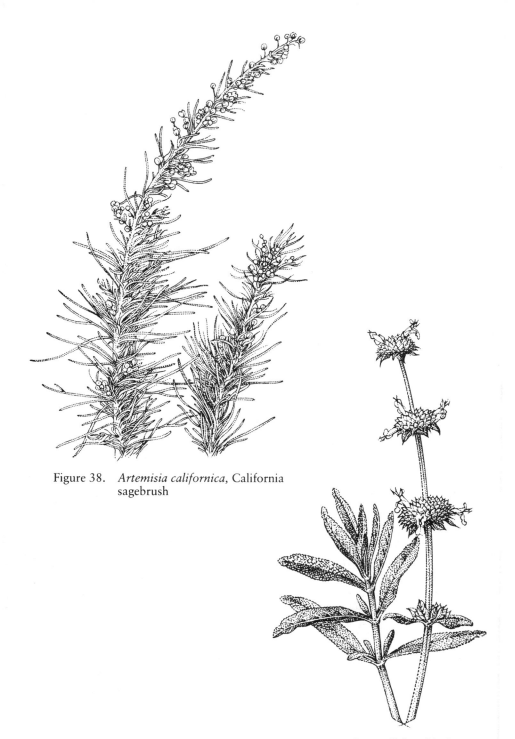

Figure 38. *Artemisia californica*, California sagebrush

Figure 39. *Salvia mellifera*, black sage

Figure 40. *Stachys bullata,* hedge nettle

Figure 41. *Artemisia douglasiana,*
mugwort

TABLE 5. COMMON COASTAL
SCRUB PLANTS

Common Name	Genus/Species
California sagebrush	*Artemisia californica*
Coyote bush	*Baccharis pilularis* ssp. *consanguinea*
Coast morning glory	*Calystegia macrostegia* ssp. *cyclostegia*
California lilac	*Ceanothus thyrsiflorus*
Sea lettuce	*Dudleya caespitosa*
Seaside aster	*Erigeron glaucus*
Dune buckwheat	*Eriogonum parvifolium*
Lizardtail	*Eriophyllum staechadifolium*
Deer weed	*Lotus scoparius*
Silver lupine	*Lupinus albifrons*
Bush lupine	*Lupinus arboreus*
Sticky monkey flower	*Mimulus aurantiacus*
Western bracken fern	*Pteridium aquilinum* var. *pubescens*
California coffeeberry	*Rhamnus californica*
Redberry	*Rhamnus crocea*
California hedge nettle	*Stachys bullata*
Poison oak	*Toxicodendron diversilobum*
Our Lord's candle	*Yucca whipplei*

The most common coastal shrub plants are listed in table 5. Coyote bush (*Baccharis pilularis*) (fig. 42), a wiry, evergreen shrub common throughout Big Sur, and shrubby lupines (*Lupinus arboreus* and other *Lupinus* spp.) are the most characteristic plants of the northern scrub. California sagebrush dominates the southern coastal scrub, which is often referred to as coastal sage scrub. California coffeeberry (*Rhamnus californica*) (fig. 43), blue blossom (*Ceanothus thyrsiflorus*) (fig. 44), poison oak (*Toxicodendron diversilobum*) (fig. 45), and toyon (*Heteromeles arbutifolia*) are other common plants. Trees in this habitat often take on a shrublike look, and few are over 2 m (6 ft) tall. California bay (*Umbellularia californica*) and coast live oak (*Quercus agrifolia*) huddle in ravines, and dense aggregations of willows (mostly *Salix coulteri* and *S. lasiolepis*) thrive wherever there is surface or near-surface water in

Figure 42. *Baccharis pilularis,* coyote bush

Figure 43. *Rhamnus californica,* California coffeeberry

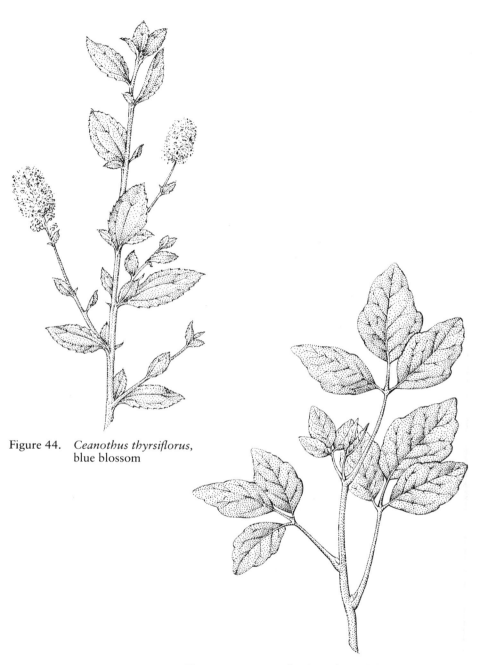

Figure 44. *Ceanothus thyrsiflorus,*
blue blossom

Figure 45. *Toxicodendron diversilobum,* poison oak

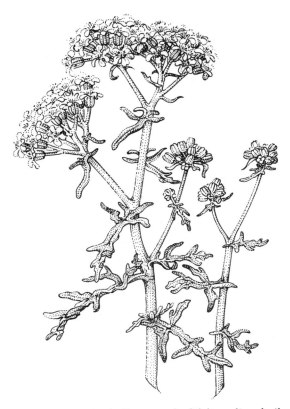

Figure 46. *Eriophyllum staechadifolium,* lizardtail

the scrub. Bigleaf maples (*Acer macrophyllum*) also find suitable habitats on more shaded slopes within the scrub.

At least four recognizable types, or *phases,* of coastal scrub can be
discerned in the Big Sur area, each with a slightly different mixture of
plants: coastal bluff scrub, coyote bush scrub, sage scrub, and ceanothus scrub.

COASTAL BLUFF SCRUB

Coastal bluff scrub grows in a narrow strip along steep coastal slopes,
bluffs, and cliffs all along the Big Sur coast. California sagebrush predominates in many areas, and lizardtail (*Eriophyllum staechadifolium*)
(fig. 46) fills the scrub with bright yellow blossoms in the summer and

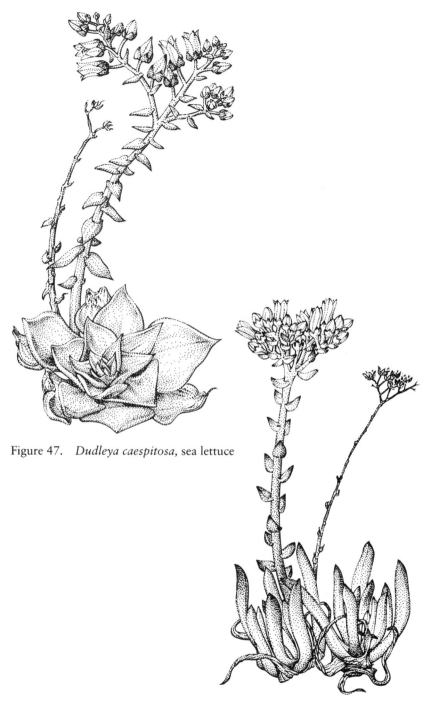

Figure 47.   *Dudleya caespitosa*, sea lettuce

Figure 48.   *Sedum spathulifolium*,
sedum

Figure 49.   *Eriogonum parvifolium*, buckwheat

fall and gives this scrub a distinctive, pleasant aroma. Black sage seems to do best on rocky, dry soils of south-facing slopes and also has a pungent odor. Succulents such as sea lettuce (*Dudleya caespitosa*) (fig. 47) and sedum (*Sedum spathulifolium*) (fig. 48) cling to rocky cliffs along with buckwheat (*Eriogonum parvifolium*) (fig. 49). Bush lupines (*Lupinus arboreus*), seaside asters (*Erigeron glaucus*), and introduced ice plant (*Carpobrotus chilensis*) add to the collage of colorful plants on more level ground.

The rigor of the bluff environment comes from the assault of wind and sea spray. The persistent, salt-laden winds on the coastal bluffs prune the bluff scrub neatly down by killing the topmost leaves. This keeps the coastal bluff plants low and rounded. The best accessible stands of coastal bluff scrub along the Big Sur coast blanket the bluffs

Figure 50.   *Mimulus aurantiacus,* sticky
monkey flower

of Garrapata State Park. There, the pastel-shaded patchwork of shrubs
is frequently dominated by mats of red ice plant and is sprinkled in
spring with an abundance of wildflowers.

COYOTE BUSH SCRUB

Coyote bush dominates this type of scrub, which grows on ocean-facing
slopes above the coastal bluff scrub to an elevation of about 300 m
(1000 ft). California coffeeberry often crowds the coyote bush, and California sagebrush, lizardtail, silver lupines (*Lupinus albifrons*), and poison oak commonly grow with it. The orange blossoms of sticky monkey
flower (*Mimulus aurantiacus*) (fig. 50) are a regular feature of the

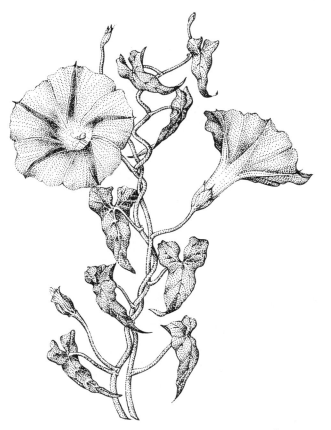

Figure 51.   *Calystegia macrostegia*, morning glory

coyote bush scrub. Morning glory vines (*Calystegia macrostegia*) (fig. 51) wind through the scrub and are hung with white trumpetlike flowers most of the year.

While walking through coyote bush scrub, it soon becomes apparent that the understory is very sparse or even devoid of plants. The dense canopy of the scrub shades the ground and inhibits germination of other plants, and rodents, rabbits, and birds graze on any seedlings that might appear. Understory plants usually survive in openings in the scrub and include bracken fern (*Pteridium aquilinum*), California hedge nettle, and California mugwort.

Flowers bloom year-round in coyote bush scrub. Monkey flowers bloom into August, when the pink puffball flowers of buckwheat first appear. California fuchsia (*Zauschneria californica*) is another late bloomer when its striking red, tubular flowers splash the scrub from August until October. Poison oak leaves turn red in late summer, adding even more color to the scrub.

Coyote bush scrub seems to favor moist locations—areas of heavy fog drip, above average precipitation, and northwest-facing slopes—and tends to grow better at lower elevations than sage scrub. It is the most common phase of coastal scrub in Big Sur. Near the coast, it is often shaped by the salt spray and wind and forms a dense, uniform cover. The Bluff Trail at Andrew Molera State Park winds through extensive coyote bush scrub, and it is also dominant near the mouth of Pfeiffer Canyon and on the austere inland slopes of Garrapata State Park. The lower portions of most coastal trails and much of Highway 1 wind through extensive coyote bush scrub.

CEANOTHUS SCRUB

Dense, impenetrable stands of blue blossom (*Ceanothus thyrsiflorus*) dominate the coastal scrub in many areas below 600 m (2000 ft). This phase is called ceanothus scrub and is found on gentler slopes and on deeper soils than other phases and seldom covers more than a few acres in any stand. The ground beneath the lilacs is piled thick with leaf litter and is often barren of other plant life. Where other plants do grow in the ceanothus scrub, they are the same species as those found in coyote bush scrub.

From a distance, ceanothus scrub stands out as a denser, taller growth amid other scrub types of Big Sur. The blue blossom shrubs are covered with fragrant blue blossoms in early spring that color the hillsides and add a lilac scent to the air. They are short-lived plants, dying in forty to sixty years, and the age of a stand can be roughly gauged by the number of dead individual lilacs. About five years after establishment, young stands are made up of widely spaced, healthy lilacs. After twenty-five years, the crowns of the trees are touching so that the ground beneath the stand is 100 percent shaded. Stands that are fifty years old are dotted with lilac skeletons draped with morning glory and wild cucumber (*Marah fabaceus*) vines, and crown cover is reduced to 50 percent. The dead wood adds greatly to the amount of fuel in the brush and increases the likelihood of a serious wildfire.

Without fire, a stand of ceanothus scrub may die completely and will probably be replaced by coyote bush scrub or another scrub type. Unlike many other plants in California scrub types, ceanothus shrubs do not resprout from their roots following fire. Instead, they rely on fire-resistant seeds that germinate after fire. Ceanothus scrub plants, as well as crown-sprouting plants in coastal scrub, are thus dependent on fire for their continued existence.

Good examples of ceanothus scrub grow on the slopes above the mouth of McWay Canyon in Julia Pfeiffer-Burns State Park, near the mouth of Salmon Creek, and in isolated patches along much of Highway 1.

COASTAL SAGE SCRUB

California sagebrush dominates coastal sage scrub, which grows at higher elevations than do other coastal scrub types. Its habitat is found on dry, steep, south-facing slopes from about 600 to 900 m (2000 to 3000 ft). It often intergrades with the other phases of coastal scrub or with chaparral or mixed hardwood forest. California sagebrush forms a low-growing cover, mixed with deer weed (*Lotus scoparius*), redberry (*Rhamnus crocea*), and Our Lord's candle (*Yucca whipplei*). Its sparse, dry appearance is reminiscent of desert terrain, and it is the major coastal scrub type of southern California. It reaches its northernmost limit in the Big Sur area.

The seeds of some coastal sage scrub plants are light, abundant, and windborne, while the seeds of others are tough and actually need to be damaged to germinate. These traits allow them to quickly colonize areas where other plants have been removed by fire, overgrazing, or other disturbances. Coastal sage scrub is often the first community to become established after fire, and another scrub type or chaparral may replace the coastal sage scrub after a number of years. Plants of the coastal sage scrub are common along road cuts on Highway 1 where they grow on dry, unstable banks.

ENVIRONMENTAL CONDITIONS

Coastal scrub plants must survive the dry conditions of south-facing and west-facing slopes. They tolerate summer drought worsened by common salt-laden wind, but the dryness is periodically relieved by summer fog. Plants grow here in abundant sunlight, with winter rainfall averaging about 25–75 cm (10–30 in.) per year. Temperatures are mild year-round due to the nearness of the ocean, and frosts are extremely rare. Many shrubs in the coastal scrub are evergreen. They do not lose their leaves all at once in the fall, but lose and replace leaves gradually throughout the year. Other plants are drought deciduous, and their leaves fall or become limp and dormant to prevent water loss as the summer drought intensifies.

Evergreen shrubs in the Big Sur region are characteristic of the northern scrub, while the drought deciduous species extend up from the south. The evergreen northern scrub species are accustomed to plentiful winter rain and a summer drought that is periodically alleviated by fog. The drought deciduous plants of the southern scrub, in contrast, are adapted to less rain and more severe drought. They come to life when the rains arrive and mitigate the effects of drought by laying dormant through much of the summer. In the Big Sur region, northern plants grow better in damper locations, while plants from southern coastal scrub are more abundant in drier locations.

The distribution of coastal scrub is also partially determined by soil types. Most plants of the southern scrub community are shallow rooted to take advantage quickly of small amounts of water. The evergreen northern scrub plants, in contrast, are deep rooted. Thus, southern coastal scrub often dominates areas of shallow clay soils where water does not penetrate deeply.

The relationship of coastal scrub to surrounding communities is poorly understood. One intriguing subject of continuing debate is the common occurrence of *bare zones*—strips of virtually bare soil—between coastal scrub and grassland. The first people to study these bare zones found that some plants in the coastal scrub, especially California sagebrush and black sage, produce chemicals that inhibit the germination and growth of seedlings of other plant species (and sometimes even their own seedlings). The volatile oils that smell so good to people are toxic to plants and also to insects and animals that would like to feed on the plants. This ability to use chemicals to discourage competition from other organisms, called *allelopathy,* is an important trait of the aromatic shrubs of the coastal scrub and chaparral.

Other researchers later implicated foraging mice, voles, birds, and rabbits in creating bare zones. The animals make short excursions into the grassland to consume young herbs and grasses, but never go far for fear of being seen and eaten by predators. The bare zones mark the limit of their boldness. Thus, the bare zones may be the product of both allelopathy and small mammal grazing.

SUCCESSION

Another matter of continuing debate is the relationship of coyote bush scrub to grassland. This is of special importance to people who graze livestock because coyote bush scrub generally invades grasslands if left alone, and coyote bush makes poor cattle feed. This change of species composition within a plant community is called *succession*. After a period of time, the brush itself may be succeeded by plants of other communities such as oak forest.

Fires, both natural and man-made, periodically kill the above ground parts of invading coyote bush scrub and maintain the grasslands. Since the early part of this century, however, fires have been suppressed, and many grasslands have become dominated by coyote bush throughout coastal California. Without fire or some other means of removal, the scrub becomes dense and grasses and understory plants are shaded out. The floor of these dense "forests" is often bare, and as blue blossoms in the stand die, it becomes more and more choked with dead wood.

The former extent of the grasslands is evident in many places in Big Sur. Fence lines that once closed in pastures now poke through dense stands of coyote bush and California coffeeberry that are largely impenetrable. In one place in Big Sur, a fire removed dense coastal scrub to reveal a mower and a plow, indicating that the area was once open farmland. Aerial photographs confirm the fact that many grasslands have been taken over by scrub in the past several decades.

Grazing alone does not always prevent a takeover of the grasslands by scrub, although it may slow it down. Thus, the deliberate lighting of fires, once a common practice of natives and homesteaders, is being used again. Without controlled fire, wildfires inevitably occur and often clear huge areas in a single burn. As described in chapter 5 on fire ecology, the coastal scrub supports its greatest diversity of plant and animal life following fire, and its diversity steadily declines as a stand gets older.

COASTAL SCRUB ANIMALS

Fire opens up dense stands of coastal scrub, and for the next several years the scrub becomes lush with herbs and grasses that were absent in the dense brush. In this state, the scrub produces more useable food for wildlife than did the dense, overmature stands. The open brush that develops also includes a diverse mixture of grassland and brush that many animals need. Thus, the number and kinds of animals that the habitat can support increases after fire.

A great variety of animals rely on coastal scrub for food, nesting, and shelter. Its dense interwoven branches provide cover where animals can hide themselves and their nests from predators. The abundant woody

Figure 52.   *Aphelocoma coerulescens*, scrub jay

plants also provide the materials for making nests. The variety of plants in healthy coastal scrub produces seeds, berries, flowers, roots, and young seedlings for herbivorous insects, birds, reptiles, and mammals. Predatory animals use the brush as cover while hunting the herbivores.

Birds are especially abundant in coastal scrub. Scrub jays (*Aphelocoma coerulescens*) (fig. 52) are bright blue and gray in color, large in size, and the most conspicuous. Wrentits (*Chamaea fasciata*) are heard more often than seen here. Their song, which they sing year-round, is a series of notes that become more closely spaced toward the end of the call, a pattern that has been likened to the rhythm of a dropped ping-pong ball. California thrashers (*Toxostoma redivivum*) (fig. 53) are large brown birds with down-curved beaks. They are secretive, but their varied mockingbirdlike song is loud and unmistakable. Song sparrows (*Melospiza melodia*), white-crowned sparrows (*Zonotrichea leucophrys*) (fig. 54), bushtits (*Psaltriparus minimus*), rufous-sided and California towhees (*Pipilo erythrophthalmus* and *P. crissalis*), and Anna's hummingbirds (*Calypte anna*) (fig. 55) are common residents of the coastal scrub. Coveys of California quail (*Lophortyx californicus*) (fig. 56) scurry through the scrub, feeding on insects and seeds. The startling flutter of their wings when they fly is part of almost any walk through the scrub. In summer, Wilson's warblers (*Wilsonia pusilla*), orange-crowned warblers (*Vermivora celata*), lazuli buntings (*Passerina amoena*), and other migrants arrive to nest and feed in the coastal scrub.

The fruits of coastal scrub plants such as California coffeeberry are a

Figure 53. *Toxostoma redivivum*, California thrasher

Figure 54. *Zonatrichea leucophrys*, white-crowned sparrow

vital source of moisture to birds, and toyon and poison oak berries are important winter food. Predatory birds such as red-tailed hawks (*Buteo jamaicensis*) and sharp-shinned hawks (*Accipiter striatus*) hunt over coastal scrub for rodents, snakes, and small birds, while several species of swifts and swallows scoop up insects.

Figure 55. *Calypte anna*, Anna's hummingbird

Figure 56. *Lophortyx californicus*, California quail

Many of the resident songbirds in scrubby vegetation have long tails and short wings. This is no accident—a long tail is extremely valuable to a bird in dense brush. It acts like a rudder as the bird makes its quick, darting flight through the brush, and it is used as a counterbalance while running. The short wings provide the sudden bursts of speed needed yet remain clear of branches during tight maneuvering. Most scrub residents do more running, climbing, and short flying than they do long-distance flying. The California thrasher, for example, will almost always run rather than fly when startled. It also uses its long tail as a lever to help it climb in brush.

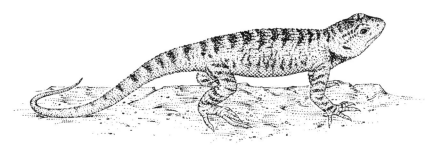

Figure 57. *Sceloporus occidentalis,* western fence lizard

A number of reptiles are common in or near coastal scrub. Most prefer the edges where scrub borders on grassland. Western fence lizards (*Sceloporus occidentalis*) (fig. 57) and western terrestrial garter snakes (*Thamnophis elegans*) are probably the most common, but alligator lizards (*Elgaria multicarinatus*) and western skinks (*Eumeces skiltonianus*) are also frequently seen.

Fence lizards are about 9 cm (3.5 in.) long and have coarse, spiny scales on their backs and fine scales on their bellies. The throats and abdomens of males are marked with patches of rich blue scales. They are most often seen basking in the sun on rocks or logs or on sunny, open slopes, and they scan surrounding territory from these perches and often bob up and down as if doing push-ups. They lack binocular vision, and this motion may help give the lizards some depth perception by providing them with slightly different perceptives on an object. This motion may also serve a social function in communicating with other fence lizards in the area. Small insects and other invertebrates are the prey of these fast lizards.

Southern alligator lizards are nearly as common as fence lizards. Their heavy scales, short legs, and long bodies do indeed make them look alligatorlike, and individuals longer than 51 cm (20 in.) have been recorded. These lizards prefer more shaded areas and sometimes climb trees using their prehensile tails for support. They may become partially nocturnal during the hottest parts of the year and hide beneath debris in both warm and cool times. They prey on insects, spiders, small mammals, and lizards and occur in grassy, shrubby, and woodland areas. Although range maps indicate that northern alligator lizards (*Elgaria coeruleus*) may be found in the Big Sur area, no survey has yet reported finding them here.

Gopher snakes (*Pituophis melanoleucus*) and both common and California mountain kingsnakes (*Lampropeltis getulus* and *L. zonata*) prey

Figure 58.   *Lampropeltis zonata*, California mountain kingsnake

on the abundant rodents of the scrub. The California mountain kingsnake (fig. 58) is banded black, red, and white and is one of the most
beautiful snakes in the Big Sur area. It is common in the Santa Lucias
but relatively rare elsewhere in California. It favors moist woodland and
scrub habitats and preys upon lizards, snakes, birds and their eggs, and
small mammals. The black-and-white banded common kingsnake is
less striking in color than the mountain kingsnake. It lives in a variety
of habitats and is well-known for its ability to kill rattlesnakes and its
immunity to their venom.

The western rattlesnake (*Crotalus viridis*) is widely distributed in the
Santa Lucia Range, and we have seen them not only in coastal scrub,
but also in mixed evergreen forest, in chaparral, and in lumber and
wood piles. This is the only poisonous snake in the area. It is not normally aggressive and will usually only bite if provoked or cornered. The
only bite in this area that we know of occurred when a herpetologist
was attempting to capture a rattlesnake.

These snakes feed on the small mammals that are plentiful in coastal
scrub such as the dusky-footed woodrat (*Neotoma fuscipes*). The stick
nests of this furry-tailed rat are scattered throughout the scrub, both on
the ground and in the branches of shrubs and trees. California mice
(*Peromyscus californicus*) sometimes build their grass-lined nests and
store seed in the woodrat piles. Other mice also live and nest in the
scrub, including brush mice (*Peromyscus boylei*), pinyon mice (*P. truei*),
and deer mice (*P. maniculatus*).

Merriam chipmunks (*Tamias merriami*), unlike many of the other
small mammals, are active during the day but are well camouflaged and
move so fast that they are difficult to see. These chipmunks are common
in the scrub and are often mistaken for birds because they climb high
and emit loud cheeps. Brush rabbits (*Sylvilagus bachmani*) (fig. 59)
never venture far from the cover of brush. Larger mammals such as
black-tailed deer (*Odocoileus hemionus*) and wild pigs (*Sus scrofa*)

Figure 59. *Sylvilagus bachmani,* brush rabbit

sometimes enter the scrub to feed in years immediately following fire, but otherwise rarely venture into it except on trails.

Gray foxes (*Urocyon cinereoragenteus*) and bobcats (*Lynx rufus*) hunt for the abundant birds and mammals in and around coastal scrub. Coyotes (*Canis latrans*) haunt the grasslands bordering the scrub in search of prey and enter the brush in less dense areas or along trails. Mountain lions (*Felis concolor*) use brush for cover as they hunt their preferred food item, deer.

CHAPARRAL

According to ecologist Steven Talley, more than half the land area of the Santa Lucia Range is covered with chaparral and coastal scrub. While coastal scrub generally predominates at lower elevations on the Big Sur coast, chaparral begins as a dark mantle of brush near the top of the Coast Ridge and continues inland where it is the dominant scrub type. Highway 1 does not pass through any chaparral, but it is encountered extensively along Nacimiento Road, the Coast Ridge roads, and most backcountry trails.

Big Sur's chaparral is often a patchwork of several kinds of shrubs, but in some areas, one shrub or another dominates the vegetation. Although the typical form of chaparral is dense brush, many chaparral plants grow sparsely on steep, rocky hillsides and form a dry, desertlike vegetation. Table 6 lists the most common chaparral plants in Big Sur.

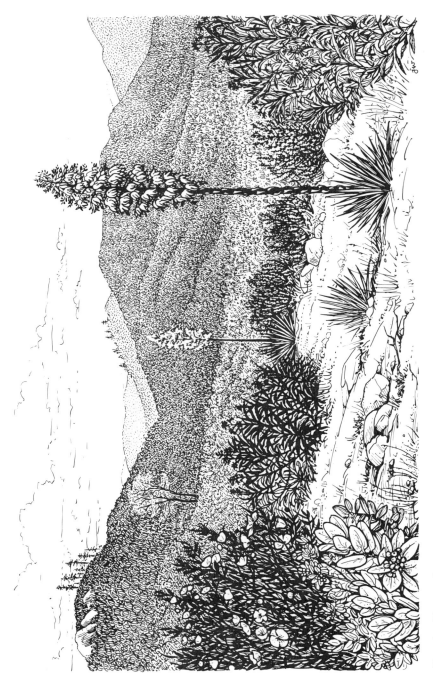

Chamise Chaparral

TABLE 6.   COMMON CHAPARRAL PLANTS

Common Name	Genus/Species
Chamise	*Adenostoma fasciculatum*
Hoary manzanita	*Arctostaphylos canescens*
Eastwood manzanita	*Arctostaphylos glandulosa*
Bigberry manzanita	*Arctostaphylos glauca*
Woollyleaf manzanita	*Arctostaphylos tomentosa*
Buck brush	*Ceanothus cuneatus*
Wartleaf ceanothus	*Ceanothus papillosus*
Jim brush	*Ceanothus sorediatus*
California mountain mahogany	*Cercocarpus betuloides*
Tree poppy	*Dendromecon rigida*
Yerba santa	*Eriodictyon californicum*
Toyon	*Heteromeles arbutifolia*
Santa Lucia sticky monkey flower	*Mimulus bifidus* ssp. *fasciculatus*
Scrub oak	*Quercus* ssp.
California coffeeberry	*Rhamnus californica*
Redberry	*Rhamnus crocea*
Poison oak	*Toxicodendron diversilobum*
Wooly blue curls	*Trichostema lanatum*
Our Lord's candle	*Yucca whipplei*

The term *chaparral* is derived from *chabarra*, a Basque word for a scrub oak of the Pyrenees Mountains, which form the border between France and Spain. Spanish explorers used the Spanish equivalent *chaparro* to describe thickets of dense scrub oak in California, and the name was eventually applied to the dense brush of the southwestern United States. Chaps were the protective leather leggings required to ride horses and work in such thick brush.

Every region in the world with a Mediterranean climate is dominated by chaparrallike plant cover, characterized by a dense growth of hardwood shrubs with stiff, evergreen leaves. This similarity of shrub types in widely separated areas is often cited as an example of evolutionary convergence, because the plants seem to have developed the same characteristics independently in response to similar environmental conditions.

In a simplified way, the majority of the chaparral in the Santa Lucias can be divided into two types, or phases: chamise chaparral and mixed chaparral. Chamise chaparral is the most widespread of the two types in California and the Big Sur area.

CHAMISE CHAPARRAL

Chamise chaparral is dominated by chamise or greasewood (*Adenostoma fasciculatum*) (fig. 60), which is a shrub with a tough woody stem, shredding bark, wiry branches, and bundles of needlelike leaves. It produces clusters of tiny white flowers in spring and earned its name because of its stringy, oily wood. A pure stand of chamise is called *chamisal* by the Spanish.

From a distance, chamisal has a dark brown, velvety appearance because of its denseness and uniform height. In summer, it takes on a reddish brown hue as its flowers wither and dry, exposing their red sepals. It borders pine and mixed hardwood forests and occasionally redwood forests. Along the coast, south-facing slopes above 450 m (1500 ft) support the most extensive stands of chamise chaparral. It covers a much more extensive area in the drier interior of the range than on the coast, growing on all slope aspects.

Shrubs in chamise chaparral are from 1 to 2 m (3 to 6 ft) tall, and the community rarely includes trees. Interior live oak (*Quercus wislizenii*), canyon live oak (*Q. chrysolepis*), California bay, and madrone (*Arbutus menziesii*) often fill shaded ravines amid the chaparral, however, and shrubby forms of the oaks grow within the chaparral. The ground beneath dense chamisal is practically barren of plant life because of the presence of toxic chemicals that many chaparral shrubs produce. The bare ground is also caused by shading by the dense canopy of branches and by the grazing of small mammals and birds.

Small numbers of other plants may grow amid the chamise. A type of yucca called Our Lord's candle is scattered in many chaparral stands, especially on rocky, open slopes where it raises its candlelike stalks of creamy white flowers in late spring. Yerba santa (*Eriodictyon californicum*) (fig. 61), which translates as "holy herb," is a medicinal herb with fragrant lavender blossoms and glossy, leathery leaves; it forms especially thick stands in recently burned chaparral. Tree poppy (*Dendromecon rigida*) (fig. 62) is also common after fire, especially on the interior slopes of the mountains. Its tall, slender stems hold up papery, yellow blossoms in April and May. Deerweed is also common in small chaparral openings.

Figure 60. *Adenostoma fasciculatum,*
chamise

Figure 61. *Eriodictyon californicum,*
yerba santa

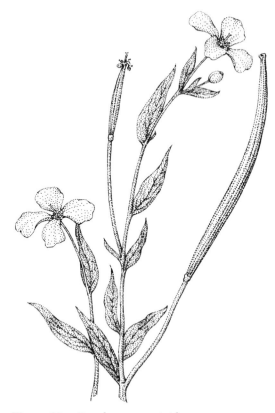

Figure 62.   *Dendromecon rigida,* tree poppy

MIXED CHAPARRAL

Mixed chaparral in Big Sur is made up of a number of shrubs, including various species of ceanothus (mostly *Ceanothus cuneatus, C. integerrimus,* and *C. papillosus*), shrubby oaks (*Quercus* spp.), Eastwood manzanita (*Arctostaphylos glandulosa*) (fig. 63) and other *Arctostaphylos* spp., toyon (*Heteromeles arbutifolia*) (fig. 64), and California mountain mahogany (*Cercocarpus betuloides*), as well as chamise.

According to ecologist Steven Talley, mixed chaparral grows on slightly less steep slopes than chamise chaparral and sometimes occupies east-facing as well as south- and west-facing slopes. The slopes of some peaks, such as Marble Peak and Black Cone, are covered with mixed chaparral. Stands of mixed chaparral dominated by wartleaf ceanothus or manzanitas are common.

The very stiff branches of the manzanita make manzanita chaparral

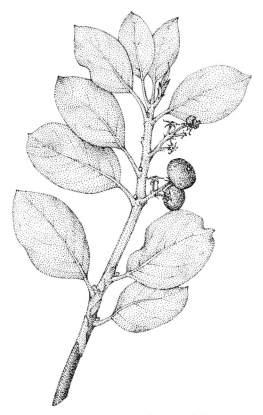

Figure 63.   *Arctostaphylos glandulosa,* eastwood manzanita

the most impenetrable of the chaparral types. As in the chamisal, the
ground in manzanita chaparral is barren of herbs because of allelopathic chemicals the shrubs produce. Manzanita (Spanish for "little
apple") often looks like a miniature tree. Its bark shreds and falls away,
leaving a deep red, bare stem that twists and branches at sharp angles.
Tiny, white to pink, bell-shaped flowers hang on the branches in winter
and spring and litter the ground like snow, and tiny red berries form in
the early summer. Woollyleaf manzanita (*Arctostaphylos tomentosa*)
predominates near the coast, while hoary manzanita (*A. canescens*) and
bigberry manzanita (*A. glauca*) are more common at higher elevations.
Hoover's manzanita (*A. hooveri*), endemic to the Santa Lucia Range,
reaches the stature of a tree and grows most commonly with ponderosa
pines (*Pinus ponderosa*) and Coulter pines (*Pinus coulteri*).

Figure 64. *Heteromeles arbutifolia,* toyon

Ceanothus chaparral is no less dense but is slightly more penetrable than mixed chaparral because its stems are straight and parallel. The dense clusters of blue flowers on ceanothus chaparral turn entire slopes blue in the springtime in the interior of the range. Walking through these stands leaves a hiker covered with blue blossoms. Wartleaf ceanothus (fig. 65) exudes a sticky resin that makes walking through it especially bothersome.

Few plants grow in the understory in chaparral, but a number of herbs and subshrubs do grow in open stands and on more fertile soils. California fuchsia (*Zauschneria californica*) (fig. 66), bird's beak (*Cordylanthus rigidus*), tongue clarkia (*Clarkia rhomboidea*), redberry (*Rham-*

Figure 65. *Ceanothus papillosus,* wartleaf ceanothus

Figure 66. *Zauschneria californica,* California fuchsia

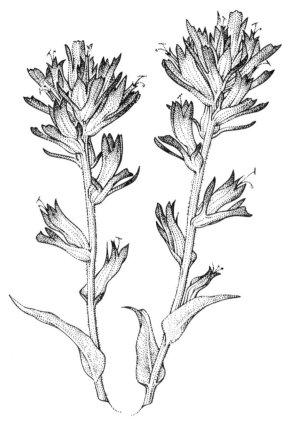

Figure 67.   *Castilleja affinis*, Indian paintbrush

nus crocea), and sticky monkey flower are common, as well as Indian paintbrush (*Castilleja affinis*) (fig. 67), the endemic Santa Lucia sticky monkey flower (*Mimulus bifidus* ssp. *fasciculatus*) (fig. 68), scarlet bugler (*Penstemon centranthifolius*) (fig. 69), chia (*Salvia columbariae*), and black sage. Two rare Santa Lucia endemics grow in interior stands of chaparral: Hickman sidalcea (*Sidalcea hickmanii* subsp. *hickmanii*) and Arroyo Seco bush mallow (*Malacothamnus palmeri* var. *lucianus*).

ENVIRONMENTAL CONDITIONS

The chaparral-covered slopes of the Santa Lucias are the driest, hottest places in the range in summer, where daytime temperatures often exceed 100°F and the relative humidity drops below 10%. These dry con-

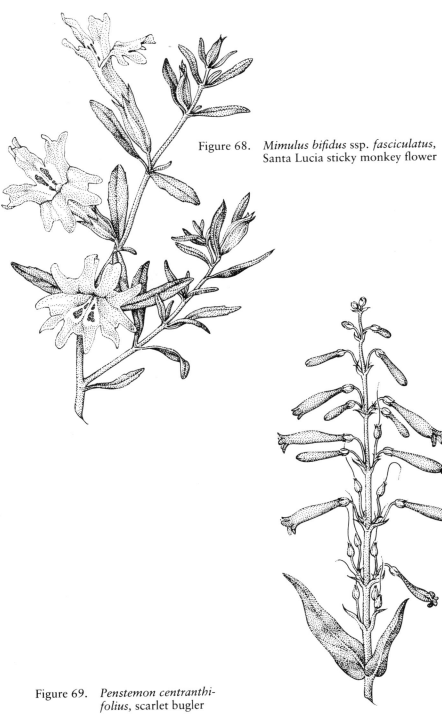

Figure 68.   *Mimulus bifidus* ssp. *fasciculatus,*
Santa Lucia sticky monkey flower

Figure 69.   *Penstemon centranthi-*
folius, scarlet bugler

ditions are often worsened by hot downslope winds in fall. Conversely, these are also among the coldest, wettest areas in winter, and freezing temperatures and snow are not uncommon.

Precipitation averages 75–200 mm (30–80 in.) per year in the chaparral, virtually all of it falling in winter. This is slightly more rainfall than the lower elevation coastal scrub receives. But the moisture in the chaparral rapidly evaporates in the late spring, while winter rainfall at lower elevations lingers because of the cooling effect of the ocean. Fog blanketing the coastal scrub also tends to keep it relatively moist into summer, but in the chaparral the soil is dry and dusty just a few weeks after the rains end.

Chamise chaparral occupies the poorest soils of any of the scrub types in the Santa Lucias, surviving on shallow, rocky soils that are very low in essential plant nutrients. It often grows directly on broken rock as well. These soils quickly lose water and are especially low in nitrogen, one of the most critical minerals to plant growth. Chamise sends its roots deep into cracks in the rocks in search of water and nutrients.

Fire is a major environmental influence on chaparral. Summer dryness, heat, wind, and the close spacing of chaparral plants make it one of the most fire-prone plant communities in the world. The prevalence of dead wood in old chaparral and the volatile oils in some chaparral shrubs add to its tendency to burn. In California, chaparral burns an average of once every 10 to 40 years.

Chaparral is also extremely important as a watershed cover. It stabilizes steep, rocky slopes so that rainfall percolates more slowly into the groundwater. Without chaparral, the steep slopes of the upper Santa Lucias would quickly discharge rainfall in massive floods. Chaparral is uniquely suited to colonizing and stabilizing steep, rocky slopes that are too poor in nutrients to support many other plants.

CHAPARRAL ADAPTATIONS

Fire and summer drought are the environmental forces that have most influenced the California chaparral. Leaves of some chaparral plants are small so that less area is exposed to the sun and the plant loses a minimum of water by evaporation. Chamise leaves, for example, are tiny and needlelike. The leaves of most chaparral plants are covered with a waxy coat, the cuticle, which seals in moisture. Leaf pores are only found on the lower leaf surface in most chaparral plants, where they are not exposed to direct sunlight. These pores, or *stomata*, are deeply recessed in the leaf cuticle in chamise where they are protected from the desiccating sun and wind.

Toyon and manzanita have broad leaves with stomata on both surfaces. But their leaves are oriented vertically, parallel to the rays of the mid-day sunlight, and are thus heated less than horizontal leaves. The leaf surfaces intercept the cooler morning and late afternoon sunlight. Manzanita leaves actually turn through the course of the day to avoid direct exposure to summer sun.

The rigidity of chaparral leaves allows them to remain stiff and functional even under severe drought stress. The leaves of other plants, especially in the coastal scrub, wilt and take time to recover from drought, but drought-stressed chamise and similar plants can start to photosynthesize only minutes after water becomes available.

Chaparral plants actively photosynthesize year-round, although they are most active in winter. They grow only when water is available, beginning in late autumn and ending in June. Most species flower in spring, when moisture availability and sunlight are optimal. Chamise begins flowering when the rains are over in June. Manzanita produces its flower buds in June, but they remain dormant over the summer and burst into bloom when the winter rains begin the following year.

Staying green year-round has advantages in the chaparral environment. When the first fall and winter rains arrive, evergreen shrubs are prepared to start photosynthesizing immediately, while deciduous plants must first produce a new set of leaves. This is one reason most plants in the chaparral are evergreen.

Rainfall comes sporadically in the winter and runs off chaparral soils quickly. Chaparral shrubs have very large root systems in relationship to their overall size to use as much of this moisture as possible. Chamise has a dual root system—a broad, near-surface system to take advantage of light winter storms and a deep root system to tap deeper sources of water during summer drought. This extensive root system allows the shrubs to monopolize water sources and helps them outcompete many subshrubs and herbs.

Some chaparral plants, like those described earlier in the coastal scrub, eliminate competitors for extremely limited water and nutrients by poisoning them. Chamise and manzanitas produce toxic chemicals that inhibit the growth and germination of other plants. These toxic, water-soluble compounds accumulate in the leaves of chamise as normal by-products of metabolism and are carried to the soil by rain and fog drip. When the chamise is removed by fire or other means, the

Figure 70. *Neotoma fuscipes,* dusky-footed woodrat

chemicals disperse and a flush of herb growth takes place. All parts of the manzanita—roots, fallen fruit, bark, roots, and leaves—produce allelopathic chemicals, and these persist in the soil much longer than those produced by chamise.

CHAPARRAL ANIMALS

Many mammals use mature chaparral for cover to escape from predators or to rest, but for food, they rely on young chaparral or clearings where seed-bearing herbs and grasses grow. Very few mammals are adapted to live in dense, homogeneous stands of chaparral. The plant community edges, or *ecotones,* where mature chaparral meets grassland or woodland are the most useful to wildlife. In a study in northern California, for example, deer were found to increase from a density of 20 per square mile to more than 50 per square mile when chaparral was opened up by fire. Other grazing animals, from insects to rodents, show a similar increase in numbers following fire. Predators follow the trend as their prey become more plentiful.

Because of the similarity in structure of coastal scrub and chaparral, the animals found in each are similar. The dusky-footed woodrat (fig. 70) is again the most noticeable mammal, with its conspicuous stick pile nests stuck in the shrubs or on the ground. Brush rabbits hide in chaparral and make cautious evening excursions into herb-rich openings for food. Many kinds of mice, including California mice, deer mice, and brush mice, live a similar existence. Merriam's chipmunk is one of the few mammals that may be more plentiful in dense chaparral than in open stands. Mountain lions, unable to stalk prey in the dense brush,

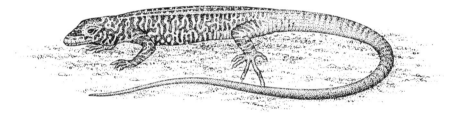

Figure 71. *Cnemidophorus tigris*, western whiptail

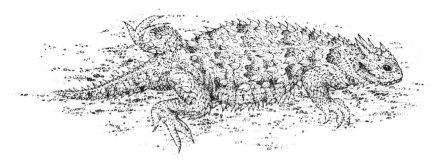

Figure 72. *Phrynosoma coronatum*, coast horned lizard

frequent its edges in search of deer and other prey. Other predatory mammals—gray foxes, bobcats, and coyotes—hunt in open chaparral to take advantage of the edge-loving herbivores.

Arid climate reptiles are at home in the chaparral. Big Sur's sagebrush lizards (*Sceloporus graciosus*), isolated from their main populations elsewhere in the state, can be found in open chaparral at higher elevations in the Santa Lucia Range. They are similar in appearance to the more common western fence lizards, but have finer scales and lighter blue bellies. The fence lizards stay on or near rock outcrops or logs in the chaparral, where they hunt insects and other invertebrates.

Western whiptails (*Cnemidophorus tigris*) (fig. 71)—fast, sleek lizards that seldom offer more than a glimpse as they disappear into brush or burrows—are common in open stands of chaparral. Widely spaced shrubs are the preferred habitat of this vision-oriented, fast-running lizard. It avoids dense brush and moves very quickly after its prey of insects, scorpions, spiders, and other lizards. We found these lizards to be especially abundant in the open, dry terrain of the upper Arroyo Seco drainage.

Coast horned lizards (*Phrynosoma coronatum*) (fig. 72) prefer this

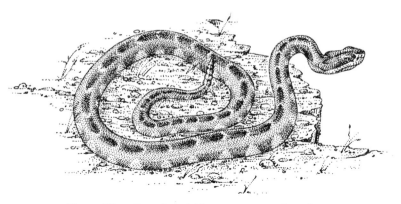

Figure 73.   *Crotalus viridus,* western rattlesnake

habitat as well, especially where the soil is soft or sandy. They are slow, colored to match their environment, and feed primarily on ants, which they capture with a flick of their sticky tongues. Horned lizards bury themselves in the soil at night and during cool winter weather, and even when unburied they are almost invisible due to their camouflaged coloration.

Western rattlesnakes (fig. 73) retire in cool shade during hot summer days but emerge to hunt the chaparral for abundant rodents in the evening. Garter snakes, gopher snakes, and striped racers (*Masticophis lateralis*) are also encountered in or near chaparral. The striped racer, known as the "chaparral snake" of California, is one of the fastest snakes in the Big Sur area. It has large eyes on which it relies to search out prey, and it favors patchy brush.

Chaparral birds are also similar to those in coastal scrub. Scrub jays, which nest in dense chaparral, swoop from shrub to shrub in search of anything edible. Wrentits (fig. 74) also nest in chaparral and are so fond of thick brush that they will not enter clearings just a few yards wide. The blue-gray gnatcatcher (*Polioptila caerulea*) snaps up insects, while Anna's hummingbird sips at yerba santa, California fuchsia, and other chaparral flowers. The mountain quail's (*Oreortyx pictus*) (fig. 75) distinctive single note "toot" is a characteristic sound of the chaparral and is seldom heard in coastal scrub. This bird feeds, nests, and roosts in chaparral.

Short wings and long tails are the rule with these birds as with those of the coastal scrub. Another adaptation these birds have for living in thick brush is the tendency to use song a great deal to communicate with other birds. Birds living in an environment where visibility is

Figure 74. *Chamaea fasciata*, wrentit

Figure 75. *Oreortyx pictus*, mountain quail

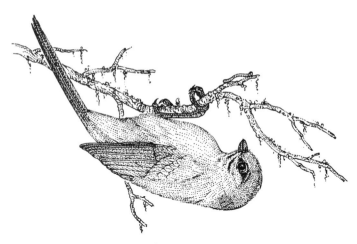

Figure 76. *Psaltriparus minimus,* bushtit

limited to a few feet rely on auditory cues for information about the
location, identity, and breeding status of fellow birds. The result is that
many birds in coastal scrub and chaparral are drab colored but sing and
call a great deal. California thrashers, wrentits, California and rufous-
sided towhees, bushtits (fig. 76), and Bewick's wrens (*Thryomanes be-
wickii*) are good examples.

A number of predatory birds hunt over chaparral. Red-tailed hawks
are the most common, soaring over the chaparral borders in search of
rodents, rabbits, snakes, and other prey. Smaller and more agile than
the soaring redtails, Cooper's hawks (*Accipiter cooperii*) and sharp-
shinned hawks fly low over the chaparral and pick up small birds from
the shrubs. Turkey vultures (*Cathartes aura*) scrutinize chaparral borders for carrion on their daily rounds of all habitats. Black swifts and
white-throated swifts (*Cypseloides niger* and *Aeronautes saxatalis*) and
barn, violet-green, and cliff swallows (*Hirundo rustica, Tachycineta
thalassina,* and *Petrochelidon pyrrhonota*) often swarm over chaparral
as they snare insects. Golden eagles (*Aquila chrysaetos*), the largest of
the predatory birds in the Big Sur area, often soar over chaparral-
covered slopes and high crags of the range.

REDWOOD FOREST

If there is one tree that most non-Californians identify with this state, it
is certainly the coast redwood (*Sequoia sempervirens*) (fig. 77). These

Redwood Forest

Figure 77. *Sequoia sempervirens,* coast redwood

giant trees, famous for their size and longevity, form dark, primordial groves in moist valleys and canyons, and large ferns and a lush understory suggest a different, earlier time. Big Sur is the southern stronghold of California's redwood forest, and the species reaches its southern distributional limit about 2.5 km (1.5 mi) from the Salmon Creek drainage in southern Big Sur. From this point, the redwood forest stretches north 725 km (450 mi) just across the California–Oregon border. The trees grow in the narrow belt of fog that hugs the California coast and are rarely found more than 48–64 km (30–40 mi) inland from the Pacific.

Redwoods have not always been restricted to this foggy belt of maritime California. Fossil evidence indicates that these trees and related plants were once widespread throughout the northern hemisphere, including Greenland, Europe, and Asia, about 50 million years ago. Climatic conditions then, even in the far north, were similar to the mild temperatures and high humidity seen today along the northern Pacific coast. In fact, a closely related species once thought to be extinct and known only from the fossil record was discovered in a remote area of China. However, due to the changing climate, says botanist Robert Ornduff, the coast redwood "should be considered a species that is on the way out in an evolutionary sense."

The redwood's distribution in Big Sur reflects this trend and is more patchy than that of the redwood forests to the north. The trees usually occupy the steep coastal canyons where summer fog is channeled. They have been recorded growing at elevations as high as 1100 m (3600 ft) and occur less frequently on the north-facing slopes of the interior valleys.

The redwood is a water-loving species and is thus restricted to areas of ample moisture. Many of the creeks flowing through the redwood-filled canyons dry up during the summer, but the summer fog supplies important supplementary moisture to the trees. The fog not only lowers temperature and increases humidity, but it also condenses on the flat needles of the redwoods and falls to the ground as fog drip. Studies in northern California have found that fog drip can add as much as 26 cm (10 in.) of precipitation to the annual total in redwood forests.

Differences in temperature and moisture are also evident within the redwood's range along the coast from Oregon to Big Sur. The warmer and drier climate of Big Sur is probably responsible for the smaller size of Big Sur's redwoods, both as individuals and the forest in general. The redwoods in Big Sur, as large as some of them are, do not come near the size of the northern redwoods of Humboldt and Del Norte counties. Those giants may be the tallest trees in the world, the largest reaching 112 m (367 ft) in height (some Australian eucalyptus trees may be as tall or taller). The largest redwoods in Big Sur are 61 m (200 ft) tall and are found in the canyons and valleys on the coastal flank of the mountains, such as along the Little Sur and Big Sur rivers and in Partington, McWay, Big Creek, and Palo Colorado canyons. To the south, the trees become noticeably smaller.

If the basic requirements of humidity and soil conditions are met, however, redwoods are extremely vigorous and competitive plants. They are not only the tallest of trees but are also some of the oldest, living longer than 2000 years. Black scars reaching far up the trees' trunks attest to their enduring many fires over the years. Their bark is fire resistant and can be as thick as 30 cm (12 in.), while their wood lacks the flammable pitch and resins that allow many other conifers to burn quickly during a blaze. Redwoods also resist disease and wood-boring insects, thus the lumber is preferred where insect and rot damage is a problem.

What remains of a tree that does succumb to a disaster, such as fire or logging, does not always die but often sprouts from its roots or stump in a process known as *stump sprouting*. The branches of a fallen tree or dormant buds grow straight up and send out new roots, becoming new trees as the parent log decays. Rings of younger trees often surround burned or logged stumps and are the shoots of those parent trees. As the young trees grow, the ring enlarges and these trees develop their own rings. The identity of the original ring is lost as the process is repeated. Redwoods most often reproduce this way, vegetatively, rather than sexually with their seed-bearing cones.

Fire-resistance, stump-sprouting, and the subsequent rapid growth of young trees are several important ways in which redwoods shape and dominate their environment. Most of the hardwood trees competing for space with the redwoods, such as the tanoak (*Lithocarpus densiflorus*) and California bay, are less tolerant of fire and have a slower growth rate. These trees, although they can also stump sprout, are quickly outgrown by the redwoods and are eventually forced to live in the shade. Shading of the forest floor inhibits the growth of tree seedlings, and the deep layer of *duff*—organic material dropped by the trees—raises the soil acidity and also discourages competitive growth.

Another adaptation of redwoods is their ability to withstand the flooding and silting that periodically occur in their canyon bottom habitat. Often after a severe summer fire, the following winter's rains wash soil and debris off the denuded slopes and into the redwood-filled canyons. Much of this soil is deposited in the flatter portions of the redwood groves, and in one storm several feet of mud and silt can bury the bases of the redwoods. In McWay Canyon at Julia Pfeiffer-Burns State Park, for example, the grove above the parking area was silted to a depth of several feet in the winter following the Rat Creek fire of 1985. Several tributaries of the Big Sur River channeled mudflows into the Big Sur Valley in 1972 and inundated redwoods there.

Redwoods lack tap roots and have an extremely shallow root system. They instead develop a wide root horizon close to the surface. After burial by a mudflow, new redwood roots grow from the old root system toward the surface and out from the buried portion of the trunk. A new shallow root system is then established, and the old one, now well buried, is abandoned. Bay, tanoak, and other trees, in contrast, are often killed by silt deposition. Geologist Lionel Jackson excavated ancient redwood root horizons in Pfeiffer–Big Sur State Park to establish pat-

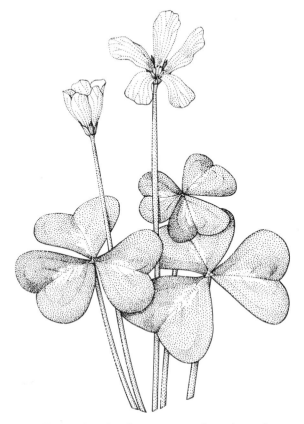

Figure 78.   *Oxalis oregana*, redwood sorrel

terns of mudflows over time. By reading the patterns of root growth, he found that severe mudflows probably occurred in the park area at least three times between the years 1370 and 1700.

Some common understory plants such as redwood sorrel (*Oxalis oregana*) (fig. 78) have also adapted to this cycle. When submerged by silt, they grow vertical shoots up through the layer and eventually reclaim their former habitat.

TYPES OF BIG SUR REDWOOD FOREST AND RELATED PLANTS

Table 7 lists the trees and understory plants most commonly found in the Big Sur Redwood forest. Redwood forests can be divided into three

TABLE 7.   COMMON REDWOOD
FOREST PLANTS

Common Name	Genus/Species
Trees	
Big leaf maple	*Acer macrophyllum*
White alder	*Alnus rhombifolia*
Tanoak	*Lithocarpus densiflorus*
Western sycamore	*Platanus racemosa*
Coast redwood	*Sequoia sempervirens*
California bay	*Umbellularia californica*
Understory	
Five finger fern	*Adiantum pedatum*
Maidenhair fern	*Adiantum jordani*
Crimson columbine	*Aquilegia formosa*
Fairy lantern	*Calochortus albus*
Toothwort	*Cardamine californica*
Hound's tongue	*Cynoglossum grande*
Fairy bells	*Disporum hookeri*
Wood fern	*Dryopteris arguta*
Redwood sorrel	*Oxalis oregana*
Goldenback fern	*Ptyrogramma triangularis*
Sword fern	*Polystichum munitum*
Bracken fern	*Pteridium aqulinum*
Red-flowered currant	*Ribes sanguineum*
Wood rose	*Rosa gymnocarpa*
Thimbleberry	*Rubus parviflorus*
Western solomon's seal	*Smilacena racemosa*
Poison oak	*Toxicodendron diversilobum*
Star flower	*Trientalis latifolia*
Western wake robin	*Trillium ovatum*
California huckleberry	*Vaccinium ovatum*
Western chain fern	*Woodwardia fimbriata*

main phases for a more accurate description: pure redwood, redwood–riparian, and redwood–mixed hardwood. The latter two types are essentially zones of overlap between redwood forest, riparian woodland, and mixed hardwood forest; these phases are widespread and consistent. Differences in exposure to wind and sunlight, availability of water,

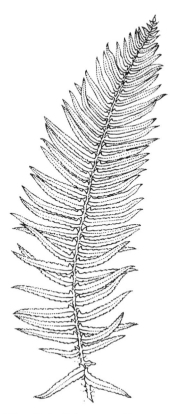

Figure 79. *Polystichum munitum,* sword fern

varying soil types, elevation differences, and disturbance history all play a part in shaping the composition of each phase.

Pure Redwood Forest   Many of Big Sur's coastal canyons, such as Partington Canyon and the Big Sur River valley, contain stands of pure redwood forest. These groves are not usually located directly along a large stream or river because sunlight can reach the forest floor through the open stream corridor. Instead, they are found on the moist, north-facing slopes of dark canyons or in small stream flats and protected bowls.

In its purest form, this forest is characterized by a lack of plant diversity. Here the redwoods so thoroughly dominate that often nothing else can grow, not even the shade-tolerant sword fern (*Polystichum munitum*) (fig. 79) and redwood sorrel. The ground, nearly bare of understory, is covered with a duff layer several inches thick. The canopy overhead systematically filters out most of the direct sunlight, and the relative humidity and temperature are kept remarkably constant.

The pure redwood forest contains some of the most magnificent and oldest redwoods, but sometimes a dense grove of young redwoods of uniform stature and age can also form a pure stand. Because the redwoods are so long lived, only severe natural or man-made disturbances can open up the forest to colonization by other plant species. On steep slopes, landslides open up patches of sunlit ground which may allow a tanoak, bay, or small shrub to move in. Fires perform the same function, but redwoods often bounce back and reclaim their territory before other species can become established.

Redwood–Riparian Forest   As the name implies, the redwood–riparian forest is restricted to the canyon bottoms where streams and rivers flow. This plant community is a melding of the redwood forest and the riparian woodland. The overall plant diversity is much greater here than in the pure redwood forest. The open stream corridor allows direct sunlight to infiltrate the forest floor, and additional moisture from the stream is available to plants along the banks. The hardwoods found here include the tanoak, western sycamore, white alder (*Alnus rhombifolia*), bigleaf maple, and California bay. The bay and tanoak trees grow interspersed with the redwoods, while the others line the stream where water and sunlight are most readily available.

This forest often forms the picturesque scenes associated with the central California redwoods. Elegant, moisture-loving flowers such as leopard lily (*Lilium pardalinum*), crimson colombine (*Aquilegia formosa*), and Andrew's clintonia (*Clintonia andrewsiana*) line deep, clear pools. Elk clover (*Aralia californica*), western coltsfoot (*Petasites palmatus*), coast boykinia (*Boykinia elata*), horsetails (*Equisetum* spp.), and several ferns give the pools a lush, almost tropical look. The riparian hardwoods, the leaves of which turn yellow and orange in autumn, contrast sharply with the towering green and brown redwoods.

Just off the streambanks, this forest can have a dense and brambly understory of vines and shrubs that includes coffeeberry, poison oak, thimbleberry (*Rubus parviflorus* var. *glutinosum*), gooseberries (*Ribes* spp.), and California huckleberry (*Vaccinium ovatum*), as well as the young saplings of tanoak and bay. Depending on moisture availability, there are often many species of ferns. Sword ferns and spreading wood ferns (*Dryopteris arguta*) (fig. 80) are common, while wetter areas near

Figure 80. *Dryopteris arguta,* spreading wood fern

springs have venus hair (*Adiantum capillus-veneris*), maidenhair (*A. jordani*), five-finger (*A. pedatum*) (fig. 81), western chain (*Woodwardia fimbriata*) (fig. 82), and bracken (*Pteridium aquilinum* var. *pubescens*) (fig. 83) ferns. The flowers include western Solomon's seal (*Smilacena racemosa*) (fig. 84), western wake robin (*Trillium ovatum*) (fig. 85), redwood sorrel, redwood violets (*Viola sempervirens*), star flower (*Trientalis latifolia*) (fig. 86), and fairy bells (*Disporum hookeri*).

Redwood–Mixed Hardwood Forest   The third phase of redwood forest is redwood–mixed hardwood forest. This forest occurs on moist, north-facing slopes above the canyon bottoms where less light is avail-

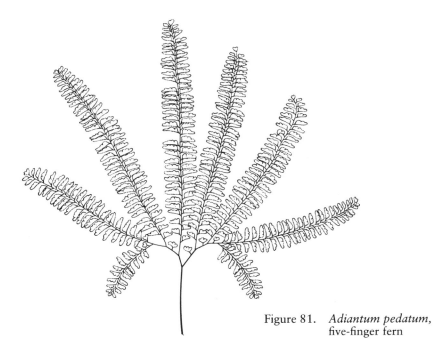

Figure 81. *Adiantum pedatum,*
five-finger fern

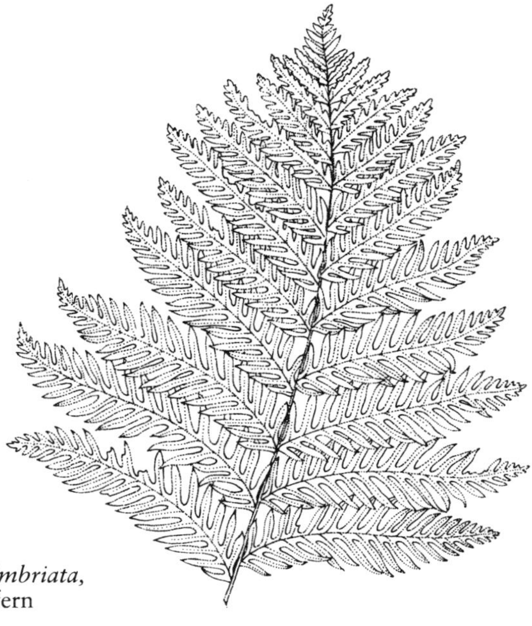

Figure 82. *Woodwardia fimbriata,*
western chain fern

Figure 83. *Pteridium aquilinum* var.
pubescens, bracken fern

Figure 84. *Smilacena racemosa*,
western Solomon's
seal

Figure 85. *Trillium ovatum,* western wake robin

Figure 86. *Trientalis latifolia,* star flower

Figure 87.   *Cardamine californica*, milkmaids

able, and it represents a transition from a redwood forest to a hardwood forest. Although conditions are drier up here, enough moisture is
present for redwoods to grow with the hardwoods.

The hardwoods adapt well to growing with the taller redwoods.
Along the Tanbark Trail in Partington Canyon, for example, tanoaks
grow almost as tall and narrow as the accompanying redwoods. California bay displays a similar tendency, while the coast live oak and madrone sometimes grow in patchy openings in and around the redwood
stands. The understory here is usually shrubbier than that of the other
two phases. There are many flowers, such as milkmaids (*Cardamine
californica*) (fig. 87), hound's tongue (*Cynoglossum grande*), Douglas'
iris (*Iris douglasiana*), and California saxifrage (*Saxifraga californica*),
and shrubs such as poison oak, California coffeeberry, and gooseberries
grow thick.

Figure 88. *Cyanocitta stelleri,* Steller's jay

The redwoods grow smaller and are less hardy near the tops of the slopes where moisture diminishes and exposure to wind and sun becomes more severe. The hardwoods, in contrast, become more numerous, and the redwoods eventually give way to a mixed hardwood or mixed evergreen forest.

REDWOOD FOREST ANIMALS

At first glance, the redwood forest seems quite devoid of animal life. The groves are unusually quiet. Aside from the occasional cries of the Steller's jay (*Cyanocitta stelleri*) (fig. 88), there is little bird chatter or insect noise. This absence is most noticeable in the pure redwood forest, where the understory has few seed-bearing plants to attract herbivores and their predators. Also, one of the most common understory plants, the redwood sorrel, is toxic to grazing animals and is avoided.

What the redwood forest lacks in diversity, however, it makes up for with a moist and stable microclimate relished by a few notable animals. The banana slug (*Ariolimax columbianus* ssp. *stramineus*) (fig. 89), for example, would perish in the hot chaparral or grassland during the heat of the summer but instead finds a suitable habitat here year-round.

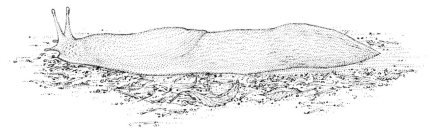

Figure 89. *Ariolimax columbianus* ssp. *stramineus,* banana slug

This bright yellow gastropod is one of the redwood forest's most visible inhabitants. It is related to the intertidal snails described earlier in this book, but its shell has been reduced to a tiny fragment hidden in its mantle. This lack of a shell explains the banana slug's need to stay in its moist environment since the shell is used by snails to lock in body moisture during dry periods.

Shells also provide snails with a measure of protection from predators, but banana slugs have developed another strategy. Their bodies secrete chemicals that are extremely distasteful, and the slug's bright yellow coloration advertises this fact to would-be predators. Thus, they are usually left alone to graze on the vegetation and fungi littering the forest floor.

Several amphibian species also prefer the moist habitat of the redwood forest. Salamanders are seen in other habitats, even the grassland if the season is wet enough, but they are most readily observed in or near the redwood forest. They belong to the family Plethodontidae, all members of which are lungless. Oxygen is absorbed directly through their thin, moist skin. Consequently, water evaporates rapidly through the skin and is lost, and any drying of the skin inhibits the animals' ability to breathe. (Some amphibians also use *buccal* respiration, a process by which they gulp air and then absorb oxygen through the linings of the mouth and throat.) As with the banana slug, these salamanders depend on the redwood forest's moist microclimate for their survival.

Probing beneath fallen wood or duff often uncovers a red salamander (*Ensatina eschscholtzi*), a slender salamander (*Batrachoseps pacificus*), or a Coast Range newt (*Taricha torosa*) (fig. 90). The Coast Range newt is essentially a terrestrial (land-based) salamander that returns to water only to breed. Like all salamanders, it is similar to a lizard in body form but has no claws, and it also has only four toes on its front feet while lizards have five.

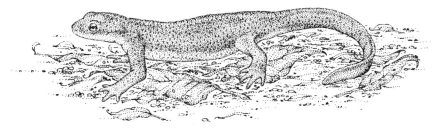

Figure 90.   *Taricha torosa*, Coast Range newt

The Coast Range newt seeks refuge beneath leaf litter, downed wood, or in the burrows of other animals to stay moist in dry weather. Large numbers of these newts can be seen traveling to their breeding sites after a rainstorm, and they are common in streams in the springtime. We saw numerous Coast Range newts in the Big Sur River, in Lost Valley Creek, and in the Arroyo Seco River in May. Breeding males have smooth skin and a flattened tail, while all others have warty skin and a round tail. The glands on the skins of newts exude potent poisons to discourage predators, and they should be handled with caution. Newt larvae have a set of feathery gills that they use to breathe in the water during their first year of life. Near the end of that time, they develop lungs and rise to the surface of the water to breathe. Once they leave the water they return annually only to breed.

Red salamanders, distinguishable from newts by the prominent grooves on their backs and sides, are entirely terrestrial salamanders. They are usually reddish brown on the back and white or light orange on the belly, are 15 cm (6 in.) long from head to tail, and have a noticeable constriction at the base of the tail. They have smooth skin and large dark eyes. They, too, spend most of their time hidden under debris, but need not return to water to breed. These lungless salamanders breathe entirely through their skins and the lining of their mouths.

The slender salamander is much thinner and smaller, and resembles a worm with four tiny legs attached to its body. Both salamanders become active with the first rains in October or November and remain so until April or May. They are carnivorous and feed on sowbugs, worms, centipedes, spiders, and ground-dwelling insects.

A few lizards are sometimes seen in the drier, sunnier portions of the redwood forest, including the alligator lizard and the ubiquitous western fence lizard. Snakes are also seen, especially near streams or in the redwood–mixed hardwood forest. The uncommon and secretive sharp-tailed snake (*Contia tenuis*) feeds almost exclusively on slugs, including

Figure 91. *Troglodytes troglodytes,*
              winter wren

the noxious banana slug. It is most active
in the spring, when its prey is out and
about. The species nears the southern extent of its range in Big Sur. It is most likely
to be seen at night or after rain.

Food for the birds, in the form of insects and seed, is scarce here compared
with most of the other plant communities.
Nevertheless, this forest is the preferred
habitat of two interesting but inconspicuous species, both of which seem to fit in
well with the overall character of the redwood forest. The winter wren (*Troglodytes troglodytes*) (fig. 91) is a tiny bird
with a pleasing song. It is more often
heard than seen in the tangled shrubs and
brambles of the darkest redwood forests,
where it builds a nest of moss in the exposed roots and rocks along the steep
streambanks.

The brown creeper (*Certhia americana*)
(fig. 92) is slightly larger than the winter
wren and depends directly on the red-

Figure 92. *Certhia
americana,*
brown
creeper

wood and other trees for its livelihood. It builds its nest behind loose strips of bark on tree trunks, where it also feeds on insects found in the cracks and crevices of the bark. It creeps up a tree trunk in a spiral pattern, poking its thin, curved beak into the bark as it climbs. A more conspicuous bird of the redwoods is the Steller's jay. With raucous outbursts it alerts the rest of the area to any unwanted intrusions, be they hawk, owl, or human. It is an omnivorous feeder, eating seeds, acorns, and insects as well as the eggs and young of smaller birds. Other occasional nesters in the redwoods include Pacific slope flycatchers (*Empidonax difficilis*), dark-eyed juncos (*Junco hyemalis*), and acorn woodpeckers (*Melanerpes formicivorus*). The woodpeckers nest in the dead crowns of redwoods, where they also locate their granaries of stored acorns.

Birds that are seen foraging in and around the redwood forests include varied thrushes and hermit thrushes (*Ixoreus naevius* and *Hylocichla guttata*), American robins (*Turdus migratorius*), chestnut-backed chickadees (*Parus rufescens*), downy woodpeckers (*Picoides pubescens*), and common flickers (*Colaptes auratus*). Other birds, such as band-tailed pigeons (*Columba fasciata*) and certain owls and hawks, often roost here. Observation of raptors, especially the great horned owl (*Bubo virginianus*), is relatively easy in these woods due to the open spacing of tree limbs.

The owls prey upon the shrews and mice that are active at night. The trowbridge shrew (*Sorex trowbridgii*) (fig. 93), a mouselike creature about 10 cm (4 in.) long, pushes through the damp redwood litter in search of insects, sowbugs, and worms. Shrews are the smallest mammals and have a correspondingly high metabolism. They are sometimes seen running frantically about the forest floor, where they must eat at least their own weight in food every day or die. During this high-paced search for food, they attack insects, spiders, worms, and even small mice, and they are one of the few mammals with venom. The shrews' above-ground habits make them the common targets of larger predators such as snakes, owls, and foxes.

Another small mammal found here is the broad-handed mole (*Scapanus latimanus*). Moles are extremely well adapted to life underground. They have eyes the size of pinheads and no external ears. At the expense of these organs, they have instead developed sensitive snouts for locating prey. Their tails are tactile, and their fur is napless, allowing it to be brushed equally well in either direction; these features enable moles to travel forward or backward in their tunnels. The tun-

Figure 93. *Sorex trowbridgii,* trowbridge shrew

nels, which are visible as long ridges of raised ground, are dug with powerful forelimbs that have large palms.

RIPARIAN WOODLAND AND FRESHWATER STREAMS

One of Big Sur's best kept secrets is the year-round presence of flowing water in most of its major drainages. Visitors see the dry, scrub-covered hills and are unaware of the many waterfalls and deep pools in the canyons. Riparian woodland is the narrow belt of trees and understory growing along these creeks, streams, and rivers. The woodland is not very large in total area, but it occurs wherever water flows in Big Sur.

The exact character of this plant community differs from creek to creek and is dependent on several factors. The steepness and orientation of a river canyon's walls determine how much sunlight reaches the canyon floor. The makeup of the riverbed—whether it is sandy or rocky—influences what plants can take hold. The grade, shape, and width of the stream channel determines where and how fast water flows. This is especially significant during floods when many plants are torn up at the roots by high water and floodplains are cut.

PLANTS OF THE RIPARIAN WOODLAND

Riparian woodland is characterized by moisture-dependent trees that have adapted to the wet conditions along streams. The most common of these are the western sycamore (fig. 94), bigleaf maple (fig. 95), red alder (*Alnus rubra*), white alder (fig. 96), and several species of willow.

Riparian Woodland

Figure 94.   *Platanus racemosa,* western sycamore

Several other trees, such as the black cottonwood (*Populus trichocarpa*) (fig. 97), valley oak (*Quercus lobata*), California bay, incense cedar (*Libocedrus decurrens*), western chokecherry (*Prunus virginiana*), and box elder (*Acer negundo*), occur less frequently. This plant community also has a lush and sometimes tangled understory of ferns, viny shrubs, and herbaceous plants. Table 8 lists the most common riparian woodland trees and understory plants.

The western sycamore is the most conspicuous and well known of the riparian trees. The tree is easily distinguished by its broad leaves and patchy bark. The fuzzy-bottomed leaves have as many as five lobes and can be up to 30 cm (12 in.) long and wide. The bark, colored brown, tan, and off-white, flakes off the tree in patterns that resemble pieces of a jigsaw puzzle. Under optimum conditions, such as along the Big Sur River in Andrew Molera and Pfeiffer–Big Sur state parks, the sycamores

Figure 95. *Acer macrophyllum,* bigleaf maple

grow as tall as 24 m (80 ft) and as wide as 1.5 m (5 ft) in diameter. Stout sycamores growing in open areas often lean precariously to one side, while those growing in the redwood–riparian forest usually grow tall and straight to compete for sunlight with the redwoods. Sycamores grow on both sides of the Santa Lucia Range.

The bigleaf maple can be confused with the sycamore because it, too, has large, five-lobed leaves that measure as large as 30 cm (12 in.) across. These are the largest leaves of any maple and are more deeply lobed than those of the sycamore. They are also a darker green and lack the yellow or silver hairs found on the underside of sycamore leaves. Autumn is perhaps the easiest time to tell the two trees apart since the leaves of the maple turn a bright yellow while those of the sycamore become a dull brown. The bark of the bigleaf maple is usually a gray or reddish brown, and on older trees it is deeply cracked and furrowed.

Figure 96. *Alnus rhombifolia,*
white alder

Figure 97. *Populus trichocarpa,*
black cottonwood

TABLE 8.   COMMON RIPARIAN
WOODLAND PLANTS

Common Name	Genus/Species
Trees	
Bigleaf maple	*Acer macrophyllum*
White alder	*Alnus rhombifolia*
Red alder	*Alnus rubra*
Western sycamore	*Platanus racemosa*
Black cottonwood	*Populus trichocarpa*
Red willow	*Salix laevigata*
Coulter willow	*Salix sitchensis*
Arroyo willow	*Salix lasiolepis*
Understory	
Five-finger fern	*Adiantum pedatum*
Elk clover	*Aralia californica*
Crimson columbine	*Aquilegia formosa*
Coast boykinia	*Boykinia elata*
Stream orchid	*Epipactus gigantea*
Horsetail rush	*Equisetum* spp.
Seaside heuchera	*Heuchera pilosissima*
Leopard lily	*Lilium pardalinum*
Scarlet monkey flower	*Mimulus cardinalis*
Common monkey flower	*Mimulus guttatus*
Western coltsfoot	*Petasites palmatus*
Thimbleberry	*Rubus parviflorus* var. *glutinosum*

The trees are usually thinner than the sycamores, with an average trunk diameter of 0.6–1 m (2–3 ft), but they can grow more than 30 m (100 ft) tall.

White alder is markedly smaller than both bigleaf maple and western sycamore, growing 0.3–0.6 m (1–2 ft) in diameter and 6–15 m (20–50 ft) tall. Lone specimens get larger, but alders usually form dense thickets of small trees. They line most of the interior waterways, such as the upper Carmel River, for several miles in unbroken stands. These stands often form a subcanopy beneath the larger riparian trees. Red alder is slightly larger than white alder and is found along the northern Big Sur coast, such as at the Big Sur River mouth. Both trees are mem-

Figure 98.   *Salix lasiolepis,* arroyo willow

bers of the birch family, and their gray, scaly bark, bright green leaves with sawtooth edges, and polelike trunks are reminiscent of those eastern hardwoods.

Willows often grow beneath the alders and along seeps and springs. Several species are common to the riparian woodland, where they grow either as shrubs or small trees in tangled forests. In some areas, such as at the Big Sur River mouth, willows form almost pure forests in which other riparian trees are excluded. In other areas, such as along the upper Nacimiento River, a few individuals will grow as large as the other hardwoods. About 32 species of willow occur in California, and in Big Sur the most common species are the red (*Salix laevigata*), Pacific (*S. lasiandra*), sandbar (*S. hindsiana*), Coulter (*S. sitchensis*), and arroyo (*S. lasiolepis*) (fig. 98) willows. The latter species was first described by botanist Theodore Hartweg in 1846 or 1847 along the Carmel River. All of these willows have thin leaves that are longer than they are broad, and even with a good field guide, the species are difficult to distinguish.

A phase of riparian woodland, known as stream mouth woodland, occurs near the creek and river mouths of the coastal slope. This community is often devoid of large trees, such as the sycamores and redwoods, which cannot tolerate the windy, salt-laden air of direct ocean exposure. When present, these trees are often severely wind-pruned and stunted. Trees that can tolerate the exposure, such as white and red alders and black cottonwood, often grow above a mixture of riparian and coastal scrub shrubs.

The composition of the stream mouth woodland is variable and dependent on the streambed's exposure and the shape of its canyon. In northern Big Sur, Garrapata Creek has a dense stand of alders that grow creekside a good distance up the shallow canyon. In contrast, Partington Creek has a small stand of alders and willows that yield to redwoods just a few meters from the ocean. Sycamore Canyon, near Pfeiffer Beach, supports a unique woodland of stunted, wind-pruned sycamores upstream from the creek mouth. The Big Sur and Little Sur rivers have thick willow forests lining their banks for several kilometers, until their respective valleys deepen and are far enough from the ocean to support redwoods. Vicente Creek mouth has a dense stand of Coulter willow, black cottonwood, and white alder with some dwarfed redwoods. Other creek mouths, such as those at Grimes and Torre canyons, are so steep and narrow that redwoods are protected by the canyon walls quite close to the ocean.

In the canyons above the stream mouth woodland, the redwood–riparian forest dominates the creekside vegetation anywhere between 30 and 900 m (100 and 3000 ft) in elevation. Above this border, redwoods (or Douglas fir in Salmon Creek and other southern drainages beyond the natural range of the redwoods) disappear and the riparian hardwoods described earlier are joined by tanoak, California bay, and several oaks.

The understory here is similar to that of the redwood–riparian forest, but it gradually thins out as elevation increases. Arroyo and Coulter willows grow in the stream bed, while elk clover (fig. 99), coast boykinia (fig. 100), western coltsfoot (fig. 101), and hedge nettle (*Stachys bullata*) line the banks. Chain fern, sword fern, Dudley's shield fern (*Polystichum dudleyi*) (fig. 102), five-finger fern, and giant horsetail (*Equisetum telmateia*) (fig. 103) are also common where water or shade is plentiful. The understory also has an impressive wildflower display

Figure 99.   *Aralia californica,* elk clover

that includes leopard lily (fig. 104), red-flowered currant (*Ribes sanguineum*), crimson columbine (fig. 105), thimbleberry (fig. 106), and stream orchid (*Epipactus gigantea*).

The riparian vegetation of the interior valleys follows the same general scheme where moisture is adequate. It is often much drier here, and the riparian woodland is even more confined to the creeksides, flanked above by chamise, ceanothus, and scrub oak chaparral. Tanoaks and bays occur less frequently and are often replaced by coast live oak (*Quercus agrifolia*), valley oak, and in some places, black oak (*Quercus kelloggii*).

The larger watercourses, such as the Arroyo Seco and upper Carmel River, have lush riparian woodlands that disguise the overall dryness of the surrounding terrain. Large oaks join maples and sycamores to tower

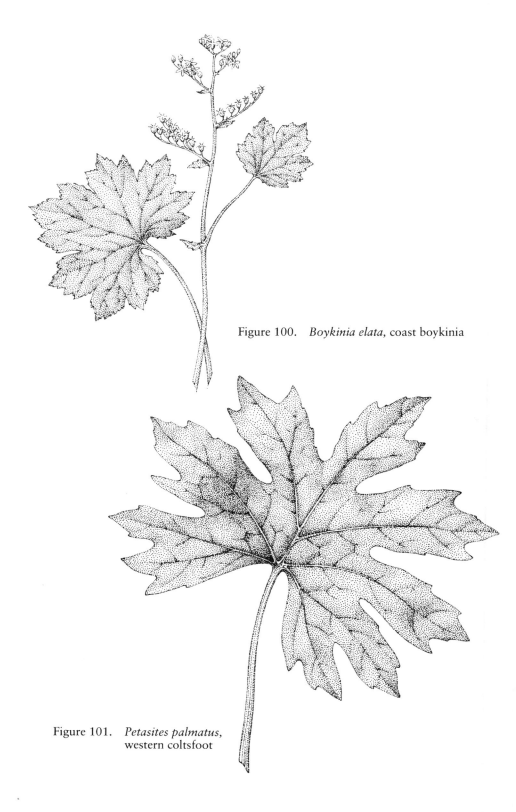

Figure 100. *Boykinia elata*, coast boykinia

Figure 101. *Petasites palmatus*,
western coltsfoot

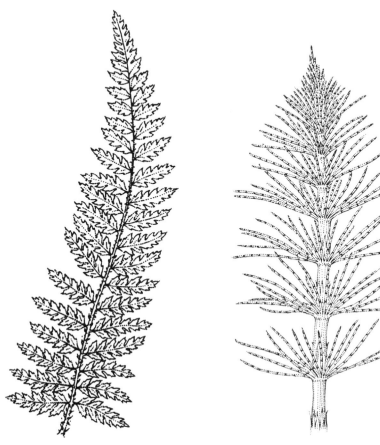

Figure 102. *Polystichum dudleyi,*   Figure 103. *Equisetum telmateia,*
        Dudley's shield fern   giant horsetail

over thickets of willow and alder. An occasional madrone, incense cedar, or ponderosa pine also grows in the river flats. The chain ferns and
elk clover grow more than 2.5 m (8 ft) tall in some places beneath this
canopy, in turn creating a canopy for horsetails and other water-loving
plants. Other understory plants grow in viny clumps and include gooseberries and currants, poison oak, California rose, and blackberry. Thickets of these plants make many of the backcountry steambanks impassable, and one must walk directly in the stream to avoid thrashing
through the vegetation.

The riparian woodland is nonetheless a favorite refuge for many
backcountry hikers during the heat of summer. The cool breezes flow

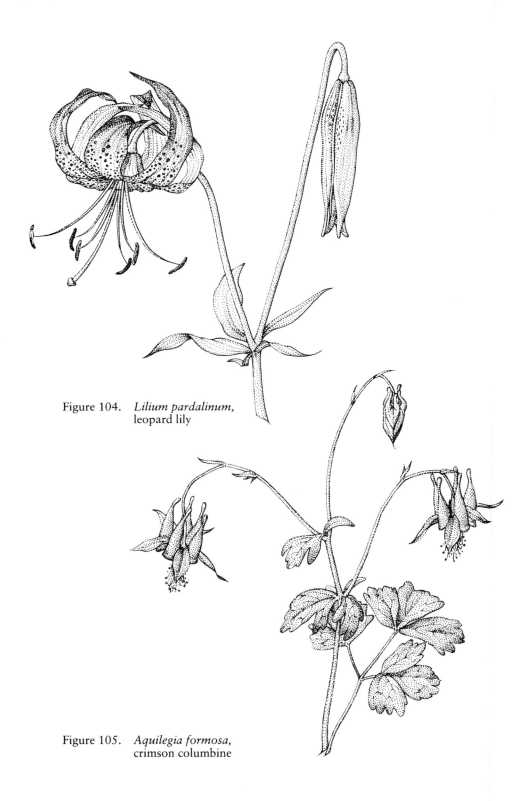

Figure 104. *Lilium pardalinum,*
leopard lily

Figure 105. *Aquilegia formosa,*
crimson columbine

Figure 106. *Rubus parviflorus* var. *glutinosum*, thimbleberry

up and down the canyons, rustling the silvery leaves of the alders and maples. These leaves turn golden yellow as summer gives way to fall and provide the most dramatic example of autumn's approach. Stream levels are at their lowest at this time, and hiking the streamcourse is easier.

Many seeps and springs also occur throughout the mountains that, although not true streams, provide enough moisture to support a distinct group of plants separate from the surrounding plant community. Willows, bays, or even a sycamore or maple tree mark such spots. The springs are often obscured by a lush growth of ferns, mosses, horsetail rushes, and other water-loving plants. One of the most obvious of these is the common monkey flower (*Mimulus guttatus*) (fig. 107), a plant with bright yellow flowers that grows directly in the waterflow. These plants are also found in roadside culverts where water is channeled.

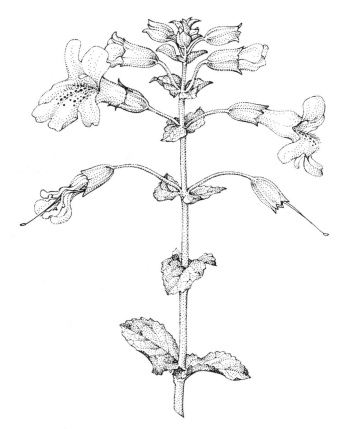

Figure 107. *Mimulus guttatus,* common monkey flower

ANIMALS OF THE RIPARIAN WOODLAND

Aside from the intertidal zone, the riparian woodland is probably the best area to view a great variety of wildlife. Insects such as butterflies and dragonflies are extremely common here. Reptiles and amphibians are seen both in and out of the water. There are several resident bird species, and many more are drawn here by the presence of water and the dense vegetation. Mammals are also lured here to drink and hunt, and their tracks are often left in the mud and sand.

Three noteworthy animals that live in many of the streams are steelhead trout, lamprey, and crayfish. A member of the salmon family, the steelhead (*Oncorhynchus mykiss*) (fig. 108) is a rainbow trout that is *anadromous*; that is, it spends part of its life at sea but returns to fresh-

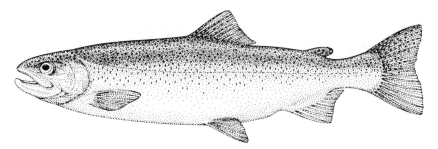

Figure 108. *Oncorhynchus mykiss,* steelhead trout

water streams to spawn. It gets its name from the steel blue color it takes on after leaving the stream for the sea. After returning to freshwater, its steel blue and silver colors gradually revert to the green and rainbow striping of the rainbow trouts. The steelheads, unlike most Pacific salmon, do not die after spawning and can return to the ocean. Quite often, though, the large fish become trapped in shrinking pools during the dry season, and they soon die without a suitable channel through which to return to the ocean. We have seen large numbers of trapped steelhead in the Little Sur and Big Sur rivers, Lost Valley Creek, Big Creek, and the Arroyo Seco. The steelhead travel up other streams except where blocked by waterfalls. They can get quite large and weigh up to 13 kg (30 lbs). They are an impressive sight when compared to the tiny trout with which they are seen in the freshwater pools.

The lamprey (*Lampetra tridentata*), like the steelhead, is also anadromous. This primitive, eellike fish harkens back to the early days of vertebrate development because it has no jaws and no paired fins. It is a parasite and uses its round mouth to attach to large marine fish and mammals, including whales. It secretes an anticoagulant while sucking the blood and body fluids of its host.

The spawning of lampreys is a very complex process. They return from the sea to freshwater streams and build nests of cobbles and gravel in the streambed. Both males and females aid in the construction, attaching to the largest rocks with their mouths and using their bodies to thrash about and clear a suitable area. They also use suction to move pebbles around the site. After the nest is complete, the exhausted couple then begins laying and fertilizing hundreds of thousands of eggs in a process that may take two days. Adults die soon after, and their decomposing bodies can be found along the streambanks as the water level drops. Such dead individuals can be a startling sight—the silver-gray body, unusual gill openings, and bizarre mouth make the creatures look out of place along Big Sur's backcountry streams. We have found lamprey in the Big Sur and Little Sur rivers and Lost Valley Creek.

Crayfish are not fish at all, but actually crustaceans that look like miniature lobsters. They walk around the streambed feeding on decayed organic matter and chasing down small fish. When threatened, they shoot backward by flexing their powerful abdomens and disappear beneath rocks or the creek bank. They are not very common in Big Sur, yet people, especially young children in the state parks, sometimes catch and take them from the streams. They are more common in the Carmel River.

The reptiles and amphibians of the riparian woodland are essentially the same as those of the redwood–riparian forest. Arboreal salamanders (*Aneides lugubris*), red and slender salamanders, and Coast Range newts are all seen here, often beneath the accumulated litter of bark and leaves. The newts are also common at the bottom of small creek pools where they breed. The tiger salamander (*Ambystoma tigrinum*) spends most of the year underground, becoming active above ground only after rain from December to January to breed in freshwater ponds and streams.

Big Sur's streams are swift and cold and are thus not very suitable for frogs and toads, which prefer slower and warmer water. The Pacific tree frog (*Hyla regilla*) is common around seeps, springs, and cattle ponds. Bullfrogs (*Rana catesbeiana*) can also be heard near marshy streams and river flats.

We observed snakes more often in this environment than anywhere else in Big Sur. The western terrestrial garter snake, the sharp-tailed snake, the ringneck snake, the rubber boa (*Charina bottae*), and the California mountain kingsnake are some of the most common ones, but even western rattlesnakes are occasionally encountered along sunny streambanks. Alligator lizards and western fence lizards are sometimes seen along the creeks, and we once watched a fence lizard actually jump into Lost Valley Creek and swim rapidly to the other side.

Another reptile, the western pond turtle (*Clemmys marmorata*) (fig. 109), is especially common in the backcountry streams such as Lost Valley Creek, Arroyo Seco, and upper Big Sur River (although populations are declining elsewhere in the west). This is the only wild turtle in the Big Sur area, and it is almost entirely aquatic. This cautious turtle is usually seen sunning itself on an old log or rock overhanging the water. When a potential predator comes near, it quickly drops into the water with a splash and buries itself in the mud or hides beneath a submerged overhang. Plants, fish, insects, worms, and carrion make up its diet.

Figure 109. *Clemmys marmorata,* western pond turtle

Birds are the most common and visible inhabitants of this woodland. Ornithologists John Davis and Alan Baldridge point out that most California plant communities are adapted to dry conditions, and birds often find available surface water and cool summertime shade only in the riparian woodland. These authors also suggest that the riparian woodland provides "edge situations" since it shares borders with many other plant communities. Birds from these neighboring plant communities that depend on surface water are often seen here.

There are several bird species that are almost exclusively riparian. The American dipper, or water ouzel (*Cinclus mexicanus*) (fig. 110), is a wrenlike bird slightly smaller than a robin with a stubby tail and peculiar white eyelids. No other local bird walks into whirling rapids to feed on aquatic invertebrates and small fish. The dipper is usually seen perched on a rock surrounded by white water and displaying a nervous bobbing motion, or flying over the stream following its course bend for bend. It is also seen in spring building a nest of moss or tending a noisy brood. The nests are almost always located on steep walls beneath waterfalls; spray from the falls keeps the moss nest green and alive.

The belted kingfisher (*Ceryle alcyon*) (fig. 111) is another waterloving bird of Big Sur's freshwater streams. It is much noisier than the shy dipper, and it usually perches on an overhanging branch from which it dives into pools after small fish. It also fishes the tidepools along the coast.

Another raucous riparian bird is the red-shouldered hawk (*Buteo lineatus*). This handsome hawk hunts along the Little and Big Sur rivers

Figure 110. *Cinclus mexicanus,* American dipper

Figure 111. *Ceryle alcyon,* belted kingfisher

and the Carmel River, both in the riparian corridor and in the adjacent grassy meadows. Pairs are often spotted in or near the eucalyptus grove in Andrew Molera State Park or in the sycamores at Pfeiffer–Big Sur State Park. The riparian willow forest at Andrew Molera State Park is also an excellent area to watch for warblers, chickadees, and other small songbirds.

Figure 112. *Procyon lotor,* raccoon

Like the many birds, large mammals are also attracted to the riparian woodland for its dependable surface water supply and the cool summertime shade. Gray fox, bobcat, and deer are occasionally seen, but the most common visitors are raccoons (fig. 112) and striped skunks, whose footprints are often seen on sandy banks or mudflats. They poke around along the banks and beneath rocks, capturing small invertebrates, reptiles, and amphibians.

BIG SUR GRASSLANDS

The grasslands bring to Big Sur what the maples bring to New England—a burst of seasonal color change. Winter rains, usually beginning in November, create an almost instantaneous green tinge on the golden brown slopes and open ridgetops. Annual plants—herbs and grasses that germinate, flower, set seed, and die in a single year—begin their yearly cycle of growth with this rainfall. This annual plant growth cycle, which begins in winter rather than spring and ends before summer, is a pattern often confusing to non-Californians since it is unique in the United States.

Within a month of the onset of the winter rains, the mountains are a bright, vibrant green as the new grasses push above the tangled mulch of last year's decaying plants. The grasses accelerate their growth in March and April as the rains diminish, temperatures rise, and the days grow longer. The soil begins to dry by early May, and the hills turn a golden brown as the grasses die. The seeds drop and lay dormant through the hot, dry summer until the rains return the following winter.

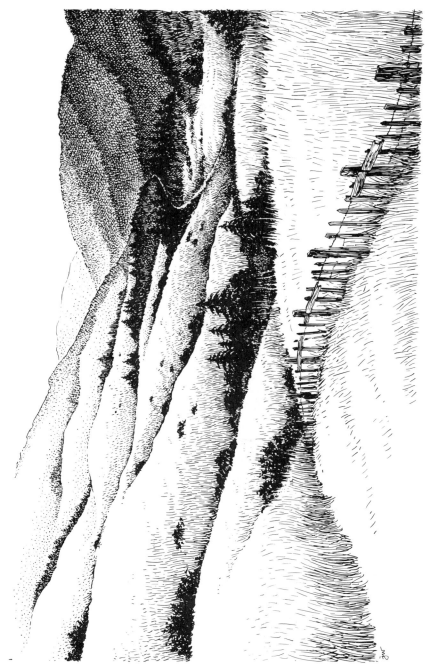

Big Sur Grasslands

TABLE 9.   COMMON
GRASSLAND PLANTS

Common Names	Genus/Species
Grasses	
Silver hairgrass	*Aira caryophyllea*
Slender wild oats	*Avena barbata*
Wild oats	*Avena fatua*
Rattlesnake grass	*Briza maxima*
Soft chess	*Bromus hordeaceus*
Red brome	*Bromus rubens*
Western ryegrass	*Elymus glaucus*
Barnyard foxtail	*Hordeum leporinum*
Italian ryegrass	*Lolium multiflorum*
Pine bluegrass	*Poa scabrella*
Forbs	
Scarlet pimpernel	*Anagallis arvensis*
Elegant clarkia	*Clarkia unguiculata*
Shooting star	*Dodecatheon clevelandii*
Red larkspur	*Delphinium nudicaule*
Storksbill	*Erodium botrys*
California poppy	*Eschscholzia californica*
Dove's foot geranium	*Geranium molle*
Sky lupine	*Lupinus nanus*
Owl's clover	*Orthocarpus purpurascens*
Popcorn flower	*Plagiobothrys nothofulvus*
English plantain	*Plantago lanceolata*
California buttercup	*Ranunculus californicus*
Sheep sorrel	*Rumex acetosella*
Milk thistle	*Silybum marianum*
Blue-eyed grass	*Sisyrinchium bellum*
Johnny jump-up	*Viola pedunculata*

GRASSES

Most of the grasses responsible for this yearly cycle are alien invaders to the California landscape (table 9). They are nonnative species, brought here both intentionally or unintentionally by settlers and explorers during the last two centuries. Some of these exotic grasses were originally introduced and grown as feed for livestock, but the great majority were probably unknowingly introduced as seed in animal feed, in dry vegetation used as packing material for cargo on ships, and by early land explorations. Thus, the grasslands have been transformed from their original composition and appearance more than any other type of vegetation in the state.

Big Sur did not escape this change despite its relative isolation from the rest of California. Of the 162 species of grasses found in Monterey County, 91 (56%) are native and 71 (44%) are introduced. Even these figures are misleading since a few select nonnative species often dominate most grasslands. In addition, the invasion process continues as slower spreading and recently introduced species continue the transformation.

Some grassland ecologists refer to the more common introduced grasses as "new natives" and begrudgingly accept their permanent status in the California flora. Wild oats (*Avena fatua*) (fig. 113) and ripgut brome (*Bromus diandrus*) (fig. 114) are some of the most common. Other exotic grasses common to Big Sur include some of the annual fescues (*Festuca* spp.), Italian ryegrass (*Lolium multiflorum*) (fig. 115), which is often seeded after a fire, rattlesnake grass (*Briza maxima*) (fig. 116), barnyard foxtail (*Hordeum leporinum*) (fig. 117), and silver hairgrass (*Aira caryophyllea*).

Common native grasses in Big Sur include California brome (*Bromus carinatus*) (fig. 118), blue wildrye (*Elymus glaucus*), pine bluegrass (*Poa scabrella*), and several species of needlegrasses, *Stipa* spp. Some ecologists believe that purple needlegrass (*Stipa pulchra*) (fig. 119) may have been a dominant perennial grass prior to the arrival of the Spanish, and this species is California's official state grass.

Unfortunately, records of the grasslands prior to the arrival of the Spaniards are scanty. Grassland ecologists believe that the northern California grasslands were originally dominated by perennial bunchgrasses. Native annual grasses probably played an important role, but little is known of their historical extent. Unlike their annual cousins, perennials live year-round and renew growth yearly from their crowns and creeping stems. Typical lawn sod, for example, is a perennial grass that is kept in a constant state of vegetative reproduction by mowing, watering, and fertilizing.

The replacement of the native grasses by nonnative annuals was probably the result of several factors working in conjunction. First, settlers introduced livestock and increased the grazing pressure on the

Figure 114.   *Bromus diandrus,*
ripgut brome

Figure 113.   *Avena fatua,* wild oats

native grasslands. The perennials were adapted to tolerate grazing by
deer, elk, and other native browsers, but not to the different grazing
patterns of cows and sheep. Many of the nonnative grasses, in contrast,
had evolved during thousands of years of intense grazing pressure in-
flicted by cattle, goat, and sheep in the Mediterranean region and elsewhere in Eurasia. When these grasses arrived in California, they were
preadapted to this pressure.

Unfortunately for the native grasses, the exotic annuals were also
preadapted to California's well-developed grassland soils and its Mediterranean climatic pattern of high winter rainfall and long summer
droughts. The exotics grow more rapidly during the critical moisture

Figure 115. *Lolium multiflorum,*   Figure 116. *Briza maxima,*
                Italian ryegrass   rattlesnake grass

period, and they produce large numbers of seeds even with low moisture availability and can reproduce well under drought conditions.

The nonnative annuals effectively outcompete the native perennials in certain situations. The latter grow much more slowly, produce less seed, and have shallower root systems than many alien annuals. Water is often used up by the annuals before the perennials have reached their peak growth in late spring. Also, once the annuals have become established due to cultivation, grazing, and other disturbances, it is difficult for the perennials to reestablish themselves within the dense annual cover. Once established, though, perennial bunchgrasses can persist and are fairly drought tolerant.

Purple needlegrass is a native perennial bunchgrass that is able to compete with the more aggressive nonnatives. Unlike many other native

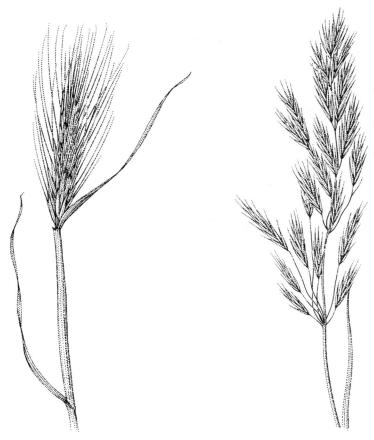

Figure 117. *Hordeum leporinum,*
barnyard foxtail

Figure 118. *Bromus carinatus,*
California brome

grasses, this species is opportunistic and can establish itself readily on bare ground. Like the annuals, it germinates quickly and produces large quantities of seed. Where the annual grass cover is thick, the needlegrass seedlings do not survive. But when this cover is disturbed by fire, grazing, or landslides, the needlegrass seedlings thrive.

One reason for this success is that a *Stipa pulchra* seed can actually plant itself. Attached to the seed is a long, thin spike called an *awn.* The awn is sensitive to changes in humidity. As it dries during the day, the awn twists and pushes the seed into the ground. When the awn unwinds at night due to higher humidity, backward-pointing hairs on the seed casing, or *lemma,* prevent the seed from being pulled back out of the

Figure 119. *Stipa pulchra,* purple needlegrass

ground. In a few days, the seed is planted in soil cracks and soft places, allowing it to colonize an area bare of vegetation and mulch cover. The seed is also protected in this way from predators such as mice and birds and from late summer and fall fires.

Many grasses have awns and other structural adaptations that serve as seed-dispersal mechanisms designed for air, water, or animal transport. A ten-minute walk in summer through a field of dry grasses usually yields socks and shoes stabbed full of seeds. These are then transported, perhaps driven in a car, by the seed carrier to a new area miles away from their point of origin.

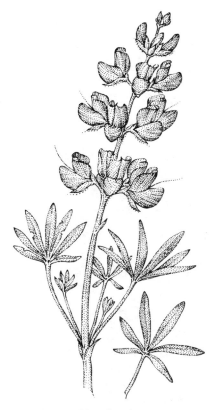

Figure 120. *Lupinus nanus,*
sky lupine

FORBS

Grasses are not the only plants of the grasslands. Forbs, or nongrass herbs, make up an important portion of the grassland ecosystem (see table 9). The native forbs provide the spectacular wildflower displays for which the Coast Range grasslands are so famous. While the grasses are still green, whole slopes and ridges are colored blue and orange by sky lupines (*Lupinus nanus*) (fig. 120) and California poppy (*Eschschol-zia californica*) (fig. 121). Delicate flowers such as the shooting star (*Dodecatheon clevelandii*), California buttercups (*Ranunculus californicus*), and Johnny jump-up (*Viola pedunculata*) bloom along many of the coastal trails. Blue-eyed grass (*Sisyrinchium bellum*), several species

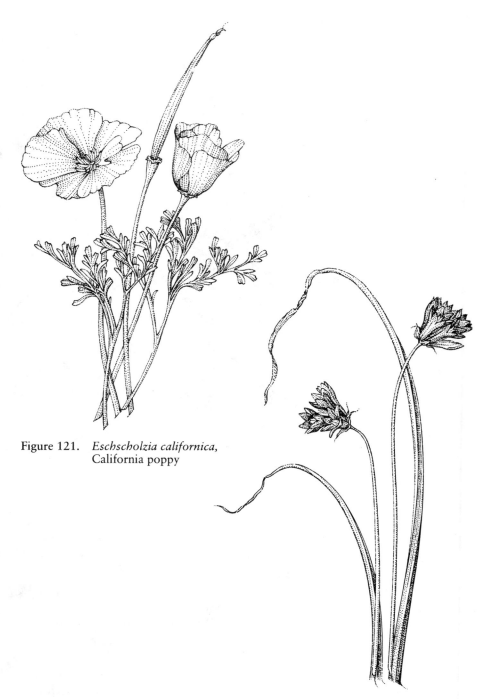

Figure 121.   *Eschscholzia californica,*
California poppy

Figure 122.   *Dichelostemma multiflorum,*
blue dick

Previous page
Waterfall on McWay
Creek, Julia Pfeiffer-
Burns State Park.
Donald J. Usner photo.

The Big Sur coast as
seen from Cone Peak,
1571 m (5155 ft).
Donald J. Usner photo.

Ventana Cone and
Ventana Double Cone,
granitic peaks in the
northern Santa Lucias.
Paul Henson photo.

Sandy marine terrace
deposits in coastal cliffs
near Pacific Valley.
Donald J. Usner photo.

Layered and deformed
rocks of the Franciscan
complex near Cooper Point,
Andrew Molera State Park.
Donald J. Usner photo.

Sandstone arch,
Church Creek.
Donald J. Usner photo

Marine terraces near
Pacific Valley.
Donald J. Usner photo

Opposite
Rocky, granitic coves of
Garrapata State Park.
Donald J. Usner photo.

Bank of coastal fog about
60 m (200 ft) thick.
Donald J. Usner photo.

Winter storm over the
Big Sur coast near Gorda.
Donald J. Usner photo.

Sky lupines (*Lupinus nanus*)
on spring grasslands.
Donald J. Usner photo.

A tangle of marine algae drapes the intertidal zones at low tide. Donald J. Usner photo.

Tidepool, Garrapata State Park. Donald J. Usner photo.

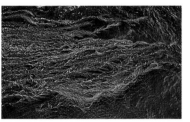

Giant kelp, Garrapata State Park. Donald J. Usner photo.

Coyote bush scrub on the coast near Lucia. Donald J. Usner photo.

Mosaic of plant
communities on the
coastal slope of the
Santa Lucia range.
Donald J. Usner photo.

Our Lord's candle
(*Yucca whipplei*) in bloom
on Partington Ridge.
Donald J. Usner photo.

A tongue of coastal fog
creeps up a coastal
canyon to a stand of
coast redwood
(*Sequoia sempervirens*).
Donald J. Usner photo.

Overleaf
Golden grassland in late
summer.
Donald J. Usner photo.

Sparse chaparral and
gray pine on arid, sandy
soils near Lost Valley.
Paul Henson photo.

Dense growth of
chamise chaparral in the
Dutra Creek watershed.
Donald J. Usner photo.

Ponderosa pine
(*Pinus ponderosa*) amid
hardwoods in mixed
evergreen forest.
Donald J. Usner photo.

Lizard tail (*Eriophyllum
stachaedifolium*) in bloom in
coastal bluff scrub on the
coastal terrace in Andrew
Molera State Park.
Paul Henson photo.

Opposite
Santa Lucia fir
(*Abies bracteata*) on the
steep, rocky slopes of
Cone Peak.
Donald J. Usner photo.

Coast redwood
(*Sequoia sempervirens*) in
the Little Sur drainage.
Paul Henson photo.

Streambank woodland in
Lost Valley.
Paul Henson photo.

Coastal scrub on fire in
the Rat Creek fire,
July 1985.
Donald J. Usner photo.

Post-fire bloom of
California poppy
(*Escholzia californica*) in
coastal scrub.
Donald J. Usner photo.

Overleaf:

Top
Gray whale (*Eschrichtius
gibbosus*) breaching.
Donald J. Usner photo.

Center left
Elephant seals
(*Mirounga angustirostris*).
Donald J. Usner photo.

Center right
Oil-covered murre
(*Uria algae*) washed up
on garnet sands near
Point Sur.
Donald J. Usner photo.

Bottom
California sea otter
(*Enhydra lutris*).
Greg Meyer photo.

Opposite
Maidenhair fern
(*Adiantum pedatum*)
and five-finger fern
(*Adiantum jordanii*) in
cool, streamside habitat.
Donald J. Usner photo.

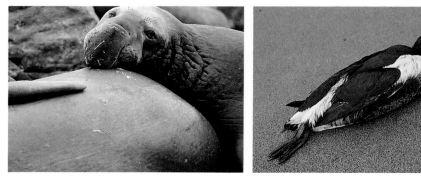

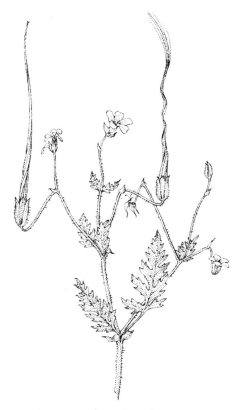

Figure 123. *Erodium botrys,*
long-beaked storksbill

of clarkia, red owl's clover (*Orthocarpus purpurascens*), blue dick (*Dichelostemma multiflorum*) (fig. 122) and popcorn flower (*Plagiobothrys nothofulvus*) are also common. Walking on a grassy slope splashed with these colors is one of Big Sur's most beautiful treats.

Many exotic forbs were introduced along with the foreign grasses, probably as seed in livestock feed, and they are just as competitive and preadapted as the grasses. The filarees (*Erodium* spp.) are the most ubiquitous. Members of the geranium family, they are found throughout the coastal and interior areas of Big Sur and elsewhere in the California grassland. Redstem storksbill (*E. cicutarium*) occurs in drier areas, while long-beaked storksbill (*E. botrys*) (fig. 123) grows on the wetter coastal slopes. The seeds of these plants have awns similar in shape and function to those of *Stipa pulchra* described earlier.

Other alien forbs common to Big Sur include English plantain (*Plantago lanceolata*), several species of clover (*Trifolium* spp.), sheep sorrel (*Rumex acetosella*), dove's-foot geranium (*Geranium molle*), which is similar to the filarees, scarlet pimpernel (*Anagallis arvensis*), and milk thistle (*Silybum marianum*). Milk thistle, a tough, spiny plant unpalatable to cattle, is especially common where grazing has been intense, such as in the Point Sur area.

GRASSLAND DISTRIBUTION IN BIG SUR

On the coastal slope of the Santa Lucia Range, grassland is usually found mixed with or above the coastal scrub but below the mixed evergreen forest. In the drier interior, it occurs adjacent to the chaparral and the coniferous and hardwood forests. This distribution follows a recognizable pattern, but there are local variations. From vantage points along Highway 1, such as at Gamboa, Partington, and Hurricane points, the border between the grasslands and the coastal scrub is an almost horizontal line ranging in elevation from about 150 to 300 m (500 to 1000 ft). Above this line, the grasslands extend up the south- and west-facing slopes and often cover the ridgetops. The north- and east-facing slopes are usually covered with coastal scrub, redwoods, or mixed evergreen forest. On the highest coastal ridges, such as near the Coast Ridge road, the grassland becomes an understory for ponderosa pine and oak woodlands.

These patterns are dictated by several factors, including exposure, fog, rainfall, soil conditions, and disturbance history. For example, there are grasslands on the low-lying marine terraces and hills near Andrew Molera State Park that were once grazed by cattle. The vegetation is quite different along the fence line separating Andrew Molera State Park from El Sur Ranch to the north, which is heavily grazed. In just a decade or so since the state land was acquired and fenced off, it has become much more shrubby in character and may gradually become coastal scrub if left unburned and ungrazed.

Other areas, however, remain grassland even if ungrazed or unburned. Grassland grows on shallow soils that are drier than those of the coastal scrub. Many steep slopes and open ridges are above the fogline and are scorched daily by the sun. Coastal scrub does not grow well under these conditions, but grasslands thrive. Inland, the hottest slopes are often covered with chaparral, and grasslands occur above these slopes and on the open ridges.

Figure 124.   *Sturnella neglecta,* western
meadowlark

GRASSLAND ANIMALS

Many insects, rodents, birds, and large mammals feed on the plants and
seeds found in the grasslands. Predators, such as snakes, lizards, spiders,
hawks, foxes, and mountain lions come to the grasslands to feed on
these herbivores. Although many of these animals feed in the grasslands, relatively few actually nest and breed here. For example, of the
many birds seen in the grasslands, only the western meadowlark (*Sturnella neglecta*) (fig. 124), grasshopper sparrow (*Ammodramus savan-
narum*), savannah sparrow (*Passerculus sandwichensis*), and lark sparrow (*Chondestes grammacus*) nest here. The burrowing owl (*Speotyto
cunicularia*) and horned lark (*Eremophila alpestris*) probably nest in the
grasslands on the eastern slope of the range.

But the list of birds that feed here is long. Raptors such as the black-
shouldered kite (*Elanus leucurus*), red-tailed and red-shouldered hawks,
American kestrel (*Falco sparverius*) (fig. 125), golden eagle, barn owl

Figure 125.   *Falco sparverius,* American kestrel

(*Tyto alba*), and great horned owl all hunt here regularly. The larger
birds take rodents and snakes, while the kestrel preys on grasshoppers
and small mice. Several species of swallows and swifts snatch insects that
fly above the grasslands. Starlings, blackbirds, California quail, mourn-
ing doves (*Zenaidura macroura*), finches, and sparrows also feed here.

The birds that do nest here divide up the habitat according to their
different feeding and nesting preferences. Meadowlarks eat primarily
insects and insect eggs and are important predators of crickets and
grasshoppers. Savannah sparrows, in contrast, eat both vegetable and
animal matter. Some birds prefer short grass while others feed in tall
grass, and some use the tops of grasses while others feed on the ground.
These preferences greatly reduce competition among these grassland
birds.

Few reptiles nest in the grasslands, and most wander into the fringes
from nearby rocky or wooded areas. Western fence lizards are the most
common, but southern alligator lizards and western skinks (*Eumeces
skiltonianus*) are also common. These lizards frequent rock outcrops in
grasslands and the borders between grassy areas and other habitats.

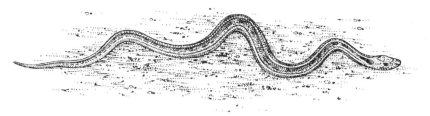

Figure 126. *Pituophis melanoleucus*, gopher snake

Figure 127. *Thomomys bottae*, pocket gopher

They hide under logs and rocks when they are inactive and feed on insects and spiders when active.

Snakes can also be seen along these fringes, where they prey upon small mammals, lizards, other snakes, birds, and insects. Gopher snakes (*Pituophis melanoleucus*) (fig. 126) seek out gopher tunnels, sliding into the gopher nests and asphyxiating the rodents. They sometimes wiggle their tails and spread their jawbones in imitation of rattlesnakes—a ploy to fool potential predators. This act, along with the snake's pale yellow coloration and dark dorsal blotches, often cause people to mis-identify it as a rattlesnake. The western yellow-bellied racer (*Coluber constrictor*) and the ringneck snake sometimes nest in this plant com-munity, and the western rattlesnake is found in the rockier grassland.

Small mammals are more common than the reptiles in the grasslands, but they are less visible due to their nocturnal habits and below ground burrows. Pocket gophers (*Thomomys bottae*) (fig. 127) use their long claws to dig elaborate tunnels and rarely venture above ground except after dusk, when they commonly become prey for owls. During the day, they feed on plant roots and grasses that they pull down to the safety of their burrows. It is not uncommon to see a long grass stem shake a bit and then suddenly disappear down a gopher hole. Small holes and fan-shaped piles of dirt are signs of gopher activity.

Figure 128. *Spermophilus beecheyi,* California ground squirrel

California ground squirrels (*Spermophilus beecheyi*) (fig. 128) are also common in some grasslands. Unlike gophers, which are solitary creatures, squirrels form large underground colonies. They spend more time above ground, feeding on seeds, grasses, herbs, and acorns. They are abundant in areas that are overgrazed by cattle because the reduced grass height allows them to spot potential predators more easily. The south-facing slopes of Prewitt Ridge, the Point Sur and Rocky Point areas, and much of the Hunter–Liggett military base support large colonies. These animals are easy to watch from a distance, and their animated behavior near their burrow entrances makes for some interesting viewing.

Squirrels and other rodents are an important food source for all the larger predators, especially hawks, eagles, badgers, and coyotes, attracting these and other predators to the grasslands. Long-tail weasels (*Mustela frenata*) hunt mice, gophers, and ground squirrels, actually crawling into burrows if necessary. These handsome predators are relatively rare along the coast, but several have been seen near Andrew Molera State Park. Other grassland hunters, such as the gray fox, bobcat, and coyote, stalk the rodents at night when they come out to feed. Mountain lions are also seen in the grasslands, where they feed on everything from small rodents to deer.

OAK WOODLAND

Some of the most picturesque landscapes to be found in Big Sur are just a short detour inland from Highway 1 along the Nacimiento Road. Just north of Pacific Valley, this road leads through an oak woodland where centuries old blue oaks and valley oaks spread their crowns over grassy hills and plains. In many places the landscape has an open, parklike

Oak Woodland

appearance, while elsewhere the oaks form enchanting forests where
limbs are draped with hanging lichens. This area represents a good example of the oak woodlands of the Santa Lucia Range.

PLANTS OF THE OAK WOODLAND

The most common trees and understory plants of Big Sur's oak woodland are listed in table 10. Blue oak (*Quercus douglasii*) (fig. 129) and
valley oak (*Q. lobata*) (fig. 130) are the dominant trees in this plant
community, but coast live oak (*Q. agrifolia*) (fig. 131), interior live oak
(*Q. wislizenii*) (fig. 132), canyon live oak (*Q. chrysolepis*) (fig. 133),
and California black oak (*Q. kelloggii*) (fig. 134) occur in many areas
as well. Coast, interior, and canyon live oaks form pure oak woodlands
on the coastal side of the range, but these stands are mostly small in size
and of local occurrence. Woodlands of blue and valley oaks are restricted to the inland areas, but these stands are large and widespread
throughout interior Big Sur.

TABLE 10.   COMMON OAK
WOODLAND PLANTS

Common Name	Genus/Species
Trees	
Coast live oak	*Quercus agrifolia*
Blue oak	*Quercus douglasii*
Black oak	*Quercus kelloggii*
Valley oak	*Quercus lobata*
Canyon live oak	*Quercus chrysolepis*
Bull pine	*Pinus sabiniana*
Understory	
Bedstraws	*Galium* spp.
Toyon	*Heteromeles arbutifolia*
Douglas' iris	*Iris douglasiana*
Pacific pea	*Lathyrus vestitus*
Bracken fern	*Pteridium aqulinum*
California coffeeberry	*Rhamnus californica*
Currants/gooseberries	*Ribes* spp.
Yerba buena	*Satureja douglasii*
Creeping snowberry	*Symphoricarpos mollis*
Poison oak	*Toxicodendron diversilobum*

Figure 129. *Quercus douglasii,*
blue oak

Figure 130. *Quercus lobata,*
valley oak

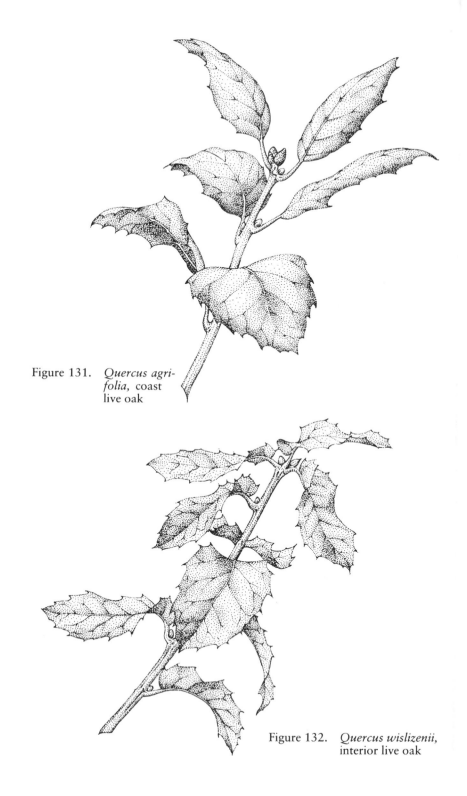

Figure 131. *Quercus agri-folia,* coast live oak

Figure 132. *Quercus wislizenii,* interior live oak

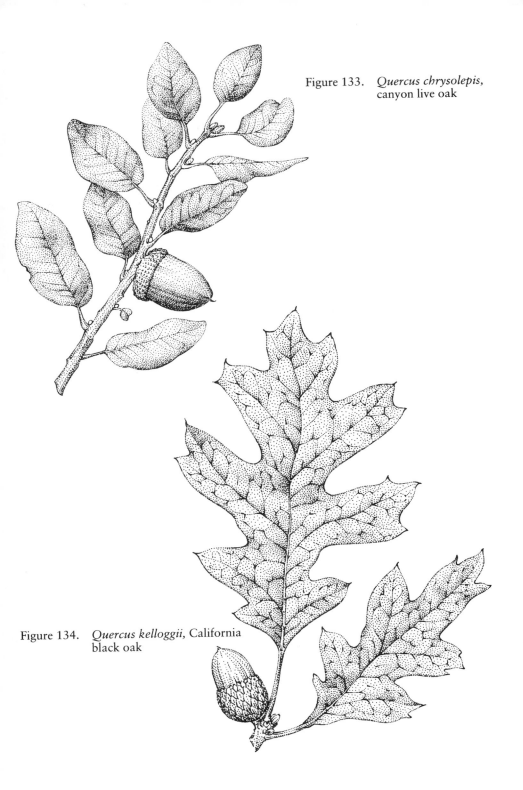

Figure 133. *Quercus chrysolepis,* canyon live oak

Figure 134. *Quercus kelloggii,* California black oak

Good examples of these blue and valley oak stands grow on the lower portions of the Carmel, San Antonio, and Nacimiento rivers and along the Arroyo Seco. Ecologist Keith White found that blue oaks are most common at intermediate elevations, while valley oaks prefer the alluvial soils of lowlands and the moist slopes of higher elevations. Gray pine (*Pinus sabiniana*) grows with blue oak in the southern Santa Lucias but is absent from the northern part of the range.

Oak woodland varies from dense forests of similar-sized trees to grassy savannas dotted here and there with large trees. It seldom forms a continuous cover over large areas but instead is a major component in a plant mosaic that includes grassland, chaparral, and corridors of riparian woodland. Mixed evergreen forest is found on slopes above the oak woodland.

Plants from neighboring communities are often part of the oak woodland understory, especially near the woodland borders. The understory is usually sparse. It is grassy and herbaceous in savannas, similar to the surrounding grassland, while a mixture of grasses, herbs, and small shrubs occurs in denser woodlands. Poison oak, toyon, California coffeeberry, creeping snowberry (*Symphoricarpos mollis*), and oak seedlings are the most common understory plants in these woodlands. In oak forests, little understory is found or it is dominated by poison oak.

Blue oaks and valley oaks are relatively easy to distinguish from one another. From a distance, blue oak trees have a bluish gray appearance while the valley oaks are a richer, moister looking green. Blue oak trees are smaller, reaching 15–25 m (50–80 ft) in height compared to the valley oaks' 28–37 m (90–120 ft). Blue oak leaves are 5–10 cm (2–4 in.) long and are either oval or oblong, occasionally having a few lobes in the margins. Valley oak leaves are about the same length but almost always have 7 to 11 rounded lobes. Blue oak acorns are the smaller of the two, about 2.5 cm (1 in.) long to the valley oaks' 2.5–6 cm (1–2.4 in.).

Blue oaks are deciduous trees, losing their blue-green leaves after the summer. In dense stands, individual trees are often small and stout, while in savannas or more open areas the trees can get quite large with spreading crowns. Such large trees often create grassy clearings in an otherwise continuous woodland. An old tree shades out smaller trees and shrubs, and when it finally dies and decomposes a large clearing is often left behind.

Blue oaks are famous for their drought tolerance, and they therefore dominate much of the Santa Lucia oak woodland. For example, of the forty-nine woodland stands surveyed by ecologist Keith White at Hastings Reserve in the northern Santa Lucias, forty-five were dominated by blue oak. University of California ecologist Jim Griffin describes the "Coast Range blue oak phase" at Hastings as occupying areas between open grassland and the extensive coast live oak–madrone forests found on that Carmel Valley reserve. The species prefers arid microclimates and forms dense stands on low south-facing slopes. It seldom grows on north-facing slopes since these are usually covered by mixed hardwood forests. Griffin also notes that the western margin of the blue oak woodland is quite irregular in these mountains, making its closest approach to the ocean—within 10 km (6 mi)—in the Nacimiento Valley.

Although not as common as the blue oaks, valley oaks are far more impressive in stature. Also known as California white oaks, many of the old trees are wider in canopy than they are tall. The best stands in the range, and perhaps even in the state, are easily reached by car along the Nacimiento Road in the Hunter–Liggett Military Reservation. According to Griffin, some of these trees were probably mature when the Portola expedition arrived in 1769 (see chap. 7). Unfortunately, many areas that were once covered with mature valley oaks—low-lying valleys with rich soil—were cleared of the trees and given over to agriculture.

Valley oaks prefer deeper, moister soils than the blue oak and often occupy such sites within the blue oak's range. The species occurs as part of the interior riparian woodland, and the most extensive stands are on the flat lowlands of the major drainages, hence the name *valley* oak. In the northern Santa Lucias, valley oaks grow adjacent to coastal sage scrub in the upper Carmel Valley. Near Plaskett Ridge, far to the south, valley oaks come much closer to the ocean—within 1.4 km (0.9 mi)—but remain well above the main fog zone at 600 m (2000 ft) elevation.

Some *Q. lobata* stands grow at 1500 m (5000 ft) elevation on Chews Ridge surrounded by mixed evergreen forest. Such high elevation occurrences are uncommon for this species, and aggressive invasion by live oaks and Coulter pines is converting many of these montane valley oak savannas.

The other oaks most common in Big Sur are the three species of live oaks. The coast live oak is probably the most familiar of Big Sur's oaks. This species is widespread near the coast but less common on the interior slopes of the range. It seems to prefer the drier portions of the coastal forest, such as the areas bordering the coastal scrub and grassland and some of the south-facing slopes. The tree grows in open woodlands along the ridgetops but forms more of a closed canopy closer to the hardwood forest. It is also found—usually along with bay trees and some shrubs—in the shallow arroyos and depressions on the upper flanks of the grassy ridges. These groves form pockets of dark green in the golden grassland.

Coast live oaks are usually seen between 300 and 1100 m (1000 and 3600 ft) in elevation. They grow near the Limekiln Creek drainage at 1075 m (3525 ft) and mix with ponderosa pines and canyon live oaks. The best developed stands in this area occur on fine-grained and clay-rich soils derived from limestone and metamorphic rocks. Near Hastings Reserve in the Carmel Valley, the species teams up with madrone to form dense forests covering many of the north-facing slopes. Pure stands of coast live oak create dark, closed canopy forests on some of the lower slopes and canyon bottoms. The species also grows in pure stands on Pfeiffer Ridge in Andrew Molera State Park. These wind-pruned trees form a bonsailike forest where their limbs are cloaked with lichens.

The interior live oak is the least common of the Big Sur's three live oaks, and it is remarkably similar in appearance to the coast live oak. The most effective, although not guaranteed, method for discerning the two species is to compare the leaves. The edges of coast live oak leaves are curled downward, making them bowl shaped; those of the interior live oak, in contrast, are usually flat or can easily be made to lie flat. Also, the interior live oak lacks the small tufts of hair that are usually found on the underside of coast live oak leaves.

The interior live oak is most common in the Sierra foothills, while the coast live oak prefers the coastal regions of the state, hence their respective names. The names are a bit misleading, though, since both species occur throughout the coastal and interior Big Sur under a variety of conditions. Ecologist Steven Talley found that the interior live oak grows in coastal canyons lacking redwoods and on north-facing slopes below 700 m (2300 ft) in elevation. This forest then mixes on the slopes above with one usually dominated by coast live oaks. Interior live oaks are also found in the upper reaches of these high elevation woodlands, such as along the De Angulo trail in the Torre Creek drainage and along the Stone Ridge Trail in the Limekiln Creek drainage. At nearby Big Creek Reserve, Eric Engles reported the interior live oak as very common on dry exposed ridges among the ponderosa pines and mixed hardwoods. The species often grows as a shrub under such conditions.

The canyon live oak resembles the coast and interior live oaks, but there are some differences. The cups that hold the canyon live oak acorns, for example, are thick and covered with a golden yellow wool. Canyon live oak leaves are usually (but not always) smooth on the margins and have a whitish or golden powder on the underside. Combined, the leaves and the acorn cup give the tree foliage a yellowish appearance.

The canyon live oak is the most widely distributed oak in California. It is also widespread in Big Sur, and portions of the mixed evergreen forest are often dominated by canyon live oak. The species is most often found above 1000 m (3200 ft) elevation, where it replaces coast live oak and marks the transition between the lower elevation hardwoods and the high elevation conifers.

This tree grows well in a variety of habitats. It forms pure stands in deeply shaded canyons as well as on dry, rocky ridges. It mixes with tanoak, madrone, bigleaf maple, and bay on sheltered slopes and ravines. It grows with Coulter and ponderosa pines on gentler slopes, and in upper Devil's Canyon and on Junipero Serra Peak it is the dominant hardwood beneath a scattered overstory of sugar pines. The tree also grows on the high summits and exposed ridgetops, areas that are covered with chaparral and swept regularly by brushfires.

The least common of Big Sur's oaks is the black oak. It is a deciduous oak, and its broad leaves are jaggedly lobed with veins that extend beyond the leaf margins. In spring the new leaves can be pink or red, while in autumn they turn from green to a bright yellow before dropping. The older trees reach as tall as 30 m (100 ft) and have blackish gray bark.

The Big Sur black oak population is disjunct from the Sierran population, where it forms extensive forests along with incense cedar and ponderosa pine. It is abundant in the northern parts of the Santa Lucia Range but is uncommon south of Plaskett Ridge. It is rarely seen on the coastal slope, instead preferring the wooded ridgetops and interior forests of higher elevations. It grows with ponderosa pines and other hardwoods along the Coast Ridge road and Skinners Ridge, and the ridges above Prewitt and Plaskett creeks support an interesting mix of black oaks, live oaks, and grassland.

OAK REGENERATION AND SUCCESSION

Hikers and travelers passing through the Santa Lucia oak woodland are often impressed by the size of old valley oaks or by the rolling hills and

Figure 135.   *Columba fasciata*, band-tailed pigeon

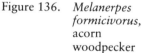

Figure 136.   *Melanerpes formicivorus*, acorn woodpecker

open savannas. But they do not usually notice the apparent absence of oak saplings in the woodland and on its fringes. There are plenty of adult trees, but where are the young oaks to replace them as they age? "In life insurance terms," writes ecologist Jim Griffin, "the whole [valley oak] community verges on disaster." The live oaks appear to be invading the blue and valley oak woodlands of interior Big Sur. This apparent failure of valley oaks and, to a lesser extent, blue oaks to compete successfully with these other species and maintain dominance is an interesting and well-documented story.

Several species of birds and mammals may be responsible for this lack of new growth. Research by Griffin and others over the past few decades has revealed that many different animals feed on oak leaves and acorns. Griffin found this list to be fairly long. Yellow-billed magpies (*Pica nuttalli*), band-tailed pigeons (fig. 135), scrub jays, acorn woodpeckers (fig. 136), mule deer, cattle, and pocket gophers are

Figure 137.   *Sus scrofa*, wild pig

Figure 138.   *Sciurus griseus*, western gray squirrel

the most important consumers of valley oak acorns. Less important acorn eaters include dusky-footed woodrats, harvest and deer mice, wild pigs (*Sus scrofa*) (fig. 137), Steller's jays, American crows (*Corvus brachyrhynchos*), California ground squirrels, and western gray squirrels (*Sciurus griseus*) (fig. 138).

Although these animals reduce the supply of acorns available for ger-

Figure 139. *Microtus californicus,* California vole

mination, they also inadvertently plant many of the seeds. When stored in the ground for future use, a number of these acorns are never recovered and instead germinate and produce seedlings. One squirrel storage chamber uncovered by Griffin during his research contained 203 germinating coast live oak acorns.

Rather than the acorn eaters, it appears that animals that browse seedlings and young saplings have the greatest adverse impact on oak regeneration. Mule deer, gophers, cattle, and certain insects are the most significant browsers, while rabbits, mice, California voles (*Microtus californicus*) (fig. 139), and ground squirrels are less important. Deer eat all foliage off the young plants, chewing them down to the stem, while gophers sever the seedlings at the base and pull them into their burrows. Cattle and sheep grazing over the last two centuries may have also reduced the number of young oaks.

All oaks are subject to heavy browsing pressure. Griffin studied a group of seventeen coast live oak seedlings that started growing before 1940. They survived continual browsing and formed hedged bushes. By 1964, a few were finally large enough in diameter to prevent deer from feeding on the central shoot. By 1969, eight of these seedlings were becoming saplings and were growing above the reach of the deer, some thirty years after germination. Both blue oak and valley oak are more sensitive to browsing pressure than coast live oak, which may explain why the live oaks are regenerating more successfully in the oak woodland of the Santa Lucias. Coast live oaks are invading many of the low elevation valley and blue oak savannas and could eventually succeed these trees.

Where there are no live oaks, open grassland usually remains as the old oaks die off. Some people believe that predator eradication may have led to artificially high deer populations, increasing the browsing pressure on oaks. Contemporary game laws allow a liberal kill of deer, but it is unclear if this culls the populations as natural predators did. In any case, many people believe that browsing pressure has increased. Not only are seedlings being prevented from growing within the woodland by increased browsing pressure, they say, but new trees do not invade and succeed in suitable grassland areas.

At higher elevations, canyon live oaks, tanoaks, Coulter pines, and interior live oaks from the nearby mixed evergreen forest are invading the valley oak stands. Old valley oaks that were probably free of understory for centuries are now choked with thickets of pine and live oak saplings. Along with the greater browse resistance of these young evergreen trees, Griffin cites the lack of frequent ground fires as the probable cause of these invasions. Regular fires would kill off invasive tree seedlings while not damaging older valley oaks.

Although the future of the valley oak woodland appears bleak, it is not hopeless. Griffin suggests that a combination of productive acorn years and wet winters in areas of low browsing pressure may produce a new generation of valley oaks to replace the aging veterans. Valley oaks are so long lived that they may be able to wait for these conditions to occur.

ANIMALS OF THE OAK WOODLAND

Acorns are the single most important food item for animals of the oak woodland. In the autumn months as the acorns ripen and fall, a number of different mammals and birds come here to harvest the nuts.

Acorn woodpeckers are the most famous of the acorn eaters, diligently collecting and storing the nuts in massive quantities. Trees throughout the mountains are riddled with holes drilled by the woodpeckers. Acorns are stashed tightly in the holes and are used as food during the winter months, while insects are eaten during the spring and summer. Ponderosa pines are the most conspicuous of granary trees, their pock-marked trunks towering above surrounding woodland. Other trees used as woodpecker granaries include valley oaks, blue oaks, dying or dead redwoods, and sycamores. In suburban areas, birds use wooden telephone poles and cause thousands of dollars worth of damage.

The annual acorn harvest is a noisy affair, bringing together Steller's and scrub jays, American crows, yellow-billed magpies, and acorn wood-

Figure 140. *Parus rufescens,* chestnut-backed chickadee

peckers. All of these birds are raucous and brash, and when in close
contact they seem to argue over the collecting rights to the acorns. The
jays and magpies usually enter the oak woodland from the neighboring
plant communities, gather acorns, and carry them off to be buried in
the ground, often in open grassland. The birds then use the nuts as
needed during the late fall and winter until spring when other foods
become available. Smaller birds such as towhees and plain titmice (*Parus inornatus*) cannot open the tough acorn husks and thus eat acorns
opened and left behind by larger birds and mammals.

Mammals also come to the oak woodland to harvest acorns, and the
food is an autumn staple. Deer wait beneath oaks as birds harvest in the
branches above and drop acorns and tender leaves. Prior to their extinction in California, grizzly bears (*Ursus arctos*) used to gorge on fallen
acorns. Squirrels collect mouthfuls of the nuts or raid the stores of the
acorn woodpecker, hiding the acorns in burrows in the ground. Small
mice also eat the acorns, and husks bearing the marks of their tiny teeth
sometimes litter the ground.

Many animals are attracted to the oak woodland for reasons other
than acorns. The dense foliage and abundant leaf litter harbors many
insects, which in turn serve as food for birds and reptiles. Flocks of
insectivorous birds, such as bushtits, chestnut-backed chickadees (*Parus
rufescens*) (fig. 140), nuthatches, warblers, vireos, and gnatcatchers often pass through the woodland from tree to tree. These birds glean insects from the undersides of leaves and twigs. Other birds, such as the
towhees, scratch around on the forest floor and uncover insects and
arthropods beneath the leaf litter.

Ornithologists John Davis and Alan Baldridge reported on the im-

Figure 141. *Sialia mexicana*, western bluebird

portance of oak woodland mistletoe for several bird species in the Santa Lucias. Mistletoe (*Phoradendron villosum*) is a parasitic plant that grows in large clumps in the upper branches of oaks and other trees. The plants are especially noticeable in the winter when the deciduous oaks have dropped their leaves. It is during this season that mistletoe produces its berries, which are eaten in large numbers by western bluebirds (*Sialia mexicana*) (fig. 141), cedar waxwings (*Bombycilla cedrorum*), and American robins, among others. These birds serve as dispersers of the mistletoe seeds. The berries are eaten, and the birds digest only the skin and part of the sticky interior of the berry that encases the seed. The birds then defecate the seed and the remaining sticky encasement. If defecation occurs while perched on a tree branch, the sticky seed adheres to the branch and eventually germinates. The new mistletoe plant grows directly into the tree branch, never touching the ground.

The presence of so many animals in the oak woodland also draws a fair number of predators. Cooper's and sharpshinned hawks hunt the woods by day, while several species of owls can be heard at night. Red-tailed hawks and American kestrels are often seen in oak savanna. Sev-

Mixed Evergreen Forest

eral lizards and snakes frequent this woodland, especially gopher snakes. Where the understory closely resembles grassland, expect animals from that plant community, and likewise where it resembles that of the mixed evergreen forest.

MIXED EVERGREEN FOREST

Travelers on Highway 1 seldom suspect that conifers other than redwoods are scattered throughout the mountains, but Big Sur is the only place on the west coast where it is possible to sit beneath ponderosa pines and look down at the Pacific Ocean almost directly below. Nowhere else do these majestic pines grow so near the ocean. It is also the only place in the world where native groves of Santa Lucia firs grow, and the only one of California's southern Coast Ranges where sugar pines are found. The mixed evergreen forest is an extremely varied forest where these and other conifers grow amid a diversity of hardwood trees.

A hiker entering the mixed evergreen forest in Big Sur may easily wander beneath more than a dozen different species of trees during the course of a day. Such variety is typical of these mountains. Certain trees prefer steep slopes while others are found on flat ridgetops, and one species does best in dry, sandy soil while another thrives in moist, lime-rich ground. Furthermore, some species grow in pure stands while others "team up" to form distinctive associations of several trees.

In general, the mixed evergreen forest covers an extensive area of Big Sur on both sides of the Santa Lucia Range, usually above the redwoods and the coastal scrub and adjacent to or above the grasslands. It occurs above the more open oak woodland on the inland side of the mountains and also on cooler, north-facing slopes. Lower and middle elevation forests are composed mostly of hardwood trees, while the upper elevation forests are a mixture of conifers and hardwoods. Some conifers, such as Douglas fir and incense cedar, are found in drainages at lower altitudes.

COMMON TREES

In the following sections we describe a little of the natural history of each tree species in the mixed evergreen forest as it pertains to the Big Sur area. Table 11 lists these trees, along with the common understory plants.

TABLE 11.   COMMON MIXED
EVERGREEN FOREST PLANTS

Common Name	Genus/Species
Trees	
Santa Lucia fir	*Abies bracteata*
Bigleaf maple	*Acer macrophyllum*
Madrone	*Arbutus menziesii*
Tanoak	*Lithocarpus densiflorus*
Coulter pine	*Pinus coulteri*
Sugar pine	*Pinus lambertiana*
Ponderosa pine	*Pinus ponderosa*
Douglas fir	*Pseudotsuga menziesii*
Coast live oak	*Quercus agrifolia*
Canyon live oak	*Quercus chrysolepis*
Black oak	*Quercus kelloggii*
Interior live oak	*Quercus wislizenii*
California bay	*Umbellularia californica*
Understory	
Jim brush	*Ceanothus sorediatus*
Mountain mahogany	*Cercocarpus betuloides*
Bedstraws	*Galium* spp.
Toyon	*Heteromeles arbutifolia*
Douglas' iris	*Iris douglasiana*
Lupines	*Lupinus* spp.
California coffeeberry	*Rhamnus californica*
Poison oak	*Toxicodendron diversilobum*

Tanoak   Tanoak (*Lithocarpus densiflorus*) (fig. 142) is not a true oak. The species resembles the oaks in that it has similar acorns and cups, but most of its other physical features are different. The most striking of these is the straight trunk that grows quite tall and gives off spirals of branches. The species is also recognized by its spiny evergreen leaves that are dark green on top and whitish green on the undersides. When viewed across a canyon, the tanoaks stand out from other trees because of their silvery sheen as the wind rustles their leaves.

Tanoaks are most common within and about the redwood forest.

Figure 142. *Lithocarpus densiflorus,* tanoak

North-facing slopes above the redwoods are often covered by almost pure forests of tanoaks, but the species also occurs on drier slopes in mixed evergreen forests dominated by live oaks. Tanoaks are found at higher elevations in the interior parts of the mountain range due to the greater precipitation there. The tree is usually absent below 500 m (1650 ft), and from 500 to 1000 m (1650 to 3300 ft) it grows chiefly in ravines and on north-facing slopes. It is abundant above 1000 m (3300 ft) in pure or mixed stands along with other hardwoods and conifers.

Most other hardwoods do not compete well with the redwoods, but tanoak has a high shade tolerance and is a vigorous stump sprouter. Trees start sprouting from the stump soon after they are cut or burned, and such second generation individuals eventually grow to be multi-trunked trees. (Stump sprouting, as a preadaptation to fire, is discussed more fully in chap. 5, Fire Ecology.) In many cases, the original trees were probably not the victims of fire but were instead felled by early settlers. Loggers stripped the bark off the trees and shipped it to tanneries, where the tannin was extracted and used to cure animal hides. Partington Cove was one shipping point for tanbark bound for the tanneries, and stands of multitrunked and even-aged trees grow along the Tanbark Trail in Partington Canyon. Many of the other coastal canyons experienced similar tanoak harvests.

Madrone   Madrone (*Arbutus menziesii*) (fig. 143) is an extremely handsome tree with glossy green leaves, colorful red-orange bark, and gracefully curved limbs. The bark is the most singular feature of the tree due to its habit of peeling off in long, thin strips or small flakes. Revealed beneath it is a shiny green or ruddy red bark that eventually turns smooth and orange. The tree also has creamy white flowers that produce bright red berries in the fall.

Madrone is a common companion to the tanoak. It sprouts faster than the tanoak following a fire or logging, but it often ends up growing beneath the taller tanoaks in much of the mixed evergreen forest. Madrone sometimes forms pure stands on the drier slopes away from the tanoaks, and it is a more common companion to black oak, ponderosa pine, and live oaks. A forest of massive madrones and black oaks covers a knoll between Bottcher's Gap and Devil's Peak. Some of these trees are so wide it takes several people clasping hands to encircle one trunk. Farther inland at Hastings Reserve in Carmel Valley, a coast live oak–madrone forest is the most widespread plant community on that reserve. Black oak–madrone forests, with an occasional bigleaf maple, form the most picturesque of the autumn woods. The canopy is lit with the yellow leaves of the oak and maple and the red of the madrone, all of which fall and blanket the forest floor with a thick, colorful carpet.

California Bay   The California bay (*Umbellularia californica*) (fig. 144) is usually smelled before seen. The tree's long, narrow leaves emit an intense fragrance that is at first pleasing, but for some can cause mild headaches or nausea after prolonged exposure. The leaves are often used as a spice, and it is said that they are four times more potent than the more commonly used Greek bay leaves. They have an oil that is composed of volatile compounds, and research suggests that these compounds often inhibit other vegetation from growing beneath the trees.

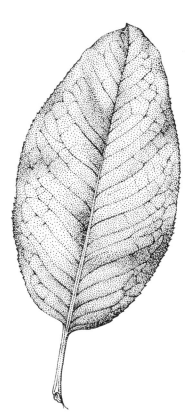

Figure 143. *Arbutus menziesii,*
madrone

Figure 144. *Umbellularia californica,*
California bay

Bays occur throughout the mixed evergreen forest and are most common along streamsides and in ravines. Conspicuous pure stands of the tree are found throughout the mountains and in coastal canyons. Dense colonies of bays grow within the canyon live oak–Coulter pine forests near Hastings. Ecologists Todd and Virginia Keeler-Wolf found that bay trees in the Limekiln Creek area do especially well in rocky, limestone-rich soils and often replace the coast live oaks in such areas. The same appears to be true near Pico Blanco and other lime-rich areas. The trees also grow in pure stands throughout the mountains, such as along the Prewitt Ridge Trail and above the Waterfall Trail in Andrew Molera State Park.

Coulter Pine   Coulter pine (*Pinus coulteri*) (fig. 145), discovered near Cone Peak by Thomas Coulter in 1832, is widespread in the Santa Lucia Range, but rarely forms pure stands. The species is found as far north as Mount Diablo, near Oakland, and southward through the Coast Ranges and the Peninsular Ranges as far down as Baja California.

Coulter pines are medium-sized pines, averaging 15 m (50 ft) in height and about 60 cm (25 in.) in diameter. They are similar in appearance to young ponderosa pines, but their dense bunches of blue-green needles contrast with the dark green needles of the larger ponderosas. Mature Coulters seldom attain the grand stature of the ponderosas, but the two species often grow together and can be difficult to tell apart. The surest identifying characteristic of the Coulter is its massive cones, and this species is also known as the bigcone pine. The cones hang like pineapples from the branches of mature trees and are the heaviest cones of any pine in the world. They can weigh up to 3.6 kg (8 lbs) and measure 36 cm (14 in.) in length. They are also armed with large, sharp spurs that make them dangerous when they fall from treetops, and it is wise not to make camp beneath these pines. Their seeds, slightly larger and harder than pinyon nuts, were an important food source to some southern California natives.

Coulter pines grow above 600 m (2000 ft) elevation in the Santa Lucia Range. They are found on all slope aspects and are most commonly scattered among canyon live oaks, but they also mix in sheltered ravines and slopes with tanoak, California bay, and madrone. They accompany sugar pines in the mixed evergreen forest on Junipero Serra and Cone peaks, and they also grow well in chaparral. They survive in drier sites than do ponderosa pines, but they are less drought tolerant

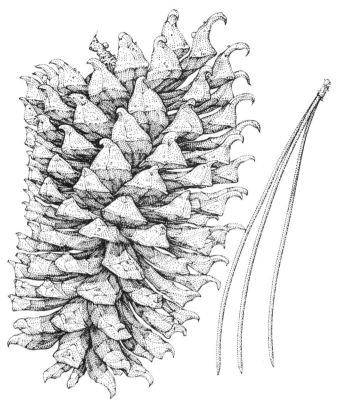

Figure 145. *Pinus coulteri,* Coulter pine

than bull pines. Often growing beneath them are the typical shrubs and herbs of the hardwood forest or chaparral, including manzanitas, chamise, ceanothus shrubs, scrubby oaks, yucca, yerba santa, and others.

Ponderosa Pine   The ponderosa pine (*Pinus ponderosa*) (fig. 146) populations in the Santa Lucias are disjunct, or reproductively isolated, from the more extensive stands elsewhere in the state. Disjunct stands of ponderosa pines occur in a few of the south Coast Ranges, but nowhere do they grow as near to the coast as they do in the Santa Lucias. On Plaskett Ridge they grow within 0.8 km (0.5 mi) of the ocean. Ponderosa pine stands are islands of Sierra-like vegetation, and several montane disjuncts from the Sierra Nevada have been found growing with the pines.

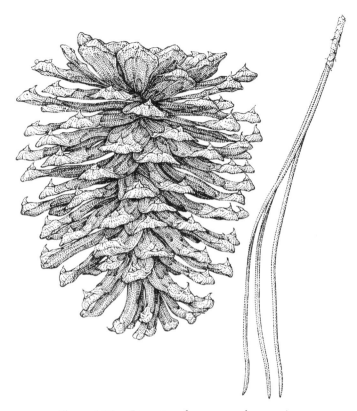

Figure 146. *Pinus ponderosa,* ponderosa pine

Ponderosas are distributed widely between 460 and 1220 m (1500 and 4000 ft) in elevation. Individual pines may be miles apart, or they may be spaced closely enough to be codominants with hardwoods. The largest, purest stands occur on nearly level ridgetops at about 760– 1070 m (2500–3500 ft), often expanding into grassland areas. Such sites include Pine Ridge, Plaskett Ridge, Prewitt Ridge, Gamboa Ridge, Alms Ridge, the ridge between Willow and Alder creeks, and parts of the Coast Ridge. Smaller stands, such as those in picturesque Pine Valley, are scattered throughout the range.

These pines in the Santa Lucias are most common in forests with black oak and madrone. They commonly mix with coast live oak in stands nearest the ocean, and the Santa Lucia Range is the only place in California where the ponderosas mingle with these coastal oaks over

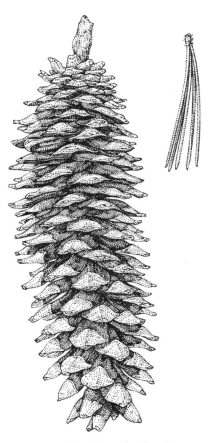

Figure 147. *Pinus lambertiana,*
sugar pine

large areas. Like the Coulter pines, ponderosa pines also grow with canyon live oak and Santa Lucia fir at upper elevations. Interestingly, the ranges of ponderosa and sugar pines seldom overlap.

Toyon, California coffeeberry, poison oak, and mountain mahogany are typical shrubs that grow with ponderosa pines. Several types of bedstraw and lupines are especially abundant beneath the pines at high elevations.

Sugar Pine   Sugar pines (*Pinus lambertiana*) (fig. 147) are the largest of all pine trees, and the largest sugar pines in the Santa Lucias are

found on the slopes of Twin Peak and at the headwaters of the Arroyo
Seco River. Some of these giants are over 1.8 m (6 ft) in diameter and
46 m (150 ft) tall. Their bark is grayish brown, and the needles are deep
blue-green in color with a slight whitish tinge. There are five needles in
each bundle, unlike the three-needled ponderosa and Coulter pines.
Their slender cones, 30–40 cm (12–16 in.) long (and occasionally up
to 61 cm [23 in.] long) and 5–8 cm (2–3 in.) in diameter, set them
apart from any other pine and are the longest in the world. Resin from
this pine is said to be sweet, "better than maple sugar," as John Muir
put it, and is the reason for this pine's name.

Like ponderosa pines, the largest populations of sugar pines are
found in the Sierra Nevada and the Cascade Range, and the Santa Lucia
population is disjunct. The nearest stands to those found here are 220
km (140 mi) away in the San Rafael Mountains of Santa Barbara
County. Sugar pines grow in only two areas in the Santa Lucias: on
Junipero Serra Peak, the highest peak in the range, and around Cone
Peak, the third highest peak in the range. The pines are concentrated on
the north-facing slopes of these peaks. The first California sugar pines
to be described botanically were found on Cone Peak by David Douglas, a Scottish botanist, in 1831.

These pines have been isolated from the Sierran and southern California sugar pines for quite some time. Analysis of chemicals from the
sugar pines in the Santa Lucias has shown that they are genetically distinct from other sugar pines in the state. They are more closely related
to southern California sugar pines than to those from the Sierra Nevada
and are also much more resistant to sugar pine blister rust.

Sugar pines on rocky cliffs near Cone Peak are small and grow with
scrubby Santa Lucia firs, Coulter pines, and oaks. On the gentler but
still steep slopes of nearby Twin Peak, the sugar pines grow to be very
large amid canyon live oak, madrone, and California bay. Large sugar
pines are mixed mostly with Coulter pines and canyon live oaks on
Junipero Serra Peak.

Where hardwood trees are abundant, the understory below sugar
pines includes such plants as manzanitas, yucca, Indian paintbrush,
burlew onion (*Allium burlewii*), bedstraws, and sword fern. The disjunct Abram's lupine (*Lupinus abramsii*), the disjunct brewer rockcress
(*Arabis glabra*), the endemic deer lupine (*Lupinus cervinus*) (fig. 148),
and the disjunct cycladenia (*Cycladenia humilis*) were noted by ecologists James Griffin and Steven Talley in these sugar pine forests.

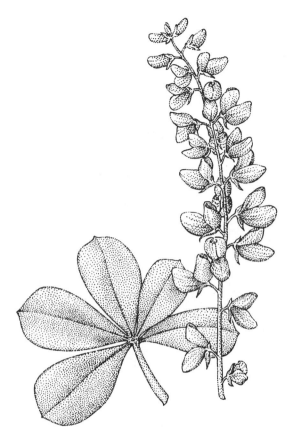

Figure 148. *Lupinus cervinus*, deer lupine

Monterey Pine Monterey pine (*Pinus radiata*) (fig. 149) is so common along coastal slopes and bluffs below 460 m (1500 ft) in Big Sur that it is difficult to imagine that the species is not part of the native landscape. Yet when Thomas Coulter first described Monterey pine in 1830, few of these pine trees grew along the coast south of the Carmel Highlands and none extended beyond Rocky Creek. Coastal scrub was the dominant plant community, and redwood trees in canyons and ravines were the only low elevation conifers.

This species is native to only three small areas: near Point Año Nuevo, north of Santa Cruz; on the Monterey Peninsula; and around the town of Cambria in San Luis Obispo County. All other Monterey

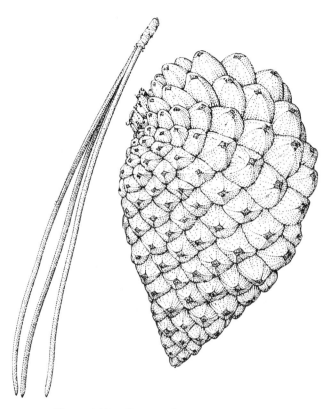

Figure 149. *Pinus radiata,* Monterey pine

pines along the California coast were planted or have spread from planted trees. In Big Sur, these pines often reveal the location of roads and houses because they are commonly used to screen development. This pine has been planted worldwide, perhaps more extensively than any other tree.

Gray Pine   The gray pine (*Pinus sabiniana*) (fig. 150), long known as the digger pine, is a familiar tree throughout the foothill woodlands of the Sierra Nevada and on the inland slopes of the Coast Range. It is the most drought adapted of all the pines, and it commonly grows in chaparral and oak woodland. Its light, blue-green foliage is sparser than that of other pines and appears silver-gray from a distance. The upper

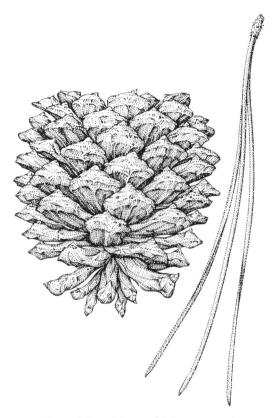

Figure 150. *Pinus sabiniana,* gray pine

branches of many gray pines form one or two open forks, while the lower branches are small and drooping and often support cones that are second only to the Coulter pine's in weight. The thin foliage, open branching, and large cones make bull pines stand out even at a distance.

Big Sur's gray pines, like the ponderosas, grow closer to the coast here than anywhere else in California, and they reach almost to the surf line in the vicinity of Gorda. They are most common, however, on the eastern side of the Santa Lucias in the dry foothills. Their presence near the coast in the Big Sur area is unusual and unexplained, as is their absence from otherwise typical gray pine habitat in the upper Carmel Valley.

In the interior valleys of the range, gray pines are particularly abundant in the vicinity of the abandoned Los Burros mines and on the Fort

Hunter–Liggett Military Reservation. They grow on the foothills surrounding the valley oak and blue oak savannas, and they often overlap
with oak woodland plants.

Knobcone Pine   The knobcone pine (*Pinus attenuata*) is a small pine
seldom more than 30 cm (12 in.) in diameter and 9 m (30 ft) tall. It has
sparse, yellow-green foliage and a wide crown that is usually forked. Its
dense, tightly closed cones are clustered close to the stems of branches
and the main trunk of the tree. The unusual location and shape of
the cones make the knobcone easy to identify among other pines of the
interior Santa Lucias. The cones remain on the tree indefinitely, and
heat from fire is necessary to open them and release their seeds. This
species and the Monterey pine are the only "closed cone" pines in the
Big Sur area.
    Knobcone pines grow in dry locations on sandy soils in a few places
on the eastern slope of the Santa Lucias, most notably in tributaries of
the Arroyo Seco drainage. Next to the bull pine, the knobcone is the
most drought-adapted pine in the range and can reproduce well on dry,
gravelly soils.

Jeffrey Pine   A stand of Jeffrey pines (*Pinus jeffreyii*) grows at an elevation of 1500 m (5000 ft) on Chews Ridge, possibly the remnant of an
effort to introduce this valuable timber tree to the Santa Lucias. Thousands of seedlings were planted in two spots along the Tassajara Road
in 1909. Some of the trees appear to be older than that, however, leading some botanists to wonder if they were growing naturally on the
ridge prior to the planting. Jeffrey pines were also planted near Cone
Peak and Anthony Creek, but these did not survive. Only about 200
trees were alive on Chews Ridge before the Marble–Cone fire.
    Most have an impressive stature and average nearly 30 m (100 ft) in
height—much taller than nearby Coulter pines. The Jeffrey pine is very
similar in appearance to the ponderosa pine, and some botanists have
considered it a form of the ponderosa. The Jeffrey's cones are distinct,
however, in having their barbs turned inward, so that picking up a Jeffrey pine cone is painless—thus the origin of the phrases "gentle Jeffrey" for this pine and "prickly ponderosa" for the ponderosa pine.

Santa Lucia Fir   The Santa Lucia fir (*Abies bracteata*) (fig. 151) has
been called the rarest and most unusual fir in North America, and it is
the most famous and significant endemic plant in the Santa Lucia

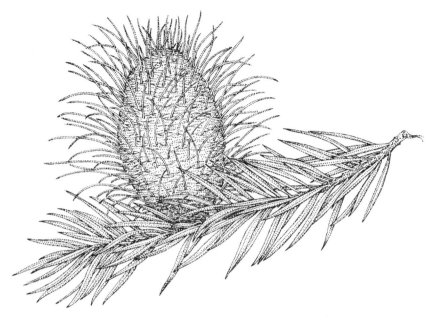

Figure 151. *Abies bracteata*, Santa Lucia fir

Range. It is found nowhere outside of the Santa Lucias and is not closely related to any living fir. Fossils believed to represent its nearest relatives have been found in western Nevada and date from the Miocene epoch, 13 million years ago.

The outline of a Santa Lucia fir—a narrow cone shape tapering to a sharp, pointed spire that often droops—distinguishes it from other trees even at a distance. Mature trees are about 18–30 m (60–100 ft) in height and are about 50–75 cm (20–30 in.) in diameter. Branches sprout from the tree almost to the ground, leaving little clear trunk. The branches droop at their tips, and side branchlets dangle downward like tassels. Their flat, deep green needles are stiff and very sharply pointed. The extremely long, narrow bracts of its small cones have earned the tree its other common name, the bristlecone fir.

Spanish missionaries used the pitch of the Santa Lucia fir as incense and called the tree "incienso." Thomas Coulter discovered this unique tree near Cone Peak in March 1831, and it was the primary reason the Santa Lucia Range received so much botanical attention in the early part of the nineteenth century. Botanists traveled to see and collect this botanical rarity and argued for a long time over just what kind of tree it was. Some even placed it in its own separate genus, *Pseudoterreya* or "false Nutmeg," because its needles resemble nutmeg needles. People still travel far to see this tree in its native habitat, and it is also cultivated and sold through nurseries.

Steven Talley conducted a thorough study of the fir in the early 1970s. He found that the tree is scattered throughout the upper elevations of the range, from Skinner Ridge near the Little Sur River south to Marmolejo Creek near San Simeon. Although a disjunct stand on the Big Sur River is located at only 180 m (600 ft) in elevation, most trees are in ravines and on steep, rocky slopes above 900 m (3000 ft). North, northeast, and northwest slopes are favored by Santa Lucia firs, but they grow on all aspects above 1400 m (4600 ft). The high elevation, south-facing stands are in locations at least partly sheltered from the sun.

Santa Lucia firs grow most commonly with canyon live oaks. Tanoak, California bay, madrone, bigleaf maple, ponderosa pine, and Coulter pine also mix with the Santa Lucia firs in some areas, and sugar pines are part of this community on Twin Peak. At lower elevations, Santa Lucia firs sometimes grow with coast and interior live oaks. They grow on serpentine soils on Pine Ridge and Bear Basin along with ponderosa pine, Coulter pine, and incense cedar. Rarely, as at Ventana camp on the Big Sur River, Santa Lucia firs grow in or near the margins of redwood forest. The stand at Ventana Camp is not reproducing well, however, and is gradually being replaced by tanoak.

More than 90 percent of the Santa Lucia firs grow in the northern part of the range, north of Nacimiento Summit. To the south the firs grow only in canyons and ravines, while to the north large stands are found on the steep slopes of Ventana Double Cone, Ventana Cone, South Ventana Cone, Devils Canyon, and Cone Peak.

The steep, rocky slopes and ravines where Santa Lucia firs are found are among the least susceptible to fire of all habitats in the range. The rocky soils do not support much brush and do not usually burn with the intensity of lower brush-covered slopes. The firs are probably concentrated here because they are very fire sensitive. They lack thick, protective bark and the ability to sprout from underground root crowns and thus have tended to survive best in fire-resistant areas. Since fires have been suppressed in the past 100 years, however, Santa Lucia firs have expanded into areas where they are more likely to suffer high mortality in a fire.

The female cones of the Santa Lucia fir are borne on the uppermost branches of the trees. As in all true firs, the cones point upward from the branches. The trees produce abundant cones and seed irregularly, depending on climatic conditions. Talley found that a year when the firs produce many cones is always followed by a year when few cones are produced.

Gray squirrels take a few cones, but by far the most serious destroyers of the seed are small wasps of the genus *Megastigmus*. Adult wasps lay eggs in the seed, and one egg per seed matures into a larva. The larva hollows out the seed and overwinters inside it. In some years, these wasp larvae destroy the entire seed crop of the Santa Lucia firs.

When the seed parasites were first noticed, many people became concerned that they would seriously impair the Santa Lucia fir's ability to reproduce. Yet seedlings and young trees of all ages are plentiful in most stands, indicating that the firs are reproducing at a healthy rate. Talley believes the firs simply produce such great quantities of seed in good years that the seed parasites cannot consume them all. Also, the wasps have no place to lay their eggs in years when few cones are produced, causing the wasp populations to drop drastically. It may take the wasps several years to become abundant again, by which time the firs may have had a productive seed year.

Douglas Fir   The Douglas fir (*Pseudotsuga menziesii*) (fig. 152), named after botanist David Douglas, is a common forest tree in mountains throughout western North America. In coastal California, it is abundant in the Coast Range as far south as the Santa Cruz Mountains, but only a few stands of Douglas fir occur in Big Sur. The largest of these is on the Little Sur River, and smaller groves grow in the Salmon Creek, Willow Creek, and Limekiln Creek drainages. Isolated individuals or groups of Douglas fir are scattered here and there.

Douglas fir is not a true fir, which are in the genus *Abies*. The cones of true firs—such as the Santa Lucia fir—point upward from the branches. Douglas fir cones hang downward and have distinctive, three-pointed bracts that protrude from between the cone scales. *Pseudotsuga* means "false tsuga" in reference to the genus *Tsuga*, or hemlock, which Douglas firs resemble in general appearance.

Among North American trees, Douglas fir is second in size only to the sequoias—the coast redwoods and the giant sequoias (*Sequoia gigantea*). In northern California, Douglas firs taller than 60 m (200 ft) and over 4.5 m (15 ft) in diameter have been found. Douglas firs in the Santa Lucias are nearly half the size of the giants in northern California. Here, they reach about 30 m (100 ft) in height and 60 cm (2 ft) in diameter.

Figure 152. *Pseudotsuga menziesii*, Douglas fir

Incense Cedar   Incense cedar (*Libocedrus decurrens*) is yet another disjunct Sierran tree that is found in the Santa Lucia Range. This tree is in the cypress family and has much smaller, simpler cones than those of the pines or firs. Its cones consist merely of three pairs of scales—only two of them obvious—that hang downward from branches.

The tree can easily be mistaken from a distance for a redwood. The two species often grow in similar habitats, and the cedars are comparable in size and appearance to small redwoods. On close inspection, however, the leaves of the incense cedar give it away. They are not needlelike as are the leaves of redwoods, pines, or most other conifers, but instead consist of small overlapping scales that form flattened sprays. The rich, green foliage of the incense cedar is dense and droopy and when crushed has a pungent, pleasant odor that is distinct from the smell of redwood needles.

Incense cedars grow mostly on north-facing slopes and in deep ravines and canyon bottoms. Occasionally, as along the South Fork of the Big Sur River, groves of fifty or more trees grow together amid other trees of the mixed evergreen forest. Smaller stands and scattered individuals are more common. James Griffin speculates that these Sierran conifers were once more widespread in the Santa Lucias, but in recent times have been increasingly restricted by wildfires. A warming climate over the past 10,000 years has probably also contributed to their range reduction.

Sargent Cypress   The Sargent cypress (*Cupressus sargentii*) grows mostly at inland locations throughout the California Coast Range, but it makes one of its closest approaches to the California coast in Big Sur's Alder Creek drainage. Extensive stands are common in the northern Coast Range, while small, scattered stands are the rule in the southern Coast Range. Most of the Sargent cypresses in the Santa Lucias are small and scrubby and are often surrounded by chaparral.

Serpentine soils form the nearly exclusive habitat of this cypress, and it is considered a serpentine endemic. According to botanist Clare Hardham, the groves in the Santa Lucias are found on serpentine soils along the Pine Mountain and King City faults, which are areas of numerous seeps and springs. The groves are at the headwaters of permanent or semipermanent streams and favor north-facing slopes. A number of water-loving plants such as sedges (*Carex* spp.) are often found with the trees in the dampest sites. The most accessible sites in the Santa Lucias are along the South Coast Ridge Road near the headwaters of Alder Creek and near Lions Den Camp. The Cruikshank Trail in upper Villa Creek passes through a stand of large cypresses that was severely burned in the 1985 Gorda fire.

Fossils suggest that Sargent cypress once grew over a very large area during the Pliocene epoch, 5–6 million years ago, when the climate was much moister than it is today. Paleobotanists Peter Raven and Daniel Axelrod believe that Sargent cypress became restricted to moist, serpentine soils as the drying climate forced it out of other areas. Near the springs, the Sargent cypress escapes competition from more drought-adapted plants that cannot tolerate the chemical conditions of the serpentine.

Monterey Cypress   Like the Monterey pine, the Monterey cypress (*Cupressus macrocarpa*) (fig. 153) is now a common planted tree along much of the California coast. At the time of the first European settlement in California, this cypress was found only in two areas in the

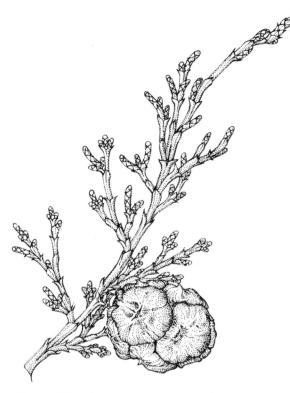

Figure 153. *Cupressus macrocarpa*, Monterey cypress

vicinity of Monterey. Similar to the Monterey pine, the Monterey cypress reveals where people have settled or built roads. All that remains of some of the homesteads in the Big Sur area are the giant cypresses and pines that the settlers planted, towering over rotting lumber and old fences.

UNDERSTORY OF THE MIXED EVERGREEN FOREST

The understory of the mixed evergreen forest is as variable as the trees that make up the canopy, and it is often influenced by shrub and herb species from neighboring plant communities. Pine–canyon live oak forests mingle with chamise, yerba santa, and wart-leaf ceanothus of the chaparral. The understory of the bay forests is especially sparse, due both to its extremely dense canopy and to the allelopathic (harmful chemical) effects of the fallen bay leaves. It is common to enter a dark

Figure 154. *Holodiscus discolor,* cream bush

bay forest and see only a few ferns and Douglas' iris pushing up through the decaying leaves and litter.

The common shrubs found throughout most forest types include poison oak, cream bush (*Holodiscus discolor*) (fig. 154), toyon, creeping snowberry, California coffeeberry, and several *Ceanothus* spp. Beneath the shrub layer are many ferns, flowers, and grasses. Bracken ferns grow on dry slopes and in grassy clearings, while California maidenhair (*Adiantum jordani*) (fig. 155), California polypody (*Polypodium californicum*) (fig. 156), and wood, chain, and sword ferns prefer the moist seeps, rock faces, and springs. California blackberry (*Rubus ursinus*) (fig. 157) also grows in moister areas.

The flowers that bloom here are more subtle than those of the grassland or chaparral, in keeping with the dark character of the forest. Cali-

Figure 155.   *Adiantum jordani,*
California maidenhair

Figure 156.   *Polypodium californicum,*
California polypody

Figure 157. *Rubus ursinus*, California blackberry

fornia hedge nettle, hound's tongue, Pacific pea, white globe lily (*Calo-chortus albus*) (fig. 158), redspot clarkia (*Clarkia speciosa*) (fig. 159), and woodland madia (*Madia madioides*) (fig. 160) all offer delicate blossoms. Those of the Douglas' iris (fig. 161), in contrast, are the most showy, with rich purple and white blossoms.

ANIMALS OF THE MIXED EVERGREEN FOREST

According to ornithologists John Davis and Alan Baldridge, the mixed evergreen forest is probably the most productive habitat for birds in this area. The insect fauna is diverse and numerous, attracting a large number of insectivorous birds. Gleaners, such as the chickadees, bushtits, and warblers, work their way through the broadleaf canopy, gleaning small insects from the undersides of the leaves and twigs. Other birds, such as the white-breasted nuthatch (*Sitta carolinensis*) (fig. 162) and

Figure 158.   *Calochortus albus*,
White globe lily

Figure 159.   *Clarkia speciosa*,
redspot clarkia

Figure 160. *Madia madioides,*
woodland madia

Figure 161. *Iris douglasiana,*
Douglas' iris

Figure 162.   *Sitta carolinen-sis*, white-breasted nuthatch

brown creeper, prefer to dig insects out of the crevices in the bark of tree trunks and limbs.

Insects are not the only source of food for birds. Madrone trees and several understory shrubs produce edible berries that attract large flocks. The fruits of California coffeeberry, toyon, poison oak, and madrone are quickly harvested by American robins, band-tailed pigeons, and cedar waxwings. A group of waxwings will sometimes launch a frenzied attack on a madrone full of ripe berries, gorging themselves and then moving on to the next tree. Acorns from the oaks also attract the acorn woodpecker, jays, and the common crow, creating a situation similar to that of the oak woodland. The mixed evergreen forest is also moister than most of the surrounding habitats, especially in the summer, and this attracts many breeding birds.

The large number of birds draws Cooper's hawks (fig. 163) and sharp-shinned hawks to these woods. These predators seem to appear out of no where, scattering a panicked bevy of quail or flock of bushtits and picking off a straggler as the birds seek cover. Warning cries from jays and crows are a good sign that a hawk is perched somewhere in the vicinity.

The jays and crows will also disclose the presence of an owl, often surrounding and harassing the predator until it is forced to leave. This behavior is known as *mobbing*. As many as a dozen birds will dive at a perched owl. When it eventually flies off, they follow it for a distance and make sure it leaves the territory. The great horned owl (fig. 164) is the most frequently heard and seen owl, and its horned silhouette on treetop or branch is a common twilight sight. A number of other owls also reside in the evergreen forest, including the spotted owl (*Strix occidentalis*), northern sawwhet owl (*Aegolius acadicus*), northern pygmy owl (*Glaucidium gnoma*), eastern screech owl (*Otus asio*), and flammulated owl (*O. flammeolus*).

Figure 163. *Accipiter cooperii*, Cooper's hawk

Figure 164. *Bubo virginianus*, great horned owl

Figure 165. *Colaptes auratus,* northern
flicker

Dead pines are important to many birds. Acorn woodpeckers use
them as granaries, leaving them riddled with holes from top to bottom.
Other woodpeckers seen on snags are the northern flicker (*Colaptes auratus*) (fig. 165) and the hairy woodpecker (*Picoides villosus*) (fig. 166).
Turkey vultures and other predatory birds have an affinity for snags as
roosting sites, using them as perches from which they scan surrounding
country. Purple martins (*Progne subis*) (fig. 167), acorn woodpeckers,
western bluebirds, and violet-green swallows (*Tachycineta thalassina*)
hollow out cavities in snags for nests. Olive-sided and ash-throated flycatchers (*Nuttallornis borealis* and *Myiarchus cinerascens*) can often be
seen darting after insects from perches on tall snags.

Some of the first ornithologists to report on the birds of the Santa
Lucia Range—H. O. Jenkins in 1906, and J. R. Pemberton and H. W.
Carriger in 1903–1905—saw mountain chickadees (*Parus gambeli*) on
the slopes of Cone Peak. The sightings were significant because these

Figure 166. *Picoides villosus*,
              hairy woodpecker

Figure 167. *Progne subis*,
              purple martin

birds are common residents of the pine forests of the Sierra Nevada and
are disjunct, like the sugar pines, in the Santa Lucia Range. These birds
are rare here and have not been noted since 1960. Flammulated owls,
also common in the pine forests of the Sierra Nevada, were first noted
in the Santa Lucias in 1966 and have since been recognized as summer

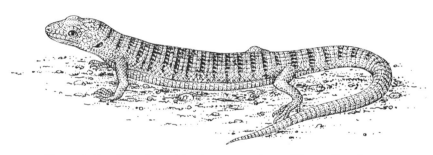

Figure 168.   *Elgaria multicarinatus*, southern alligator lizard

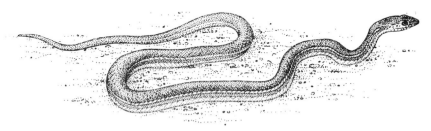

Figure 169.   *Masticophis lateralis*, striped racer

residents here. They nest in mixed evergreen forests above 1160 m (3800 ft).

Fallen wood and bark from dead pines is important for reptiles. Western fence lizards and southern alligator lizards (*Elgaria multicarinatus*) (fig. 168) sun themselves and scan surrounding territory from fallen logs. Western skinks, sharp-tailed snakes, western rattlesnakes, and other reptiles often retreat beneath fallen logs and other debris to avoid the midday heat in summer; they also hide there in cool weather when inactive. The shading canopy of conifers and hardwoods softens the sun on the forest floor, lowering the temperature so that snakes such as striped racers (fig. 169), western terrestrial garter snakes (fig. 170), gopher snakes, and California mountain kingsnakes can function during the summer days.

The deep duff that accumulates on the floor of mixed evergreen forests provides a microhabitat that remains cool and moist long after surrounding areas have become very dry. A similar habitat can be found beneath fallen bark and logs and inside rotting logs. Salamanders, which are highly moisture dependent, take advantage of these microhabitats to escape the summer drought.

Figure 170. *Thamnophis elegans*, western terrestrial garter snake

Figure 171. *Peromyscus maniculatus*, deer mouse

Mammals also take advantage of the diversified understory and accumulating duff. In a study at Big Creek Reserve, biologist Liz Block
found that pine–mixed hardwood forests supported more kinds of
mammals than any other vegetation she sampled. Deer mice (fig. 171),
dusky-footed woodrats, California pocket mice (*Perognathus californicus*), and rabbits are found in mixed evergreen forests. Western gray
squirrels and Merriam chipmunks are often abundant. These two species are both fairly omnivorous, eating a mix of nuts, berries, insects,
seeds, fungi, small mammals, and birds' eggs. Chipmunks go underground to establish burrows in tree roots and decaying stumps, while
the gray squirrel spends most of its life in the trees. Large squirrel nests
made of bark, twigs, and leaves are often seen high up on tree limbs.
Coyotes, gray foxes, bobcats, and mountain lions find ample prey here,
move through the habitat easily, and find plentiful stalking cover.

SUGGESTED READING

Barbour, M. G., and J. Major, 1988. *Terrestrial vegetation of California*. 2d ed. California Native Plant Society. Special Publication no. 9.

Bickford, C., and P. Rich, 1984. *Vegetation and flora of the Landels-Hill Big Creek Reserve*, 2d ed. Environmental Field Program Publication 15, University of California, Santa Cruz.

California Native Plant Society, 1988. *Inventory of rare and endangered vascular plants*, Special Publication #1, 4th ed. Berkeley.

Crampton, B., 1974. *Grasses in California*. California Natural History Guide 33. Berkeley: University of California Press.

Engles, E., ed. 1984. *The natural features of the Gamboa Point Properties, Monterey County, California*, Vol. 1. Environmental Field Program Publication 13, University of California, Santa Cruz.

Griffin, J. R., 1971. Oak regeneration in the upper Carmel Valley, California. *Ecology*, 52: 862–868.

Griffin, J. R., 1973. Valley oaks: The end of an era? *Fremontia*, 1(1): 5–9.

Griffin, J. R., 1975. *Plants of the highest Santa Lucia and Diablo range peaks, California*. U.S.D.A. Forest Service Research Paper PSW-110. Berkeley: Pacific Southwest Forest and Range Experiment Station.

Griffin, J. R., 1976. Regeneration in *Quercus lobata* savannas, Santa Lucia Mountains, California. *American Midland Naturalist* 995(2): 422–435.

Griffin, J. R., 1980. *The natural history of Hastings Reservation*. Unpublished manuscript on file at University of California Hastings Natural History Reservation, Carmel Valley, California.

Griffin, J. R., and W. B. Critchfield, 1976. *The distribution of forest trees in California*. U.S.D.A. Forest Service Research Paper PSW-82. Berkeley: Pacific Southwest Forest and Range Experiment Station.

Head, W. S. 1972. *The California chaparral*. Healdsburg, Calif.: Naturegraph Publishers.

Howitt, B. F., and J. T. Howell, 1964. The vascular plants of Monterey County, California. *The Wasmann Journal of Biology*, 22(1): 1–184.

Kruckeberg, A. R., 1984. *California serpentines: Flora, vegetation, geology, soils, and management problems*. Berkeley: University of California Press.

McMinn, H. E., 1974. *An illustrated manual of California shrubs*. Berkeley: University of California Press.

Mooney, H. A., and F. diCastri, 1973. *Mediterranean-type ecosystems*. Berlin: Springer-Verlag.

Munz, P. A., and D. D. Keck, 1968. *A California flora and supplement*. Berkeley: University of California Press.

Neihaus, T. F., and C. L. Ripper, 1976. *A field guide to Pacific states wildflowers*. Boston: Houghton-Mifflin.

Raven, P. H., 1966. *Native shrubs of southern California*. California Natural History Guide 15. Berkeley: University of California Press.

Ray, D. G., 1966. *Silvical characteristics of redwood*. U.S.D.A. Forest Service Research Paper PSW-28. Berkeley: Pacific Southwest Forest and Range Experiment Station.

Shreve, F., 1927. The vegetation of a coastal mountain range. *Ecology*, 8: 27−44.

Stebbins, G. L., 1978. Why are there so many rare plants in California? Part 1. Environmental factors. *Fremontia*, 5(4): 6−10.

Talley, S. N., 1974. The ecology of the Santa Lucia fir (*Abies bracteata*), a narrow endemic of California. Ph.D. Thesis, Department of Botany, Duke University, Durham, N.C.

White, K. L., 1966. Structure and composition of foothill woodland in central California. *Ecology*, 47: 229−237.

White, K. L., 1967. Native bunchgrass (*Stipa pulchra*) on Hastings Reservation, California. *Ecology*, 48: 949−955.

CHAPTER V

Fire Ecology

It is an awesome and spectacular event when wildfire sweeps over the mountainsides of Big Sur. The thick, dry brush, especially in summertime, ignites explosively as the flames climb up the steep slopes. Hardwood forests crackle and blaze, and even the redwood trees sometimes burn fiercely to their crowns. Homes are threatened and often destroyed. It seems an all-consuming and wholly destructive event. Yet, frightening as it is, wildfire is an intrinsic part of the ecology of the Big Sur area. In spite of massive efforts to extinguish all fires, virtually no part of the Santa Lucia Range has escaped fire in the past century.

Periodic fire is a factor in all Mediterranean ecosystems, where abundant winter rain encourages luxuriant growth in plants that the summer drought dries to tinder. Many plants are dry to begin with because they retain little moisture in their tissues so as to minimize their need for water. Also, many shrubs contain volatile oils that make them particularly flammable. Furthermore, the decomposing action of fungi and bacteria is inhibited by the dry climate, so that dead vegetation accumulates in large quantities. All these factors lead to the creation of a large amount of dry, dead and living vegetation that is ideal for carrying fire.

Fires have regularly burned in the Big Sur area for many thousands of years. The plants and animals that live here have adapted to fire in a remarkable variety of ways. People have also survived for millennia with fire. Ecologists and land managers once regarded fire as an alien and destructive factor in ecosystems, and past suppression of fires has significantly altered the character of the Big Sur landscape. But the perception of fire has changed radically in the past twenty years. People now realize that fire is a natural event that can be a beneficial tool for management purposes.

FIRE IN THE SANTA LUCIA RANGE

It is almost impossible to hike any distance in the Santa Lucia Range without seeing some evidence of fire. The evidence may be faint or glaringly obvious, depending on how long it has been since the last fire. On Pine Ridge, for example, the towering, blackened ponderosas that were killed during the Marble–Cone fire (1977) will be noticeable for decades. In the mixed evergreen forest, evidence of the Marble–Cone fire is less obvious because many of the oaks have resprouted and the understory is draped with vetch (*Vicia* spp.) and lush new growth.

In an area more recently burned, such as in the Rat Creek fire (1985), the brown foliage of singed redwood boughs still filled the ravines and canyons two years after the burn, and redwoods weakened at their bases were still toppling in the wind. A lush, green growth of whispering bells (*Emmenanthe penduliflora*), hedge nettle, and several types of vetch spread here amid the burned stems of coastal scrub. The chaparral became filled with new growth within two years, including large areas of blooming tree poppy. Although the dead stems of the fire were still obvious then, they are mostly hidden by now.

At the site of a grassland fire such as the Molera fire of 1986, the grasses were vibrant green soon after the fire, in contrast to the muted brownish green of nearby unburned grasslands. This is probably a consequence of the removal of mulch by the fire. Mulch—accumulated dead grass stalks—piles up in the absence of fire and may take several years to decay. This matt of dead material inhibits germination of new grass. The fire exposes the soil to sunlight and causes a burst of new growth. Increased nutrients after fire may also be a factor in creating the lush green growth. A year after the Molera fire, it was almost impossible to tell that the grasslands had burned.

The presence of very large trees that are fire sensitive, such as the Santa Lucia fir, indicate areas a fire has not burned for a long time. The largest canyon live oak and the largest Santa Lucia fir known to ecologist James Griffin in the Santa Lucias grow in lower Miller Canyon. They grow there, Griffin says, not because the habitat is particularly favorable but "because fuel and topographic conditions preclude all but minor ground fires."

In other areas, the only trace of fire may be charred, living tree trunks. Redwoods retain fire scars on their bark for decades after the surrounding forest growth shows no sign of fire. Blackened trunks on redwoods are the rule rather than the exception throughout the Santa Lucia Range.

Burned tree trunks provide clues of how often fires have burned an area. When a fire burns a tree, it leaves a scar in the tree's outermost growth rings. One of the best indications of the frequency of prehistoric fires is found in the fire scars of long-lived trees such as redwoods and pines. Counting the number of rings (which represent annual growth) between fire scars is an indication of the interval between fires, although short interval fires may not be noticeable in tree rings because scarring is slight or absent. Ecologists Talley and Griffin used this technique in the sugar pine forest on Junipero Serra Peak to date the major fires that have burned the forest over the past 300 years. They found that the time between fires was shortest before 1800, when the average interval was just 21 years. These frequent fires were probably relatively light and did not damage the pines, but actually enhanced their reproductive abilities.

Fire ecologist Jason Greenlee applied the same technique to redwood forests at Big Creek Reserve, concluding that the average period between fires exceeded seventy years. This figure does not contradict Talley and Griffin's findings in the sugar pine forest. Rather, it points up a basic fact of fire ecology: fire burns with different frequencies in different plant communities. Redwood forests are generally damper and cooler than pine forests and ignite less easily, leading to a lower frequency of fires.

In addition to lightning-caused fires, Native Americans in many parts of California deliberately used fires to make the land more productive (see chap. 7, Human History). The natives burned to improve wildlife habitat and to encourage the production of edible plants and seed-producing oaks and pines. Salinans and Costanoans (also known as Ohlone) periodically burned grassland and oak woodland, and these fires must have spread into the mountains at least occasionally. The Esselen of the Big Sur area probably burned in a similar fashion.

Human-caused and lightning-caused fires continued during the Spanish–Mexican period (1800–1847), but records of how often and where these fires occurred were not kept. Spanish diaries from the period indicate that natives continued burning. Other records indicate that loss of summer and fall livestock forage led the missions to ban native burning. As the natives left their homelands to join the missions, much of the Big Sur coast outside the northern ranchos became very sparsely inhabited during this period and was probably subject to less frequent fire than before European settlement.

American settlers resumed the practice of igniting fires in Big Sur in the mid-1800s to clear land for agriculture and settlement, to facilitate the passage of livestock, and to expand grazing land. Ecologists debate whether the settlers burned more or less land than the natives had. Gilbert Harlan, grandson of homesteader Wilbur Harlan, remembers that the settlers in the Lucia area lit fires every fall, after the first light rains. Not all settlers burned, however. George Gamboa, grandson of homesteader Sabino Gamboa, recalled that his father and uncle were "terrified of fire" and never burned. They cleared brush by hand instead.

Burning by settlers, including prospectors, hunters, and ranchers, was sometimes indiscriminate. Some fires may have gotten out of control and caused the huge wildfires reported in newspaper accounts and government reports around the turn of the century. In 1894, a fire burned "for weeks, covering the upper parts of every permanent stream in the central [Santa Lucia] mountains." As many as 20,000 ha (50,000 acres) burned in a human-caused fire in July 1903, and a 60,000-ha (150,000-acre) fire occurred in 1906.

The U.S. Forest Service took charge of all public land in the Big Sur area in 1907 when the Monterey National Forest (now the Monterey District of the Los Padres National Forest) was created. The practice of deliberate burning abruptly stopped and was replaced by a policy of strict fire suppression. Regulations forbade residents from burning wildlands. Homesteader George Harlan was one of the few who persisted in burning, and he was arrested and fined.

The number of fires that burned in the mountains dropped markedly at this time even though suppression was difficult in the rugged Santa Lucias. According to U.S. Forest Service records, an average of 3200 ha (7900 acres) of the Monterey District of the Los Padres National Forest burned each year through the 1920s. The annual burn declined to about 160 ha (400 acres) by the 1960s as fire detection and suppression techniques became more effective.

More than 70 years of fire suppression led to a dangerous accumulation of dead and live vegetation that was extremely prone to burning. Large fires began to occur once again in the Santa Lucias in the 1970s and 1980s. The human-caused Buckeye fire burned 24,000 ha (60,000 acres) in the southern Santa Lucias in 1970. In 1977, fires originating with four lightning strikes merged to become the famous Marble–Cone fire. This was the second largest fire ever recorded in California, covering 72,000 ha (178,000 acres). More recently, on July 6, 1985, lightning strikes on Big Creek Reserve and on Gorda Mountain started two fires: the Rat Creek fire, which burned over 24,000 ha (60,000 acres) in the central portion of the range, and the 8000-ha (20,000-acre) Gorda fire.

Many ecologists consider it unlikely that such large fires could have occurred if small fires had been allowed to burn periodically. Frequent small fires can reduce and break up the continuity of fire-prone vegetation, limiting the range and intensity of fires. Talley and Griffin found that the Marble–Cone fire was the most intense fire to burn the pines on Junipero Serra Peak in more than three centuries, and they cite the buildup of fuel for the past 80 years as the most important factor leading to its high intensity. The entire population of sugar pines on the peak was burned. Old trees that had withstood many fires finally perished in the intense heat of this blaze.

Similarly, the pines on Pine Ridge suffered their worst burning ever during this fire. Although pine seedlings are scattered throughout the area, large parts of the Pine Ridge pine forest will not regenerate for a long time and will probably be replaced by scrub. Coulter pines suffered high mortality as well. Some pines on rocky bluffs and north-facing slopes survived and new trees originated from their seed. There is evidence that conifers such as these were once more widespread in the Santa Lucias, but in recent times have been increasingly restricted by wildfires. A warming climate over the past 10,000 years has probably contributed to a restriction of these trees, but human intervention with fire frequencies has also had a strong effect.

The human alteration of fire cycles over the past century may have a major and lasting effect on the character of the vegetation in the entire Santa Lucia Range. The present pattern of infrequent, very hot fires seems to be slowly reducing the range of conifers in the area. Many hardwood forests of large, old trees are being replaced by dense stands of even-aged, small-diameter trees. Fire-resistant shrublands may be expanding at the expense of more fire-sensitive forest types. These changes are gradually shaping a new vegetational pattern in the mountains, and the fire policies of the coming years will determine what the range will look like for decades to come.

FIRE BEHAVIOR

How a fire behaves depends primarily on how much dead and live vegetation, or fuel, is available to burn. The amount of fuel, or *fuel load,* is proportional to the amount of time since the last fire occurred, but other factors contribute as well. For example, an unusual fall of heavy, wet snow in the Santa Lucias in the winter of 1974 crushed a great many shrub and tree limbs. These added to the already high fuel loads that had accumulated in the absence of fire. In addition, the broken branches leaned to the ground and acted as "fuse limbs" during the Marble—Cone fire, carrying fire from the ground up into the crowns of trees.

The moisture content of fuels also determines the behavior of fires. Moisture levels are highest in mid-winter in Big Sur and decline drastically over the summer months, making late summer and fall the times when fire is most likely to start and spread. Severe droughts in the winters of 1975–1976 and 1976–1977 dried plants until their moisture content was extremely low. Fuels were further dried by the normal summer drought, creating the optimal conditions that occurred for the Marble—Cone fire. Exceptionally wet winters can have the opposite effect, and fog also tends to keep fuels moist, lessening their likelihood of igniting. Heavy fog virtually extinguished parts of the Rat Creek fire near the coast and has probably kept low elevation coastal areas free of fire for long periods. Shaded areas such as north-facing slopes and canyon bottoms also retain moisture longer than south-facing slopes and fuel tends to burn less easily.

Fire spreads more rapidly uphill than downhill, and the steeper the slope, the more pronounced the effect. In the steep terrain of Big Sur, fires tend to "run" very quickly uphill and are practically impossible to stop. However, they slow at ridgecrests and move slowly down the other side. Attempts to stop fires are made at these points where the fire is slow moving. Nearly every major ridgecrest in the Santa Lucia Range bears a scar of a bulldozer cut placed there to stop a fire.

Wind increases the oxygen flow to fires, making them burn hotter and spread faster. The consistent northwest winds coming off the ocean along the Big Sur coast can be especially significant in this regard. The daily increase in afternoon wind was an anathema to firefighters in the

Rat Creek fire. Wind speed also increases when moving through narrow ravines or canyons, which funnel wind into a blast that can make a fire race explosively. Its many deep, narrow canyons and steep ravines make Big Sur an ideal place for this to occur.

Depending on the combination of all these factors, fire burns with widely different behavior at different times and places. While on one slope it is burning quickly through dense brush, it may be smoldering downhill on the opposite slope. Because of this, even large fires such as the Marble–Cone and Rat Creek fires did not burn every place severely or uniformly. Islands of lightly burned and unburned vegetation remained in the midst of the charred landscape. The effects of fire on plants, animals, and soils vary with a fire's behavior.

EFFECTS OF FIRE

Soil erosion is one of the most visible effects of fire. Removal of vegetation by fire leaves soils exposed to sunlight, wind, and rain. The soil cannot readily absorb the direct impact of raindrops. In the Marble–Cone burn, James Griffin noted rills 30 cm (10 in.) deep incised into slopes following rain, and nearby drainage channels were eroded 50 cm (20 in.) deep. Channels several meters deep were cut into lower slopes.

High runoff after fire in chaparral areas is also due to the soils in chaparral becoming water repellent after fire. Water-repellent organic compounds are leached from the leaf litter of plants such as chamise and mountain mahogany. During a fire, the compounds vaporize and are distilled downward in the soil where they condense into a water-repellent layer. Rainwater penetrates the upper layers of the soil and then moves downhill when it contacts this subsurface layer. When heavy, brief rainfall occurs under these circumstances, the surface layer weakens and slides downhill *en masse*. The resulting watery mass of soil sometimes concentrates in drainages to start mudflows, which quickly carry away enormous amounts of soil.

Big Sur residents became acutely aware of this effect during winter rains following the 1972 Molera fire. This was a relatively small fire, but a burst of heavy rainfall on water-repellent soils in a very short period—more than 1 cm (0.4 in.) in fifteen minutes along the Big Sur River—triggered massive mudflows in Pheneger Creek and other small tributaries of Big Sur River. Several thousand cubic yards of mud overflowed the streambanks and swept away cars and buried houses and buildings along the river.

Mudflows are nothing new to the Big Sur area. Many layers of old mudflows lay beneath these recent flows. Using various dating techniques (described on p. 133), geologist Lionel Jackson determined that massive mudflows occurred in the same vicinity of the 1972 mudflows at least three times between 1370 and the late 1700s.

Increased runoff and sedimentation after fire has drastic effects on streams. No habitat is altered more radically than streambeds following fire. Where streams drop steeply, the stream bottom is completely scoured of algae and invertebrates, and fish are flushed out by the high currents. Where the turbid water slows, deep pools fill with gravel; pools on Big Creek more than 4.5 m (15 ft) deep were filled almost completely following the Rat Creek fire. Yet creeks also recover from the changes and are by no means permanently destroyed. Fish were numerous in coastal drainages only two years after the Rat Creek fire. Steelhead spawned in new gravel beds, and the pools that were filled were gradually flushed clear again.

Exposure of burned-over soils to wind also leads to increased erosion. Griffin noted areas where ash and soil were blown off steep slopes in severe winter winds following the Marble–Cone fire. Significant soil erosion after fire also takes place on steep slopes without wind and even before any rain has fallen. This is particularly noticeable on chaparral-covered slopes, where gravel soil slips downhill in a process known as *dry creep*. Griffin noted significant soil loss due to dry creep immediately after the Marble–Cone fire on slopes steeper than 27 degrees.

Perhaps the most important effect of fire in Big Sur's ecosystems is on soil nutrients. Levels of essential plant nutrients are marginal at best in most soils in the Santa Lucias, and as vegetation cover increases after fire, more and more of the scant nutrients are bound up in living and dead plant tissues. This leaves the nutrients inaccessible for new plant growth. In humid areas such as tropical rainforests, plant and animal remains are quickly broken down and recycled, but this activity is very slow in arid Mediterranean climates. Fire is very important because it releases the nutrients back into the soil where a new generation of plant growth can use them to grow and reproduce.

Periodic fire is thus essential to keeping Big Sur's soils fertile. Nutrient levels are increased in the soil after fire in several ways. Nitrogen, the most critical plant nutrient, volatilizes at relatively low temperatures (about 200°C or 400°F), and is easily lost to the atmosphere during fire. (Temperatures of 700–1000°C, or 1300–1800°F, have been recorded at the ground surface in chaparral fires.) But this loss is compensated for after fire when nitrogen-fixing soil organisms in the soil increase in number. Some bacteria produce nitrates from ammonium salts in warm soils exposed to sunlight following fire, while other types of bacteria in nodules on plant roots "fix" nitrogen, transforming atmospheric nitrogen into a usable form. Root nodules are especially abundant in legumes, which are encouraged by decreased soil acidity after fire. Vetch is an especially common legume that thrives after fire in Big Sur's scrub and woodland habitats, where it enriches the soil with nitrogen.

Other important plant nutrients, including calcium, phosphorus, potash, and magnesium, volatilize at higher temperatures than nitrogen and remain in the ash on the soil following fire. Runoff and erosion during winter rains after fire can result in a loss of these nutrients, and the ash can also be carried away by wind during and after fire. If the ash layer is not washed away or leached into the soil, however, it elevates the levels of these nutrients for several years after fire.

PLANT ADAPTATIONS TO FIRE

Plants have adapted to fire in two basic ways: some are equipped to survive fire, while others avoid fire by growing where fire is least likely to occur. Santa Lucia firs, for example, live in high, rocky ravines that lack the fuel to carry hot fire, and they usually escape severe fire damage. Maples, alders, sycamores, and other water-loving plants also effectively escape hot fires by living in moist canyon and ravine bottoms. Over the course of centuries, hot fires burn much less frequently in these areas than in exposed brushlands or forest, but they still occur occasionally. The suppression of fires may make these areas more fire prone by allowing fuels to accumulate in them. The buildup of fuel before the Rat Creek fire was so great and the fuel so dry that riparian vegetation burned easily in many places.

There are two strategies in plants that are adapted to survive fire: seeding and sprouting. Some seeders produce plentiful seed early in life so that it is abundant in the soil when fire destroys the parent plant. Seeds of these plants are able to withstand very high temperatures, and some even require heat to germinate. With the first rains after fire, the seeds germinate in ideal conditions: reduced competition from other plants, increased sunlight and nutrients, and decreased soil toxins. Also, the blackened ash on the soil increases heat absorption and prolongs the growing season on burned-over soils.

Sprouters concentrate their energy on developing a large underground burl or root crown early in life. When fire (or any other disturbance, such as logging) damages or destroys the aboveground plant parts, the root crown sprouts a new generation of stems. Sprouts may appear within weeks after fire if stored nutrients and soil moisture are sufficient.

Some plants can only sprout and others can only seed. Chamise uses both strategies. California coffeeberry, coyote bush, California sagebrush, and toyon are common sprouters of the coastal scrub, while chamise, tree poppy, and mountain mahogany are sprouters of the chaparral. Many large trees also sprout from a root crown or directly from the bole of the tree. Sprouting trees include redwood, live oaks, tanoak, and madrone.

EFFECTS OF FIRE ON ANIMALS

Fire is not nearly as destructive of animal populations as most people believe. Some animals do die during fire, but the overall benefit to animal communities after fire outweighs the losses. The increase in food plants and the greater mobility afforded by the clearing of dense vegetation benefit most animals in the long run. Animals cannot survive high heat nor can they regenerate like plants do, but they can survive a fire in a number of ways.

Most small animals, including lizards, snakes, small mammals, and large insects, can crawl into underground tunnels or burrows to escape the heat of fire. It is remarkably cool only a few inches from the soil surface during most fires because of the insulating qualities of the soil and because most of the fire's heat rises up into the atmosphere. Oxygen is a different matter, however. Fire rapidly consumes oxygen, so much that animals who are cool and safe in burrows may suffocate for lack of it. Combustion also produces poisonous gases, such as carbon monoxide, that can be fatal to animals. These effects are minimal if a fire moves quickly over an area.

Large animals can flee, and most are aware of the dangers of fire. Some may leave too late, however. Woodrats, for example, may wait until their stick nests are on fire before fleeing. It may be the woodrats' well-known attachment to their home territories that compels them to wait so long. The landscape was littered with rat carcasses after the Rat

Creek fire passed. They were concentrated on roads, trails, and other cleared and level areas. They probably congregated in these areas because fuel was more scarce there or because gravity rolled them there. They died from indirect heat or by suffocation because few were burned.

Rabbits, like woodrats, fall into a category of animals that are too large to escape underground and too small to flee quickly from the fire. These animals may suffer high mortality during fire. Deer can escape more easily, but can be caught by fast-moving fires. After the Rat Creek fire, a group of five bucks was found together in a pile with several domestic cows in the corner of a clearing near Lucia; this was an area where the fire had moved very quickly. In general, very few dead deer were found, and healthy deer browsed in burned-over land almost immediately after the fire.

Birds usually escape fire easily, but a few dead Steller's jays were seen at Big Creek. Red-tailed hawks were observed very near an advancing front of the Rat Creek fire, apparently hunting rats and rabbits that were fleeing the blaze.

There is a shift toward a greater abundance of animal life after fire, but some species may become less common. Wrentits and other brush-adapted birds may decrease until shrubs develop. Woodrats and brush rabbits may take many years to reach their prefire abundance; recolonization is especially slow when these animals must travel long distances after large fires. Overall, though, the increase in young, edible plants greatly increases animal activities and numbers for several years after fire.

FIRE MANAGEMENT

The U.S. Forest Service is responsible for managing fire over most of the Big Sur area. The era of Smokey the Bear, with its emphasis on the negative aspects of fire, still lingers in management practices. But land managers are recognizing the importance of fire and are beginning to implement it as a management tool. After eighty years of fire suppression and fuel accumulation, changing to a more fire-tolerant policy is not easy, especially because of the enormous amounts of fuel that have accumulated in that period. Fire suppression remains a primary function of the Forest Service, and rightly so, since increasing human developments need protection.

However, the practice of lighting fires to manage wildlands, once used by natives and settlers alike, is again being employed throughout the west. The imprecise methods of natives and settlers are not appropriate now that homes and private property are scattered throughout the Santa Lucias. Thus, the modern procedure has developed into a science. Only small, carefully monitored fires that can be controlled are set. The primary goal of these controlled burns is to minimize the fire hazard by reducing the amount of fuel in the area. Benefits to the ecosystem result as well since wildlife habitat is improved and plants are stimulated to reproduce.

Controlled burns in the Santa Lucia Range are usually set in the fall after rain has slightly dampened fuels. Spring burns are also sometimes used. Fire is started only under optimum conditions for the desired intensity of fire, with sufficient personnel on hand to keep it contained. Over 800 ha (2000 acres) of the Santa Lucias have been burned with controlled fire, most of them in the vicinity of the Nacimiento River watershed. But there are also hundreds of thousands of acres of land that need to be burned. It is a costly process (even though it may be cheaper in the long run than fire suppression), and the U.S. Forest Service cannot possibly keep pace with the need. Controlled fire is nearly impossible in the Ventana Wilderness because of the lack of access. Private lands are seldom burned because of lack of expertise and funding.

In some areas, such as Yellowstone National Park, fires that start by natural causes are allowed to burn under certain circumstances. This is not feasible in the Santa Lucias because of the extreme volatility of the fuel types and the nearby presence of homes and businesses.

Wildfires, traumatic as they are to the human community, will continue to be part of the normal course of events in the Big Sur area unless the limitations on controlled fire discussed here are overcome. People will have to continue to live with fire, protecting their homes with wide zones of cleared land and avoiding building in extremely fire-prone vegetation or in mudflow channels or floodplains. Increasing support should be given to controlled burning so that one day it can be widely used to maintain ecosystems and to minimize extensive, damaging fires.

SUGGESTED READING

Agee, J. K., ed., 1979. *Fire and fuel management in Mediterranean-climate ecosystems: Research priorities and programmes.* UNESCO, Man and the Biosphere Technical Notes 11.

Biswell, H. H., 1989. *Prescribed burning in California wildlands vegetation management.* Berkeley: University of California Press.

Boerner, R. E. J., 1982. Fire and nutrient cycling in temperate ecosystems. *Bioscience*, 32(3): 187–192.

Cleveland, G. B., 1977. Marble Cone fire: Effect on erosion. *California Geology*, 30(12): 267–271.

Griffin, J. R., 1978. *Vegetation damage, Marble Cone fire, Los Padres National Forest, Junipero Serra Peak, Report 1.* U.S.D.A. Forest Service Research Paper PSW-77. Berkeley: Pacific Southwest Forest and Range Experiment Station.

Hanes, T. L., 1971. Succession after fire in the chaparral of southern California. *Ecological Monographs* 41(1): 27–52.

CHAPTER VI

Big Sur Fauna Overview

INTRODUCTION

There are not many places in the world where one can hike in the woods and stumble upon a deer carcass buried by a mountain lion. Or from an ocean cliff watch gray whales mate a few hundred meters offshore. Or see golden eagles snatch squirrels from the mouths of their burrows. Big Sur is a place where one can experience these and many other exciting wildlife encounters, all within a relatively small geographic area. The diversity of habitats, the productivity of the marine and terrestrial environments, and the wild and inaccessible character of the landscape all combine to make the region extremely rich in wildlife.

Most animals are found in one or a few plant communities, and these species are discussed in the appropriate sections in chapters 3 and 4. Gophers and western meadowlarks, for example, are described in the grassland and oak woodland sections. This chapter, in contrast, provides a quick overview of the amphibians, reptiles, birds, and mammals found in Big Sur, including species lists, a review of the latest faunal surveys in Big Sur, and general points regarding unusual or important wildlife. Excluded here are the marine animals, which were discussed in chapter 3, Big Sur Shoreline.

REPTILES AND AMPHIBIANS

The small number of reptile and amphibian species found in Big Sur runs contrary to the otherwise strong trend of biotic richness and diversity found here. The *herpetofauna* (reptile and amphibian fauna) of Big

Sur has not been systematically surveyed, but studies have been conducted at Big Creek Reserve and Hastings Natural History Reservation. Herpetologist James Hanken found nine amphibians and eighteen reptiles at Hastings. Only five amphibians and sixteen reptiles have been reported from Big Creek Reserve and its neighboring properties by herpetologists J. C. Carothers and Anthony Draeger. Most of these species are common and widespread throughout California, and the majority were discussed earlier in the individual plant community descriptions (see chap. 4). Table 12 lists the common species and their Latin names.

An intriguing explanation for this lack of species diversity has been put forth by herpetologist Kay Yanev, and her scenario is a good example of how climate, geology, and biology can combine to determine the distribution of animals. Central to Yanev's ideas is that the Santa Lucia Range was not always located where it is today. The rocks that compose the mountains have drifted northward during the past 30 million years and were often submerged or formed offshore islands during that time. Yanev proposes that a general warming trend in the climate that began about 10 million years ago eliminated cool climate species from this archipelago. Subsequent cooling then further reduced the herpetofauna by eliminating warm climate species.

When the mountains became connected to the mainland, recolonization of the archipelago was slow for several reasons. A seaway persisted to the north near Monterey Bay until Pleistocene time, forming a barrier to migration. Also, the moist climate of the coastal mountains discouraged migration of dry climate animals from the arid east. Finally, the height and ruggedness of the range were themselves barriers to dispersal. The consequence of this history is a herpetofauna that includes relatively few species.

The overlap and intermixing of northern and southern biotas in the Big Sur area, discussed in detail in chapters 3 and 4, is evident in the herpetofauna. Anthony Draeger reported three species on the Gamboa Point properties that seem to be intergrades between northern and southern subspecies of reptiles and amphibians. He identified intergrades of red salamander, fence lizard, and western rattlesnake.

The Big Sur area also includes an endemic salamander, the Santa Lucia slender salamander (*Batrachoseps pacificus luciae*). Yanev believes this salamander has evolved in the Santa Lucias in the past 8–10 million years. The sagebrush lizard, found in isolated patches throughout the upper elevations of the Santa Lucias, is an example of a disjunct species. This lizard may eventually evolve into a unique species if its geographic isolation there continues.

TABLE 12. REPTILES AND AMPHIBIANS OF THE BIG SUR AREA

Common Name	Genus/Species
Amphibians	
Tiger salamander	*Ambystoma tigrinum*
Arboreal salamander	*Aneides lugubris*
California slender salamander	*Batrachoseps attenuatus*
Pacific slender salamander	*Batrachoseps pacificus*
Western toad	*Bufo boreas*
Red salamander	*Ensatina eschscholtzii*
Pacific tree frog	*Hyla regilla*
Red-legged frog	*Rana aurora*
Foothill yellow-legged frog	*Rana boylei*
Coast Range newt	*Taricha torosa*
Reptiles	
Racer	*Coluber constrictor*
Sharp-tailed snake	*Contia tenuis*
Western rattlesnake	*Crotalus viridis*
Ringneck snake	*Diadophis punctatus*
Common kingsnake	*Lampropeltis getulus*
California mountain kingsnake	*Lampropeltis zonata*
Striped racer	*Masticophis lateralis*
Gopher snake	*Pituophis melanoleucus*
Long-nosed snake	*Rhinocheilus lecontei*
Western terrestrial garter snake	*Thamnophis elegans*
Common garter snake	*Thamnophis sirtalis*
California legless lizard	*Anniella pulchra*
Western whiptail	*Cnemidophorus tigris*
Western skink	*Eumeces skiltonianus*
Southern alligator lizard	*Elgaria multicarinatus*
Coast horned lizard	*Phrynosoma coronatum*
Western fence lizard	*Sceloporus occidentalis*
Sagebrush lizard	*Sceloporus graciosus*
Side-blotched lizard	*Uta stansburiana*
Western pond turtle	*Clemmys marmorata*

When looking for reptiles or amphibians in Big Sur, it is good to keep in mind a few points about their habitat needs. Most lizards and snakes bask on rock outcrops or logs until they are warm enough to move about efficiently. Pond turtles and frogs sun themselves on the banks of streams, sometimes leaving parts of their bodies in the water to achieve the proper temperature. Newts and salamanders adjust their body temperature by contact with the duff or soil.

As a consequence of their temperature regulating requirements, reptiles and amphibians are most abundant where a range of microclimates is available to them. Grasslands are generally the least populated by these animals because they offer little shelter from the sun or the cold. Reptiles and amphibians in grasslands tend to live around rock piles or dead wood where they can find shelter. Partially sunny forests provide a wide range of environmental conditions and are rich in reptiles and amphibians. Patchy sunlight and shade, plentiful deadfall, and moist leaf litter and duff create a range of temperatures and humidities. Scrubby vegetation, although drier and warmer than forests, also provides the necessary microclimatic variation.

BIRDS

INTRODUCTION

Big Sur, quite simply, is a great place for birdwatchers. One blustery December afternoon near Andrew Molera State Park, we observed eight species of raptors within about 30 minutes from one spot. A pair of black-shouldered kites were hunting mice, a golden eagle (fig. 172) dove after ground squirrels, several red-tailed hawks (fig. 173) and turkey vultures circled high overhead, two northern harriers cruised low over the scrub, a rough-legged hawk perched on a fencepost, and two American kestrels pursued mice or grasshoppers near the roadside. Also, a pair of red-shouldered hawks were heard calling from the riparian woodland along the Big Sur River. Such days are not common, but this example illustrates Big Sur's great potential for birdlovers.

Much of Big Sur's bird life is still a mystery because details of distribution and population size are hard to obtain from the rugged backcountry and inaccessible coastline. The entire area has yet to be systematically surveyed, but piecing together several localized studies gives a good idea of the region's great diversity of avifauna (bird species).

Of the more than 500 species found in California, ornithologist Don Roberson (1985) lists an impressive 427 species that occur in Monterey

Figure 172. *Aquila chrysaetos*, golden eagle

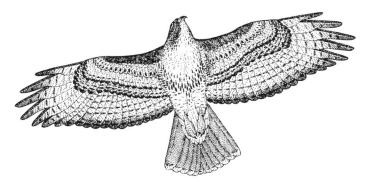

Figure 173. *Buteo jamaicensis*, red-tailed hawk

County, ranking the county fourth in California behind San Diego, Los Angeles, and Santa Barbara counties in number of species. Studies at Big Creek Reserve by ornithologists Fiona Wilson, David Melchert, and R. Cull revealed a total of 109 species for that area, but this work does not include fall migrants and wintering birds nor the seabirds and shorebirds. *Birds of Point Lobos* (Frincke and Francis, 1984) lists about 160 species that occur on this small reserve, which is located just north of Big Sur. A review of forty-two years of census work at Hastings Reserve, located inland from the coast in the upper Carmel Valley, is more thorough and chronicles the occurrence there of 166 species (Davis et al., 1980). Thus, probably at least 200 to 275 species are found in the Big Sur region, including some of the open-ocean birds. Table 13 lists

TABLE 13. BIRDS OF THE BIG SUR AREA (COMMON NAMES)

Nearshore and rocky shore

Red-throated loon
Pied-billed grebe
Western grebe
Double-crested cormorant
Pelagic cormorant
Great egret
Greater scaup
Surf scoter
Red-breasted merganser
Common murre
Marbled murrelet
Common loon
Eared grebe
Brown pelican
Brandt's cormorant
Great blue heron
Snowy egret
Lesser scaup
White-winged scoter
Peregrine falcon
Pigeon guillemot

Rocky shore intertidal and sandy beach

Black oystercatcher
Wandering tattler
Snowy plover
Killdeer
Whimbrel
Ruddy turnstone
Surfbird
Sanderling
Least sandpiper
Dunlin
Long-billed dowitcher
Bonaparte's gull
Mew gull
California gull

Rocky shore intertidal and sandy beach (cont.)

Thayer's gull
Glaucous-winged gull
Elegant tern
Common tern
Willet
Black-bellied plover
Semipalmated plover
Spotted sandpiper
Marbled godwit
Black turnstone
Red knot
Western sandpiper
Baird's sandpiper
Short-billed dowitcher
Red-necked phalarope
Heerman's gull
Ring-billed gull
Herring gull
Western gull
Caspian tern
Arctic tern
Forster's tern

Coastal scrub and chaparral

California quail
Greater roadrunner
Anna's hummingbird
Allen's hummingbird
Black phoebe
Ash-throated flycatcher
Bushtit
House wren
Wrentit
Rufous-sided towhee
Rufous-crowned sparrow
Black-chinned sparrow
Fox sparrow

Coastal scrub and chaparral
(cont.)

Golden-crowned sparrow
American goldfinch
Mountain quail
Common poorwill
Costa's hummingbird
Common flicker
Dusky flycatcher
Scrub jay
Bewick's wren
Blue-gray gnatcatcher
California thrasher
California towhee
Song sparrow
Sage sparrow
Lincoln's sparrow
White-crowned sparrow
Lazuli bunting

Grassland

American kestrel
Burrowing owl
Horned lark
Savannah sparrow
Western meadowlark
Say's phoebe
Barn owl
Western kingbird
Lark sparrow
Grasshopper sparrow
Brewer's blackbird

Riparian woodland
and thickets

Common merganser
Black-chinned hummingbird
Downy woodpecker
Chestnut-backed chickadee
Canyon wren
Swainson's thrush

Riparian woodland
and thickets (cont.)

Nashville warbler
MacGillivray's warbler
Wilson's warbler
Red-shouldered hawk
Belted kingfisher
Black phoebe
Rock wren
American dipper
Orange-crowned warbler
Yellow warbler
Common yellowthroat
Yellow-breasted chat

Open air

Turkey vulture
Northern harrier
Golden eagle
Black swift
White-throated swift
Tree swallow
Northern rough-winged
  swallow
Barn swallow
Black-shouldered kite
Red-tailed hawk
Prairie falcon
Vaux's swift
Purple martin
Violet-green swallow
Cliff swallow

Redwood forest

Spotted owl
Brown creeper
Swainson's thrush
Varied thrush
Steller's jay
Winter wren
Hermit thrush

TABLE 13. (*cont.*)

Oak woodland and hardwood forest	*Oak woodland and hardwood forest (cont.)*
Sharp-shinned hawk	Warbling vireo
California quail	Chipping sparrow
Band-tailed pigeon	Northern oriole
Western screech owl	Lesser goldfinch
Cooper's hawk	
Mountain quail	*Mixed evergreen and coniferous forests*
Mourning dove	
Great horned owl	Flammulated owl
Northern saw-whet owl	Spotted owl
Acorn woodpecker	Olive-sided flycatcher
Nuttall's woodpecker	Steller's jay
Pacific-slope flycatcher	Red-breasted nuthatch
Yellow-billed magpie	Brown creeper
Chestnut-backed chickadee	Western bluebird
White-breasted nuthatch	Cedar waxwing
Loggerhead shrike	Townsend's warbler
Hutton's vireo	Western tanager
Black-throated gray warbler	Brown-headed cowbird
Dark-eyed junco	Pine siskin
House finch	Northern pygmy owl
Lawrence's goldfinch	Hairy woodpecker
Lewis' woodpecker	Western wood pewee
Red-breasted sapsucker	Mountain chickadee
Common flicker	Pygmy nuthatch
Scrub jay	Golden-crowned kinglet
American crow	American robin
Plain titmouse	Yellow-rumped warbler
Ruby-crowned kinglet	Hermit warbler
Solitary vireo	Black-headed grosbeak
	Purple finch

the common names of these birds under the general environment where they occur most often.

There are several reasons for this great diversity. Big Sur's coastal location puts it on the migration route of many western birds, and the mild climate allows many species to winter here. The area remains relatively wild and undisturbed, an important criterion for many birds. And most significant, perhaps, is Big Sur's great variety in topography, vegetation, and habitats. Along the coast, for example, the continental shelf drops off sharply and provides upwelling currents that are rich in food. These currents attract flocks of open-ocean birds, such as shearwaters and jaegers, that can sometimes be seen from Highway 1. Closer to shore, extensive kelp forests and productive fisheries support many diving and wading birds, including cormorants, grebes, pelicans, and herons. The rocky shoreline, cliffs, and offshore seastacks provide rich feeding grounds and nesting sites for seabirds and shorebirds such as oystercatchers, turnstones, gulls, and murres. These were discussed in some detail in chapter 3.

Land birds find ample food and shelter among Big Sur's many terrestrial plant communities, and Big Sur's great allure to birdwatchers lies in the fact that one can quickly move from one type of bird habitat to another and see a correspondingly different set of birds. The only major bird habitats lacking in Big Sur that are found elsewhere in Monterey County are the extensive marshlands, sloughs, and freshwater ponds to the north. It is good to keep in mind, as local ornithologist John Davis points out, that some birds, such as the western meadowlarks in the grasslands, are restricted to just one plant community, while others, such as the great horned owls, are seen in virtually every plant community.

The description of plant communities in chapter 4 presented most of the typical birds that are associated with each plant community, while part II highlights specific sites that offer good birdwatching.

SENSITIVE AND ENDANGERED BIRD SPECIES

Big Sur is or was home to several endangered species and is a haven for many other birds with declining populations. California condors and bald eagles used to breed here, and today the eagle is a rare migrant along this coast. This bird was more common here prior to the construction of Highway 1, and there were once nesting pairs in Lafler and Torre canyons during the early 1930s. A number of bald eagles spend winters at Lake San Antonio, located in the southeastern Santa Lucia Range. Captive-bred eagles have been reintroduced to the central Big Sur coast, but the program is still too young to judge if it will be successful.

The last confirmed California condor sighting in the Big Sur area was near Mount Mars in 1980. The last remaining wild condors were captured in the mountains southeast of Santa Barbara in the late 1980s,

Figure 174.   *Falco peregrinus,* peregrine falcon

with the goal of breeding them and then reintroducing a stable population into the wild. Two condors were reintroduced into the wild in early
1992. Later in the year, one was found dead of unknown causes, casting
a shadow on the hopes of establishing a wild population of these rare
birds. However, the captive breeding program continues. If the program
is successful, it remains to be seen whether the condors will reclaim Big
Sur as part of their range. (The decline of this species, along with that
of the brown pelican and peregrine falcon, is discussed in more detail in
chapter 8, Changes in the Big Sur Environment.)

Big Sur's importance to many species of resident and migratory raptors is worthy of note. Raptors, or birds of prey such as hawks, falcons,
owls, and vultures, can often be seen here in relatively large numbers
and great diversity. Such groupings sometimes occur in winter on the
marine terraces near Point Sur, Pacific Valley, and the Hearst ranch.
These terraces are the only expansive flatlands along the coast.

Big Sur is also one of the best areas in central California to look for
falcons. Peregrine and prairie falcons are rare breeding residents, but
their numbers are increased in winter by migrants from the north. The
endangered peregrine (fig. 174) is usually seen along the coast, perched
on seastacks and cliffs. It hunts seabirds and shorebirds as well as birds
of the coastal scrub and grasslands. The prairie falcon is seen in the dry,

Figure 175. *Strix occidentalis*, spotted owl

open country of the upper Carmel, San Antonio, and Nacimiento valleys. Specific breeding locales of both species cannot be revealed due to the continued threat of illegal nest robbing.

Woodland raptors are also relatively common in Big Sur. Cooper's and sharpshinned hawks frequent the hardwood forests, and migrants are often seen circling above coastal canyons. The high country and dense forests of the Ventana Wilderness support several types of owls, including the flammulated, spotted, western screech, northern saw-whet, northern pygmy, and great horned owls. The spotted owl (fig. 175), a very rare species elsewhere in the west, is fairly common in old-growth forests in Big Sur. This species has received much recent publicity regarding the controversy of logging its old-growth forest habitat in the Pacific Northwest. The rare long-eared owl has been recorded in riparian woodland in southern Big Sur in the Salmon, Soda Springs, and Villa Creek drainages and in the north in Miller Canyon. Owls of the open country include the barn owl and the burrowing owl.

Other sensitive species are the black swift, purple martin, snowy plover, and yellow warbler. Populations of these birds are declining or are considered vulnerable. Black swifts are rare but are seen at several coastal and inland areas where they nest on cliffs and behind waterfalls.

Local purple martin populations experienced a sharp decrease in the 1970s, but appear to be rebounding today. This bird is most common in the woodlands of the interior national forest, but groups have been seen along the coast of Andrew Molera State Park. The rare snowy plover is more common in the Monterey Bay area, but a few pairs have nested near the beaches of Point Sur. This bird is extremely sensitive to disruption of its sand dune nesting habitat, much of which has been lost to development and recreational interests. The yellow warbler has experienced a serious decline in numbers throughout California, but it is still fairly common in the riparian woodlands of the interior valleys.

TERRESTRIAL MAMMALS

Most Big Sur residents and regular visitors have at one time or another seen a few of the larger mammals found in Big Sur. It is not unusual to see bobcats, gray foxes, coyotes, and badgers in Big Sur, provided one knows where and when to look for them. It is rare to observe the elusive mountain lion, but signs of these predators, such as tracks, droppings, and the remains of kills, are not uncommon. Other carnivores such as the ringtail cat and long-tailed weasel are also seen occasionally. This relative abundance of carnivores, which are usually the first animals to disappear in the face of encroaching human development, is due primarily to Big Sur's large undeveloped wilderness, the great diversity and productivity of its plant communities, and the rugged nature of its backcountry.

There are probably 50 species of terrestrial mammals residing in the Big Sur area. As with the avifauna, however, a thorough survey of the entire region has yet to be done. Jim Griffin (1980), in an unpublished paper on the natural history of Hastings Reservation, lists 46 species resident or periodically occurring there. Biologists Todd and Virginia Keeler-Wolf (1977) estimated the presence of 43 mammals in the Limekiln Creek–Cone Peak area. Studies in the Big Creek drainage by mammalogist Elizabeth Block confirmed the occurrence there of 28 species excluding the bats. Table 14 is a compilation of these lists and includes the species' Latin names.

Most mammals, such as rodents and deer, are discussed in chapter 4 in relationship to the environments where they are most often encountered. But some mammals are found in a variety of plant communities searching for their food and cannot be relegated to a specific one. The

TABLE 14.   TERRESTRIAL MAMMALS OF THE BIG SUR AREA

Common Name	Genus/Species
Opossum	*Didelphis marsupialis*
Ornate shrew	*Sorex ornatus*
Trowbridge shrew	*Sorex trowbridgei*
Broad-handed mole	*Scapanus latimanus*
California myotis	*Myotis californicus*
Long-eared myotis	*Myotis evotis*
Yuma myotis	*Myotis yumanensis*
Long-legged myotis	*Myotis volans*
Big brown bat	*Eptesicus fuscus*
Silver-haired bat	*Lasionycteris noctivagans*
Western pipistrelle	*Pipistrellus hesperus*
Hoary bat	*Lasiurus cinereus*
Red bat	*Lasiurus borealis*
Townsend's big-eared bat	*Plecotus townsendii*
Mexican free-tailed bat	*Tadarida brasiliensis*
Pallid bat	*Antrozous pallidus*
Desert cottontail	*Sylvilagus audubonii*
Brush rabbit	*Sylvilagus bachmani*
Black-tailed jackrabbit	*Lepus californicus*
Merriam chipmunk	*Tamias merriami*
Western gray squirrel	*Sciurus griseus*
California ground squirrel	*Spermophilus beecheyi*
Pocket gopher	*Thomomys bottae*
California pocket mouse	*Perognathus californicus*
Heerman's kangaroo rat	*Dipodomys heermanni*
Narrow-faced kangaroo rat	*Dipodomys venustus*
Western harvest mouse	*Reithrodontomys megalotis*
Brush mouse	*Peromyscus boylei*
California mouse	*Peromyscus californicus*
Deer mouse	*Peromyscus maniculatus*
Pinyon mouse	*Peromyscus truei*
Dusky-footed woodrat	*Neotoma fuscipes*
Desert woodrat	*Neotoma lepida*
California vole (meadow mouse)	*Microtus californicus*

TABLE 14.   (cont.)

Common Name	Genus/Species
House mouse	*Mus musculus*
Gray fox	*Urocyon cinereoargenteus*
Coyote	*Canis latrans*
Raccoon	*Procyon lotor*
Ringtail	*Bassariscus astutus*
Long-tailed weasel	*Mustela frenata*
Badger	*Taxidea taxus*
Western spotted skunk	*Spilogale gracilis*
Striped skunk	*Mephitis mephitis*
Mountain lion	*Felis concolor*
Bobcat	*Lynx rufus*
Wild pig	*Sus scrofa*
Black-tailed deer	*Odocoileus hemionus columbianus*

striped skunk (fig. 176) is seen in several plant communities, especially riparian woodland. The ringtail (fig. 177) wanders in chaparral, rocky areas, and woods looking for small birds and rodents. It will often climb trees to reach fruit or to elude predators. This evasive mammal is rarely seen and there are no reliable estimates of its population size in Big Sur.

Other predators, such as the mountain lion, gray fox, bobcat, and coyote, range throughout almost all of Big Sur's plant communities in search of food. Coyotes are true scavengers, eating carrion and fruit as well as any live animals they can capture. They are not choosy and will eat insects, reptiles, birds, and mammals. They are seen in the grassy and brushy areas of the coast and the interior, and their howls and cries are sometimes heard at night by campers at Andrew Molera State Park and elsewhere. The gray fox (fig. 178) is also a far-ranging predator. It is even more omnivorous than the coyote, feeding on fungi, fruit, and nuts as well as animal prey, including fish. It is most frequently seen in chaparral and coastal scrub. These foxes climb trees to escape predators and to forage for food—a unique habit among canines.

The bobcat (fig. 179) is often about during the day in wooded and shrubby areas. They are commonly seen on coastal terraces and grassy meadows where they prey on small mammals. They will also occasionally take a gray fox and or a small deer, and it is not unusual to find the

Figure 176. *Mephitis mephitis*, striped skunk

Figure 177. *Bassariscus astutus*, ringtail

Figure 178. *Urocyon cinereoargenteus*, gray fox

Figure 179. *Lynx rufus*, bobcat

Figure 180.   *Felis concolor*, mountain lion

Figure 181.   *Odocoileus hemionus columbianus*, black-tailed deer

disembowled remains of a brush rabbit or cottontail left in a neat pile by a feeding bobcat.

Mountain lions (fig. 180) are also out and about during the day, but they are extremely shy and difficult to find. Accurate estimates of the lion's population size are hard to obtain due to the species wary nature. They feed mostly on black-tailed deer (fig. 181) and are the primary control on the deer populations, but they will also take smaller mammals and birds as well as some domestic stock. Llamas, goats, pigs, and geese have reportedly been taken by lions, but some of these attacks are probably made by wild dogs.

The black bear is a relative newcomer to Big Sur. It has recently been seen in the Big Sur area, both to the north, near Monterey, and to the south. The species is not believed to be native to the Coast Range south of San Francisco, but recent sightings indicate that it may be colonizing this area. In the spring of 1987, we found bear tracks and excrement along the South Fork of the Big Sur River. Black bears have been seen regularly in recent years in the southern Santa Lucia Range and near San Luis Obispo and Paso Robles, and a few have been killed by cars at Cuesta Pass on Highway 101. Perhaps individuals are moving north to Big Sur from southern California ranges since grizzly bears, which used to prey upon black bears, no longer inhabit the area. Big Sur is certainly good bear habitat, providing most of the berries, insects, nuts, honey, small mammals, and other foods that they feed upon.

The human impacts on certain mammal species, especially the larger predators such as the mountain lion, wolf, and grizzly bear, are discussed in chapter 8.

SUGGESTED READING

Davis, J., and A. Baldridge, 1980. *The bird year: A book for birders.* Pacific Grove, Calif.: Boxwood Press.

Davis, J., W. D. Koenig, and P. L. Williams, 1980. Birds of Hastings Reservation, Monterey County, California. *Western Birds,* 11(3): 113–128.

Engles, E., ed., 1984. *The natural features of the Gamboa Point properties, Monterey County, California, Vol. 2: Terrestrial vertebrates.* Environmental Field Program Publication 13, University of California, Santa Cruz.

Frincke, M. M., and W. J. Francis, 1984. *Birds of Point Lobos.* Pacific Grove, Calif.: Boxwood Press.

Griffin, J., 1980. Natural history of the Hastings Reservation. Unpublished manuscript on file at Hastings Natural History Reservation.

Grinnell, J., 1902. Birds of the Little Sur River, Monterey County. *Condor,* 4: 125–128.

Jameson, E. W., Jr., and H. J. Peeters, 1988. *California mammals.* California Natural History Guide 52. Berkeley: University of California Press.

Keeler-Wolfe, T., and V. Keeler-Wolfe, 1977. *A survey of the scientific values of the proposed Limekiln Creek Research Natural Area, Monterey Ranger District, Los Padres National Forest.* U.S.D.A. Forest Service Research Paper PSW-76. Berkeley: Pacific Southwest Forest and Range Experiment Station.

Linsdale, J. M., 1947. A ten-year record of bird occurrence on the Hastings Reservation. *Condor,* 49: 236–241.

Pemberton, J. R., and H. W. Carriger, 1915. A partial list of the summer resident land birds of Monterey County, California. *Condor,* 17: 189–201.

Roberson, D., 1985. *Monterey birds.* Monterey, Calif.: Monterey Peninsula Audubon Society.

Stebbins, R. C., 1972. *Amphibians and reptiles of California.* California Natural History Guide 31. Berkeley: University of California Press.

CHAPTER VII

Human History

INTRODUCTION

It is difficult to imagine Big Sur as the first Europeans saw it. Condors fed on beached whale carcasses. Thousands of sea otters and seals swam in the surf and lounged on offshore rocks. Wolves, mountain lions, and grizzly bears were common. The Native Americans of Big Sur moved with the seasons up and down the steep mountains, from the rich shellfish beds of the shore to the oak groves laden with acorns.

The prehistory of the Big Sur area has not yet been thoroughly studied, and as a result there are more questions than answers regarding who lived here before the coming of the Spanish. It is generally assumed that California was first settled about 10,000 years ago, but it is unclear when humans first arrived in Big Sur. The most ancient aboriginal site near Big Sur is found in San Luis Obispo County, near Cambria, and has been dated at 8430 years before present (B.P.). In contrast, the oldest sites discovered so far in Big Sur, such as the Church Creek rockshelter and one near Esalen Institute, yield dates in the range of only 3390 to 4630 years B.P. It is still a mystery whether Big Sur was settled earlier than is indicated by these dates. The steep terrain and dense brush may have discouraged early people, and the area may have become settled after other nearby places such as the Monterey Peninsula.

We do know that when the Spanish arrived, Big Sur was home to people of three separate groups: the Ohlone (or Costanoan), the Esselen, and the Salinan. Each of these groups was further broken down into subgroups, and each probably spoke different languages. The Ohlone, for example, had eight subgroups. These subgroups were still not small enough to be considered politically cohesive units, and anthropologists have divided them even further into *tribelets* or nations. Tribelets spoke different dialects and were the political unit recognized by the people. They averaged up to 250 people and usually consisted of a village and several outlying camps, all within clearly defined boundaries. There was contact among tribelets through trade and food-gathering excursions, but each village was also quite independent. The Ohlone had as many as fifty separate tribelets.

OHLONE

The Ohlone were the largest of the three groups, numbering as many as 10,000 people. Their range stretched north from Point Sur to present-day San Francisco's Golden Gate, and they were most concentrated around Monterey and San Francisco bays. In the Big Sur area, the Ohlone Rumsen subgroup occupied the northern coastline and the lower reaches of the Carmel and Salinas rivers. They totaled about 800 people and consisted of at least six tribelets. The Ohlone Chalon subgroup occupied the central Salinas Valley.

Each of the eight Ohlone subgroups differed from one another in language, religious beliefs, marital customs, and patterns of dress. Subsistence methods, depending on the particular food resources available, further defined the subgroups. It is believed that the Ohlone may have moved into the San Francisco and Monterey Bay areas between 500 B.C. and A.D. 500, probably arriving from California's Central Valley. They may have then displaced the Hokan-speaking peoples, who may have been ancestors of the Esselen, forcing them south and deeper into the Santa Lucia Range.

ESSELEN

The Esselen occupied the heart of Big Sur and are one of the least known California Indian tribes. They also had one of the smallest native populations in California, estimated between 750 to 1300 individuals living over a 1500 km² (580 mi²) territory. They were found from south of Point Sur to the Big Creek drainage along the coast and inland within the watersheds of the upper Carmel River and the Arroyo Seco. These boundaries are unclear to researchers, and areas of overlap with neigh-

Figure 182.   Approximate boundaries of Coastanoan, Esselen, and Salinan
tribes and tribelets (after Jones et al., 1989).

boring groups may have existed both to the north and the south. It is
unclear, for example, whether villages near Point Sur and the Little Sur
River, known collectively as Sargenta-Ruc, belonged to the Ohlone or
the Esselen (fig. 182).

According to anthropologist Alfred Kroeber, the Esselen had disappeared in the early part of the nineteenth century and were the first
California Indian group to become virtually extinct. Kroeber came to
this conclusion after his failure in 1902 to find a single living Esselen
to interview. Anthropologist Terry Jones suggests that Kroeber's failure
to locate any full-bred Esselen people was due to the destruction of the

Esselen culture and integration of the people into the Spanish-Mexican culture, rather than the wholesale physical disappearance of all the people. Many Esselen did indeed die at the missions, but there are people living today who can trace their lineage to the mission Esselen. Unfortunately, these people know little or nothing of traditional Esselen lifestyles and language.

Kroeber suggested that the Esselen were the remnants of an older, larger group that once occupied territory to the north. They were then gradually cut off and isolated by an influx of another tribe, perhaps the Ohlone. This theory concurs with the belief that the Ohlone are relative newcomers to the area.

SALINAN

The Salinan lived to the south and east of the Esselen. They extended as far south as San Carpoforo Creek along the coast and occupied the inland mountains south of Junipero Serra Peak and north up the Salinas River valley to the Ohlone border. Traditionally, Lopez Point had been considered as the Esselen–Salinan boundary. Recent research conducted at the Big Creek Reserve, however, has pushed this boundary to the north somewhere in the vicinity of the Big Creek drainage.

Population estimates for the Salinan range from 2300 to 3000 people. The tribe may have been separated into two distinct groups— the inland people and the coastal people, or "Playanos." Some ethnologists feel that these two groups had different languages. The inland villages were located along the Nacimiento and San Antonio rivers near Jolon and in the Salinas Valley. The coastal sites were usually located in grassland and woodland settings far above the ocean.

NATIVES AND THE BIG SUR ENVIRONMENT

The Big Sur Indians were a Stone Age people. They were hunter–gatherers and had no agriculture. They followed certain food sources through the seasons, moving in fall to the oak groves to collect acorns, in spring to the open meadows full of tender greens, and in winter to the bountiful coastal waters.

Most of what we know of Big Sur's first settlers comes from two different types of sources: the written records left by Spanish explorers, missionaries, and early anthropologists; and the analysis of the middens that mark the sites of Indian villages and encampments. The word *mid-*

den derives from a Scandinavian term meaning "muck" or "dunghill." Middens are, for the most part, trash heaps. They are giant shell-mounds, full of discarded mollusk shells and rock and dirt, and they are the prehistoric equivalent of today's landfill or town dump. They also contain small amounts of animal bones, stone tools, and other artifacts. One of the largest middens in California is 400 m (1300 ft) wide and 10 m (30 ft) deep, but most in Big Sur are small hummocks or knolls along streambanks and marine cliffs.

Middens are built up year after year, century after century, by people living atop or adjacent to them and depositing the unwanted materials of everyday life. As the days go by, layer upon layer is deposited, and a stratified testimonial to the culture remains. What is on top of the midden is younger than what is beneath it, and by reading these materials in the proper sequence, we can get some idea of the cultural and material development of those people through time.

Big Sur has numerous middens lining the shore and dotting the hillsides. Coastal middens are usually located on terraces directly above the intertidal area. In places, waves have cut into the cliffs and exposed the midden soils, which are dark black mixed with bits of white shell and rock. Many coastal sites are also sheltered behind dunes or hills that offer wind protection. Inland middens are most often found along streambanks and on sunny knolls with southern exposure. Many of these are also located above the fogline, an indication that the natives preferred the sun to fog. Proximity to a dependable water supply was another criterion for site selection.

Midden analysis, combined with the review of historical accounts, reveals that the Big Sur natives, like their counterparts elsewhere in California, were essentially omnivorous. They ate most everything that was edible. A large midden in northern Big Sur, for example, is composed primarily of shells of mussels, abalone, chitons, and barnacles. Other shells include those of several species of limpets, snails, and sea urchins. Also found are the bones of seabirds such as cormorants and marine mammals such as the sea otter and California sea lion.

Other marine foods included eggs and fish. The mission padres at Carmel described how the natives went out to the offshore rocks in tule rafts and collected cormorant eggs from nests, and how they used nets to fill barrels with sardines during a 20-day sardine run near the mouth of the Carmel River. Indians living along the coast also used terrestrial resources. Midden diggings often include the bones of mule deer, skunks, raccoons, coyotes, gray foxes, rabbits, squirrels, mice, and pocket gophers. One ingenious method of deer hunting involved the donning of a deerskin complete with head and antlers. The camouflaged hunter then slowly worked his way out among an unsuspecting deer herd until he was close enough to easily kill one with a bow and arrow.

Sites located well inland have a significant amount of shells, but the importance of marine foods seems to decrease and that of nonmarine foods increases the farther one gets from the coast. The Ohlone are known to have dried and smoked mussels, abalone, and chitons, preserving them for storage. Such a practice may explain the presence of shells in middens many miles inland from the ocean.

Many items other than food remains are found in middens, including tools, weapons, and ornamental artifacts. Such finds are rare, and their deposit in the middens was probably unintentional. A shell bead may have fallen from a necklace or an arrowhead was dropped in passing. Perhaps a stone mortar, used to grind acorns to flour, was abandoned when worn out or as a call to leave camp was heard. Other artifacts include shell fishhooks, spear tips, scrapers, abalone prybars, hammerstones, choppers, net sinkers, and so on.

Even small flakes of stone, scattered on the midden as they were chipped off to make arrowheads or speartips, provide useful information. Obsidian, a black volcanic glass popular among natives because of its hard, sharp edges, has been found in several Big Sur middens. There are a limited number of sources in California where obsidian can be found, and most of these are in the eastern Sierras or the northern Coast Range. None are in central California. The specific quarry from which the obsidian originated can be determined using a technique known as X-ray fluorescence spectrography.

Samples from a midden near Soberanes Creek were analyzed with this method and are believed to have originated near northern Napa Valley. Samples recovered at Big Creek, however, are from the eastern Sierra Nevada. Such revelations shed light on the tribal boundaries and the trading patterns used by the coastal Indians. It is also interesting to note that shell beads and abalone trinkets, which could only have come from the coast, have been found as far east as the deserts of the Great Basin.

Unfortunately, plants do not preserve as well as animal bones and stone artifacts. There have been a few recoveries in the Santa Lucia Range of plant-related artifacts, such as woven baskets and nets, but these are extremely rare. More weight, then, must be put on historical accounts to appreciate the intimate and thorough understanding the Indians had of the plants available to them.

The most important plants to the Indians were probably the several species of oak that grow here. Most northern and central California natives relied heavily upon acorns as a food staple. Even coastal people, with their great marine resources, depended to some extent on the oaks. According to some early Spanish sources, native population densities were highest in areas rich in oak trees. Malcolm Margolin, in *The Ohlone Way,* describes the importance of oak trees and acorns to these people: "For most Ohlone groups, acorns were the staff of life, the food people ate nearly every day of their lives. . . . Time itself was measured by the oaks. . . . The rhythms of the oaks marked the passage of the year and defined the rhythms of Ohlone life."

These rhythms reached a peak in mid-fall when the acorns were harvested. Black oaks and tanoaks were the favored trees. The acorns were collected in baskets and laid out in a clearing to dry in the sun. After drying, they were taken back to the villages and stored in granaries above ground to keep them dry through the winter. The women prepared several foods from the acorns. They first split the nuts open, peeled off the husk, and removed the kernel. These were then ground with a stone mortar and pestle. Bedrock mortars, large exposed rocks with a dozen or more deep mortar bowls worn into them, are located throughout Big Sur. The women sat at these communal sites and ground the nuts to a fine flour.

They then leached the flour with water to remove the bitter tannin. It was cooked by bringing a flour and water mixture to a boil and stirring until the desired consistency was achieved. The resulting mush was eaten like porridge. Bread was made by boiling off more water and baking the batter on hot rocks or in earthen ovens. European visitors described it as oily, rich, and flavorful. It was also nutritious, comparable to bread made from wheat or barley.

Along with the oaks, there were probably few plants for which the people did not have some use. Tule reeds were used to construct small rafts that would hold up to four people. Such crafts gave hunters access to offshore rocks and islets where bird eggs and baby seals could be taken. (It is unknown to what extent, if any, the Esselen and Salinan may have used such rafts; it is known that the Ohlone in the Carmel area used them.) Branches of willow and poison oak were woven into fish traps and watertight baskets. Scores of plants, such as buckwheat and monkey flowers, were employed to cure everything from rashes to ringworm and warts to kidney disorders. Others, such as wavy-leaf soap plant (*Chlorogalum pomeridianum*), were used to stupefy and catch fish in the streams and to make a shampoolike soap.

The variety of edible plants was extensive. Spring greens were plentiful, among them clovers, watercress, poppies, and miner's lettuce (*Montia perfoliata*). Berries followed in summer and fall: thimbleberries, blackberries, toyon, madrone, Virginia strawberries (*Fragaria virginiana*), gooseberries, currants, and manzanitas, to name a few. Gray pine nuts, hazelnuts, and many types of seed were harvested in fall along with the acorns.

Contrary to some of the more romantic stereotypes of "naive natives living lightly on the land," California natives exerted a strong manipulative pressure on their environment. They had a definite impact on the local ecosystems. Historian Burton Gordon suggests that parts of the Monterey County coastline were occasionally stripped bare of mollusks by the Ohlone and that the people were the principal control of animal populations along the shoreline. He also points out, though, that pressures brought to bear by these people were spread throughout the ecological spectrum and did not focus on any one species. This is in sharp contrast to Spanish, Russian, Chinese, and American hunters who exploited and nearly exterminated single species, such as the red abalone, gray whale, sea otter, and elephant seal.

The natives also manipulated the vegetative landscape. They selectively and consciously set fire to large tracts of land, opening it up, clearing brush, and essentially making it more productive. They had an understanding of the successional effects of fire on the vegetation (see chap. 5, Fire Ecology), and they were usually rewarded with an increased supply of seeds and edible greens and an enhanced habitat for wild game. Fires also helped perpetuate important trees, such as the bull pines and oaks, and prevented the buildup of dead wood that might have eventually led to a truly destructive wildfire.

It is not known to what extent the Esselen may have used fire, but it is known that the Ohlone used it as a regular tool of land management. Early French and Spanish explorers repeatedly commented on this practice. In July 1774, a Spanish captain at the Monterey presidio wrote of Indians "to the south," probably Carmel Valley, burning grasslands and that the smoke was visible from Monterey. The job of burning, like that of gathering most plant food and firewood, belonged to the women.

EARLY EXPLORATION AND SETTLEMENT

PORTOLA EXPEDITIONS

Europeans first saw Big Sur and the Santa Lucia Range from the sea. Juan Cabrillo, sailing by in 1542, was quite impressed: "There are mountains which seem to reach the heavens, and the sea beats on them; sailing along close to land, it appears as though they would fall on the ships." Sixty years later, Sebastian Vizcaino followed Cabrillo's route and visited Monterey and Carmel bays. He surveyed the immediate area and proclaimed both bays to be excellent harbors. No settlement was established, though, and for the next century and a half, the Spanish limited their colonization efforts to Baja California and mainland Mexico.

Captain Gasper de Portola and his men were the first Europeans known to actually set foot in the Santa Lucia Range. Traveling north from Baja (Lower) California in 1769, the Portola Expedition was seeking an overland route to Alta (Upper) California. Fearful that Russian explorers were moving south along the coast from Alaska, the Spanish were anxious to reach Monterey Bay and claim the area.

Portola and his men, guided by crude charts based on Vizcaino's explorations, marched slowly from San Diego up the California coast toward Monterey Bay. They stayed close to the coast and avoided the mountains and foothills wherever possible until they reached the southern Santa Lucias. Here the sheer mountain wall at San Carpoforo Canyon rises straight up from the surf.

It must have disheartened the men to view these impassable cliffs and brush-covered slopes. Their only alternative was to cut inland and hack their way through the scrub. After several difficult days, they descended into the Nacimiento River Valley and were greeted by friendly Salinan Indians. The expedition continued northeast, reached the Salinas River, and followed it around the Santa Lucias to the ocean. Big Sur, protected by its mountain walls, was bypassed entirely.

The harbors of Monterey and Carmel, the goals of the expedition, were also mistakenly bypassed. After discovering San Francisco Bay, Portola turned south to retrace his route. The expedition soon reached Monterey Bay and the Carmel River, but did not recognize the area as their goal. By this time, scurvy and dissension were taking a toll among the men, and a return trip to the south was planned. They left almost the exact way they had come, following the Salinas Valley around the Santa Lucias, hooking up with the Nacimiento River and then following San Carpoforo Creek out of the mountains to the coast. They arrived back at San Diego on January 24, 1770, six months after their departure.

Portola did not give up. Fresh supplies arrived at San Diego from Mexico, and a new trip was organized. Father Junipero Serra, anxious to establish a mission in the unknown territory, sailed north, while Portola and twenty men went by land. The trip was much easier this time, and the land expedition arrived at Carmel Bay, north of Point Lobos, on May 24, 1770. This was the very spot where they had given up on their last trip.

MISSION PERIOD

After some initial hardships, Monterey was soon the thriving capital of Alta California. Big Sur, in the meantime, remained unexplored. In 1771, Father Serra moved his mission from Monterey and established Mission San Carlos near the Carmel River mouth. Missions were also founded at Soledad (1791) in the Salinas Valley and in the San Antonio River Valley (1771), both on the eastern flank of the Santa Lucias. These sites were selected for their proximity to good farmland, an adequate water supply, and a large population of "unbaptized heathens."

It remains unclear just how the Big Sur natives—members of the Esselen, Ohlone Rumsen, and Salinan tribes—were drawn to the missions. Anthropologist Terry Jones says the Salinan have been repeatedly described as welcoming the padres and that it is unknown whether the Esselen were forced to convert or went to the missions peacefully. Historian Augusta Fink describes how a Rumsen chief from the Carmel Valley willingly presented himself and his four-year-old son to Father Serra for baptism. Many were undoubtedly attracted by the strange and exciting gifts offered by the Spanish: the glass beads, the brightly colored cloth, and the metal knives, pots, and tools. They were also curious about the bizarre animals: the cows, sheep, mules, and horses. It is generally agreed, Jones says, that forced conversion of natives was not mission policy prior to 1800, but after this time, as the natives resisted, the padres at some missions may have turned to more coercive methods.

The severe change in lifestyle could never have been anticipated by the Indians. Once baptized, they were required to reside at the mission. They worked the fields and abandoned their "primitive" ways, no longer to wander the oak groves, stalk deer, or take trips to the shore for abalone and mussels. Instead, they grew wheat and corn, spun wool, and wove cloth. They became blacksmiths, shepherds, and cowboys. They were to pray two hours a day, and after ten years of indoctrination and worship, they would be given land upon which to raise a family. This was the "Catholic utopia" envisioned by the missionaries.

Escapees from the mission were often hunted by soldiers and returned. One early French explorer, la Perouse, likened the Spanish missions to a Caribbean slave colony. He described "with pain" the regimented lives, frequent imprisonment, and corporal punishments suffered by male and female converts.

Indian numbers at the missions rose steadily until the early 1800s. By this time, there were supposedly no unbaptized natives within seventy-five miles of Mission San Antonio, which would include all of the Big Sur area. Mission life during this period took an especially tragic turn as introduced diseases began decimating the new converts. Smallpox, venereal disease, and measles, to which they had no previous exposure and thus no immunity, took a horrible toll. One account from Mission San Antonio claimed that during these years, there were three deaths for every two baptisms.

The missions began suffering from a depletion of Indian labor. Problems included an increasing infant mortality, a lack of new converts, and the emigration of converts from the missions. To make matters worse for the padres, Mexico seceded from Spain in 1822, and in 1826, the governor of Alta California emancipated from mission control all Indians who met certain criteria and could become Mexican citizens. Many took advantage of this opportunity. The final blow came with the Secularization Act of 1833, when the extensive mission lands were transferred to public domain. Without their land and their laborers, the missions rapidly declined.

RANCHO AND HOMESTEADING PERIOD

The vast mission lands were distributed by the Mexican government to qualified citizens as land grants. These were the famous California ranchos. Although Monterey continued to grow during the rancho period, Big Sur maintained its aura of mystery. There were several grants made in the outlying areas of Big Sur, such as in the Carmel, Nacimiento, and San Antonio river valleys, but only two were made in Big Sur itself. In 1834, Juan Bautista Alvarado received title to the 8949-acre Rancho El Sur, covering most of the Point Sur area. Much of it is still a working ranch today. The second grant, the 8876-acre Rancho San Jose y Sur Chiquito, stretched from the Carmel River to Palo Colorado Canyon and has since been divided up into private holdings and Garrapata State Park.

Between this time and the 1860s, Big Sur was settled by Spanish, Native Americans, and Spanish married to Native Americans, but records are sketchy. These people probably left the Monterey Bay and Salinas Valley areas because of their declining economic and social status in the face of an influx of Americans. Some Esselen and Salinan natives lived in the backcountry, while some prospectors and Mexican "vaqueros" may have roamed the canyons.

In 1848, California was ceded to the United States. The next year, gold was discovered in the Sierra Nevada foothills. Statehood followed in 1850. Prospectors and settlers flocked to California. The choice lands in the Monterey and Salinas areas were already privately owned, so any newcomers wishing to homestead in the area looked to Big Sur.

The steep land was rocky and not well suited to agriculture, and it remained open to homesteading well after most of California was settled. This period, from the 1860s to the early 1900s, saw the establishment of an independent but loose-knit community of Big Sur pioneers. Parcels of 160 acres could be claimed by a man or a family. Improvements—a house, a fence, and a barn—were made over a period of years, and the family received title to the land. Most of Big Sur's canyons and ridges are named for the families that settled them: the Pfeiffers and Posts, Phil Dolan, the Partingtons, Tom Slate, the Castros, the Harlans, the Danis, Sam Trotter, the Plasketts and Prewitts, Jim Anderson, and the Borondas and Avilas, to name a few. Several books give detailed reporting of this era in Big Sur's history, for example, Fink (1982), Georgette (1981), and Woolfenden (1981).

These people carved out a rough lifestyle for themselves. Initially, most families hunted, fished, and foraged along the shore for much of their food. As they became settled, they raised pigs and cattle and grew much of their food instead. Orchards and gardens were planted, and abandoned homestead sites are today often marked only by fruit or walnut trees.

Pioneer life in Big Sur was one of isolation. Families were separated from one another by deep canyons and tall mountains. Big Sur as a whole was separated from the rest of Monterey County by a lack of roads and safe harbors. The coast road from Monterey, a primitive wagon trail, reached only as far as the present-day Ventana Inn. Winter storms caused frequent washouts and slides, and wooden bridges crossing the many creeks were swept away during storms. Travelers farther south had to follow the narrow horse trail that connected the various homesteads. It was a long and sometimes dangerous trip.

There was a marked division between Big Sur's northern and southern coasts back then, with the area around present-day Esalen Institute being the boundary. The northern coast did business mostly with Monterey, while the southern coasters went east over the mountains to King City for their mail and supplies. Fishing ships sometimes brought supplies to the southern coast, tying up near Gamboa or Lopez points to deliver the essentials that could not be produced at home or carted over the mountains. This was the preferred method of commerce. Ranchers in the area, such as the Harlan family, drove their cattle and pigs along the Gamboa Trail, near Cone Peak, and into the market at King City. Cattle took three days to drive, while pigs took a week.

Several small-scale industries were started in Big Sur that provided some homesteaders with other sources of income. Tanoak trees throughout the range were harvested for their bark, with Partington Cove being a major shipping point for bark from that canyon. Limestone was mined and processed at Limekiln and Bixby creeks. Gold was discovered near Alder Creek, and the mining town of Manchester sprang up to service the brief but exciting rush. All these operations were relatively short lived, and life in Big Sur always seemed to close in on itself, safe and isolated from Monterey and the outside world.

HIGHWAY 1 AND RECENT SETTLERS

The homesteading period gradually faded in the early 1900s and a different era of land ownership and use began. Isolation and the rugged landscape were no longer features with which to do battle, but instead became qualities sought after by the adventuresome, the wealthy, and California's growing body of tourists. Big Sur was slowly coming to be recognized as one of America's most spectacular scenic areas. Artists and writers from nearby Carmel, such as Robinson Jeffers, Ansel Adams, and Edward Weston, extolled the area's many wonders in their work. Local residents began providing services to visitors. Hunting, camping, and fishing trips led by first- or second-generation pioneers became available. Pfeiffer's Resort Hotel and other tourist services appeared. The completion of Highway 1 in 1937 ensured a steady stream of tourists to these and subsequent hotels and parks.

Funds were first approved to build the road in 1919 when voters in the state passed a $1.5 million bond issue. Many settlers were against the building of the road, not only because it went across much of their land, but because the devastation caused by dynamite and bulldozers seemed too large a price to pay. They also knew that it would bring an invasion of outsiders. But differences between residents and roadbuilders were gradually smoothed out, and the road was completed eighteen years and $8 million later.

The opening of Highway 1 in 1937 brought a great influx of visitors to Big Sur. It changed the lifestyles of the residents, allowing them to make a quick drive to Monterey for supplies rather than take a three-day trip. It also opened the coastline to increased settlement. Many of those to take advantage of this opportunity included artists, writers, musicians, and philosophers. These people, although different from the original breed of pioneers, were similar in spirit to those settlers. They maintained—and continue to maintain—a fierce intellectual and artistic independence and an appreciation of the isolation and inspiration found in Big Sur. Different decades have brought different settlers: the 1940s and 1950s saw writers such as Henry Miller and Nicholas Roosevelt; the 1960s and early 1970s were filled with hippies, communes, and New Age establishments such as the Esalen Institute; and the mid-1970s and 1980s brought in celebrities from the television, movie, and business worlds. The mingling of these people with the descendants of homesteaders and other early settlers creates a diverse and intriguing local community.

SUGGESTED READING

Cook, S. F., 1974a. The Esselen: Territory, villages, and population. *Monterey County Archeological Society Quarterly,* 3(2): 1–10.

Cook, S. F., 1974b. The Esselen: Language and culture. *Monterey County Archeological Society Quarterly,* 3(3): 1–10.

Fink, A., 1982. *Monterey County: The dramatic story of its past.* Santa Cruz, Calif.: Western Tanager Press.

Georgette, S. E., 1981. *In the rough land to the south.* Environmental Field Program Publication 5, University of California, Santa Cruz.

Gordon, B. L., 1979. *Monterey Bay area: Natural history and cultural imprints.* Pacific Grove, Calif.: Boxwood Press.

Jones, T., Anderson, S., Garsia, A., Hildebrand, K., York, A., and Brown, M., 1989. *Surface archeology at Landels Hill–Big Creek Reserve and the Gamboa Point properties, Monterey County, California.* Environmental Field Program Publication 18, University of California, Santa Cruz.

Margolin, M., 1978. *The Ohlone way: Indian life in the San Francisco–Monterey Bay area.* Berkeley: Heyday Books.

Woolfenden, J., 1981. *Big Sur: A battle for the wilderness.* Pacific Grove, Calif.: Boxwood Press.

CHAPTER VIII

Changes in the Big Sur Environment

INTRODUCTION

Big Sur may look wild and natural, but the area has undergone some significant changes as a result of human activities. The landscape has been altered by ranching, logging, road building and maintenance, home and commercial development, farming, deliberate burning as well as fire suppression, mining, and introduction of nonnative plants and animals. The passage of time has a healing effect and seems to smooth over many of these changes—the logged forest grows back, as does the burned field. But it is important to recognize patterns of disturbance to understand why an area looks like it does and to better anticipate the short- and long-term consequences of such activities.

RANCHING

The commercial raising of cattle, hogs, goats, and sheep has had a noticeable impact on the vegetation and pastures of public and private lands. Grazing cattle have worn distinct terraces and deep gullies into many hillsides. These terraces remain long after grazing is stopped and are familiar patterns on many hillsides above Highway 1 and in the backcountry. Grazing compacts the soil in some areas and accelerates erosion. When an area is overgrazed, the runoff from heavy rains forms small channels on the semidenuded slopes. Subsequent rains deepen and widen the channels to form gullies and eventually larger arroyos. Small landslides and slips are also common on overgrazed slopes.

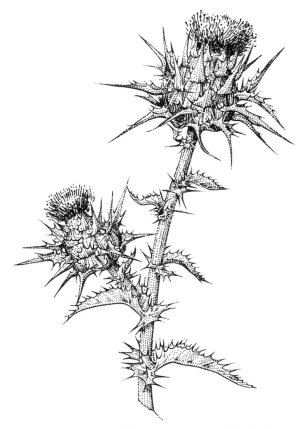

Figure 183. *Silybum marianum*, milk thistle

Ranching has also been responsible for the introduction and prolif-eration of many nonnative species of grasses and weeds. Grasses are discussed in detail in chapter 4, but it should be noted here that several hardy and troublesome exotic weeds such as the milk thistle (*Silybum marianum*) (fig. 183) favor grazed areas. This weed is especially ap-parent in the heavily grazed area near Point Sur and Andrew Molera State Park.

Cattle excrement on public lands is another unfortunate consequence of the ranching industry, and many streams and springs have become contaminated and unfit for drinking as a result. The aesthetic quality of certain areas is also compromised by the presence of cattle and their effect on the landscape.

Unlike cattle ranching, the commercial raising of hogs, sheep, and goats has almost disappeared in Big Sur since the homesteading days. In the 1860s, Monterey County had the largest sheep population in the United States. For many early settlers, hogs and sheep were better suited than cows to the rough terrain here. The hogs ran semiwild at times, and many escaped and interbred with wild pigs (see chap. 6), which were introduced for sport hunting purposes in upper Carmel Valley.

LOGGING

Because of its inaccessibility and forbidding topography, Big Sur did not experience logging to the same extent as did other forested areas of central California. The nearby Santa Cruz Mountains, for example, were logged extensively during the latter nineteenth century. The cost of harvesting and then transporting lumbered goods from Big Sur was excessive, and except for some small commercial redwood, pine, and tanoak operations, much of the harvesting that did take place was for local use. Nonetheless, the State Board of Forestry reported in 1924 that half of the virgin timber in the Big Sur area had been cut.

The Santa Lucia Range was an important source of tanoak bark for the leather-tanning industry. According to one report, accessible tanoaks were nearly exhausted in this range by the early 1900s. Gamboa Point, Notley's Landing (near Palo Colorado Canyon), Partington Cove, and Bixby Creek were a few shipping points for the exportation of the bark to tanneries in Santa Cruz and San Francisco. At its height, the operation at Partington Cove employed 40 men and produced 10,000 cords of tanbark. In 1889, as much as 50,000 cords of tanbark were hauled out from the Little Sur River and Big Sur River watersheds.

The harvesting of tanoaks was particularly disruptive to the forest. Since tanoaks do not usually form extensive pure stands under natural conditions, many paths were made throughout the forest to reach the trees. The tanoaks were cut in spring when the bark peels easily, and the trees were felled with care so that the bark could be stripped off. The wood was left to rot even though it was of good quality for building and firewood. Even-aged stands of large, multitrunked trees have stump sprouted and grown in areas that were logged during the early part of this century. Such trees grow in many coastal canyons, for example, along the Tanbark Trail in Julia Pfeiffer-Burns State Park.

Unlike tanoak, redwood was highly valued as a building material. Most homesteaders used it to build their barns, homes, and fences. Redwood shakes were cut by hand for roofing material and were sometimes carried into Monterey or King City to be sold. The Pfeiffer–Big Sur State Park area was logged around the turn of the century, and most coastal canyon bottoms have large redwood trunks surrounded by rings of smaller trees. These smaller trees are stump sprouts and probably grew after the primary tree was cut. Fortunately, redwoods are aggressive regenerators and quickly produce second growth forests, but these second growth forests will need many more centuries of growth to match the magnificence of the virgin stands.

Logging continues today in several areas of Big Sur. Woodcutters harvest downed trees on national forest property for firewood. Some private landowners are harvesting the pines, redwoods, and other trees that were damaged by recent fires. Such trees were killed but their wood was not destroyed, and many are still standing and provide high-quality lumber. The negative effects of such operations include increased erosion due to the building of access roads and bulldozer trails to remove the timber, and the loss of habitat for a variety of wildlife— woodpeckers, squirrels, and insects—that depend on dead trees for food and shelter.

Due to the high commercial value of certain conifers, especially redwood, the economic pressure to harvest these trees is great. In May 1984, for example, a proposal was submitted by a private landowner to cut redwoods on about eighty acres along the West Fork of Limekiln Creek. Concerns were raised not only regarding the usual negative side effects of logging, but more importantly, there was fear that the special ecological significance of the area would be impaired. The Limekiln drainage harbors several rare and endemic plants, and the land's steep rise from sea level to the summit of Cone Peak supports an especially diverse and rich assortment of plant communities.

In recognition of these features, the area has received special status from several government agencies: the U.S. Forest Service proposed it as a candidate Research Natural Area in 1975; the U.S. Department of the Interior suggested making it a National Natural Landmark in 1980; and in 1983, it was included with several other watersheds in the area as part of the United Nations' Man and the Biosphere Reserve system.

The proposed logging operation would have included some of the oldest, healthiest, and largest redwoods in Monterey County, and there was no guarantee that the trees would have grown back. These redwoods are also significant in that they have been geographically separated from the main redwood forests to the north and may represent a distinct subspecies or variety of redwood. The local Land Use Plan discourages logging in Big Sur, particularly old growth redwoods, but it does not outlaw it. Due to action by the Big Sur Land Trust, this particular logging proposal was eventually stopped and the property was acquired.

MINING

The only large-scale mining operation in Big Sur is the limestone quarry located on the south face of Pico Blanco. This mine and its access road is within the Little Sur River watershed and is partially on National Forest property. Limestone is a sedimentary rock composed of calcium carbonate. It is most often formed from the skeletons of tiny marine invertebrates that are deposited on the ocean floor. This particular deposit contains an estimated 640 million tons of limestone and is probably the largest mass of good quality limestone within 150 miles of San Francisco. The Los Padres National Forest Management Plan estimates that the annual rate of mining the deposit increased from 3000 tons to 30,000 tons by 1988.

Due to some developments in the 1980s, however, it remains to be seen just how much of the limestone will actually be removed. In 1983, after receiving a permit from the U.S. Forest Service to dig a 5-acre open pit mine, the Granite Rock Company refused a State Coastal Commission request that the company also apply to them for a permit. The Coastal Commission was concerned about the negative side effects that the operation might have on the quality of the Little Sur watershed and its wildlife, including the silting of the river, noise from explosions and heavy machinery, and more roads. Animals that would be affected included prairie and peregrine falcons, golden eagles, mountain lions, and steelhead trout. A road leading up to the pit was built and is visible from Andrew Molera State Park and the Old Coast Road.

Granite Rock Company refused to apply to the Coastal Commission and instead took the case to court. The company claimed, in accordance with the federal Mining Act of 1872, that the state had no jurisdiction over private activities on federal land. The case reached the U.S. Supreme Court in March 1987, which decided in favor of the Coastal Commission by a narrow margin. The company is now seeking state permission to mine.

Other than this large claim, the Big Sur region is almost without mining operations. Historically, there was limestone extraction in Limekiln Creek by the Rockland Lime and Lumber Company and in Bixby

Creek. The impact of these short-lived operations, which took place during the late 1880s, was probably greatest on the surrounding forests since many redwoods were cut to fire the kilns. About the same time and a little farther south, there was a brief gold rush in the headwaters of Alder Creek; this is described in part II of this book. Today, a few small gold and jade claims exist in the National Forest, and diving for jade at Jade Cove has become increasingly popular.

OFFSHORE OIL DRILLING

The Big Sur coast is not immune to the threat of oil drilling on the outer continental shelf. Public and Congressional sentiment appears to be against such activities in this area, but the Department of the Interior may include Big Sur in its offshore lease sales. Even if Big Sur is excluded from offshore drilling activities, operations in neighboring waters near San Luis Obispo to the south and Santa Cruz to the north could have an impact on this area. Oil spills and increased pollution would have devastating effects on the marine flora and fauna, especially on sea otters and marine birds. Local and state governments are opposed to any drilling off the California coast, but their power to regulate and restrict offshore oil drilling is limited.

RECREATION

Recreation and tourism are the mainstay of Big Sur's small economy. About 3 million visitors drive along Highway 1 each year. Many of these people stay more than the day and, depending on the campground or hotel, pay anywhere from $1 to $200 for a place to sleep. Others choose to park on highway pullouts for the night, a practice that was recently outlawed by the county. Still others pack into the backcountry, walking trails to camp far from the highway and hotels.

These activities have a definite impact on Big Sur's natural environment. Human feces have polluted several of the coastal streams, especially the Arroyo Seco, Big Sur River, and Salmon Creek. Water from the lower portions of these drainages must now be boiled before drinking. Hiking trails on steep slopes have accelerated erosion and caused small landslides. The ground at many campsites, particularly in the redwood groves, is trampled and compacted by overuse and threatens the very health of the trees.

Litter is another problem, both in the backcountry and along the highway. Bottles, cans, and even disposable baby diapers are regularly tossed out of moving cars. Cigarette butts are thrown along trails and the roadside, greatly increasing the risk of fire. Smog sometimes accumulates and settles in Big Sur Valley during times of heavy summer traffic, and rain runoff from the road surface washes engine oil and gasoline residues into the creeks and streams.

NONNATIVE PLANTS

Nonnative, or exotic, plants are those species that were not part of a region's original flora but were instead introduced here by humans. Table 15 lists some of the most common nonnatives in Big Sur. About 20 percent of Monterey County's plant species are nonnative. Such a large percentage is alarming because of the disruptive nature of the exotics. These plants are usually weedy, aggressive, and hardy, and they often displace less vigorous native plants. This in turn can have repercussions for the animal life that is part of that ecosystem. There is also a less tangible loss, one of both a visual and philosophical nature, when an area as pristine and natural as Big Sur is overrun with foreign weeds.

The grassland plant community is the hardest hit by the exotics. Of Monterey County's grass species, 44 percent are from other parts of the world and some of these were introduced here as forage for cattle and sheep. Nongrass exotics, such as the filarees and milk thistle, are also common in the grasslands.

Aside from the grassland species, many of the most troublesome exotics in Big Sur were introduced accidentally, as ornamentals, or as dune and roadcut stabilizers. Many of these plants are confined to roadsides and other disturbed areas around homes and landslides, while others use the roads as dispersal routes. Ice plant (*Carpobrotus edule*) from South Africa is used to stabilize roadcuts and dunes along Highway 1 and is also a popular ornamental. Once established, it spreads from the road and encroaches on native dune and coastal scrub vegetation. French broom (*Cytisus monspessulanus*) (fig. 184), a green shrub with bright yellow flowers, is another persistent nonnative that invades the coastal scrub and forest understory from roadsides. Wild radish (*Raphanus sativus*), a bright pink and white flower, and shortpod or summer mustard (*Brassica geniculata*) (fig. 185) are also common roadside exotics.

Pampas grass (*Cortaderia atacamensis*) (fig. 186) is a roadside exotic that perhaps poses the most serious threat to native vegetation in Big

TABLE 15. COMMON NON-NATIVE PLANTS OF THE BIG SUR AREA

Common Name	Genus/Species
Common yarrow	*Achillea millefolium*
Pimpernel	*Anagallis arvensis*
Slender wild oat	*Avena barbata*
Wild oat	*Avena fatua*
Field mustard	*Brassica rapa*
Shortpod mustard	*Brassica geniculata*
Rattlesnake grass	*Briza maxima*
Ripgut grass	*Bromus diandrus*
Soft chess	*Bromus hordeaceus*
Foxtail chess	*Bromus rubens*
Poison hemlock	*Conium maculatum*
Pampas grass	*Cortaderia atacamensis*
Monterey cypress	*Cupressus macrocarpa*
Bermuda grass	*Cynodon dactylon*
French broom	*Cytisus monspessulanus*
Gum trees	*Eucalyptus* spp.
Long-beaked filaree	*Erodium botrys*
Red-stemmed filaree	*Erodium cicutarium*
Sweet fennel	*Foeniculum vulgare*
Barnyard foxtail	*Hordeum leporinum*
Italian ryegrass	*Lolium multiflorum*
English ryegrass	*Lolium perenne perenne*
Bur clover	*Medicago polymorpha*
Ice plant	*Carpobrotus edule*
Watercress	*Nasturtium officinale*
Monterey pine	*Pinus radiata*
English plantain	*Plantago lanceolata*
Wild radish	*Raphanus sativus*
Milk thistle	*Silybum marianum*
Stinging nettle	*Urtica dioica*
Winter vetch	*Vicia villosa*
Spring vetch	*Vicia sativa*

Figure 184.   *Cytisus monspessulanus*, French broom

Figure 185.   *Brassica geniculata*, shortpod
mustard

Figure 186.   *Cortaderia atacamensis*, pampas grass

Sur and elsewhere in California. It is an attractive plant with long, thin leaves and graceful white plumes. But the leaves are razor sharp and the plumes release millions of hardy seeds to the wind. Entire slopes, such as those near Lucia and Esalen, are covered thick with the large clumps. The plant is making inroads into the coastal scrub and grassland areas, pushing aside native shrubs and herbs. Other exotic plants common in the coastal scrub are common yarrow (*Achillea millefolium*) (fig. 187), poison hemlock (*Conium maculatum*) (fig. 188), sweet fennel (*Foeniculum vulgare*) (fig. 189), and stinging nettle (*Urtica dioica*) (fig. 190).

Pampas grass is native to an area of barren plains, the pampas, in Argentina and Chile. In California, this species does well on the bare,

Figure 187. *Achillea millefolium,* common yarrow

Figure 188. *Conium maculatum,* poison hemlock

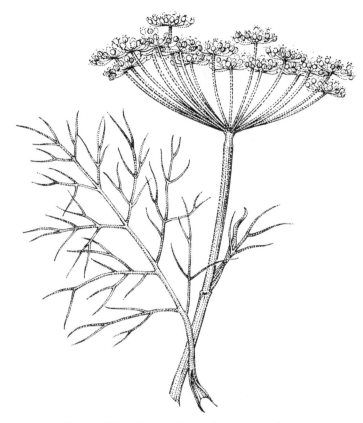

Figure 189.   *Foeniculum vulgare,* sweet fennel

disturbed slopes of roadcuts, logging cuts, landslides, sand dunes, erosional gullies, and overgrazed pasture. In these areas, the plant has sometimes been used as an erosional deterrent and soil stabilizer. But as the pampas grass colonies grow, they serve as a stable base from which seeds are dispersed throughout the neighboring plant communities. Any areas that show the least sign of disturbance are often invaded. Just south of Lucia, for example, the slopes are covered with large pampas grass plants that moved in after the area was logged.

Most visitors and local residents are unaware of the botanical havoc caused by this plant. Many actually plant it in their yards and unwittingly spread the seeds. One means of seed dispersal, perhaps helping to account for the roadside distribution of the plant, has been termed by frustrated ecologists as the "honeymoon dispersal mechanism." Motor-

Figure 190. *Urtica dioica,* stinging nettle

ists visiting Big Sur, some of whom are newlyweds, often attach a pampas grass seed plume to the radio antennae of their cars and scatter the seeds as they drive along the highway.

Eradication of the plant is costly and labor intensive. Herbicides have been used in parts of the Monterey Peninsula and Big Sur, but these poisons can have undesirable side effects. Manual removal, however, is nearly impossible on Big Sur's vertical slopes, and it remains to be seen what will be done to check this plant's expansion.

There are several exotic tree species that have also found a suitable habitat in Big Sur. Gum trees (*Eucalyptus* spp.) are the most common and should be familiar to any Californian. Native to Australia and the South Pacific, gum trees were sold as ornamentals in San Francisco nurseries as early as 1850. Since that time, the trees have been planted commercially for a variety of reasons, including use as firewood, as a hardwood in the making of furniture, and as a supposed deterrent of malaria in the late nineteenth century. There is a difference of opinion among ecologists whether *Eucalyptus* are expanding their range in California or if they are only holding on to territory provided for them by early large-scale plantings. Some researchers believe that the trees' range is in fact decreasing in the face of competition with native redwoods, tanoaks, and live oaks.

Ecologists and planners for the California State Park System feel otherwise, and in 1986 they implemented plans to remove blue gum (*E. globulus*) trees, the most common *Eucalyptus,* from Andrew Molera and Julia Pfeiffer-Burns State Parks. The blue gum at Molera are located near the Cooper Cabin and perhaps constitute the largest single grove in Big Sur. This grove appears to have grown from the original trees that were planted around the cabin by homesteaders. Park officials are concerned that younger blue gum trees are invading the nearby riparian habitat and are crowding out the native willows and western sycamores. The trees also appear to be spreading elsewhere in Big Sur, such as at the mouth of Hot Springs Creek near Esalen Institute and near the Dolan Creek bridge.

At this writing, the eradication program at Molera has proceeded, but there has been some opposition. Members of the Big Sur Historical Society were concerned that trees of historical value—that is, the original blue gum trees planted alongside the cabin—were going to be destroyed. Biologists were concerned that the removal program would adversely affect the monarch butterflies (fig. 191) that migrate along the coast during winter and use the grove to roost and mate. The monarchs are sensitive to even the slightest changes in temperature and wind at their roosting sites.

Nectivorous birds, such as orioles and yellow-rumped warblers, use winter-flowering eucalyptus flowers as a sole source of nectar prior to the winter rains. Orioles probably did not overwinter in coastal California prior to the introduction of the gum trees. Aside from these birds, and butterflies, bees, and hummingbirds, all of which feed on the gum flowers, few native plants and animals grow, nest, or feed in the gum groves. The understory at the Molera grove consists primarily of poison oak, but often such groves lack even that much of an understory. Most birds and mammals tend to avoid the gum and instead prefer the hardwood forests, oak woodlands, and scrub. Notable exceptions are the red-shouldered and red-tailed hawks that roost and nest in the blue gum. But these birds, like others that are sometimes seen in the Molera grove, tend to find most of their food in neighboring habitats.

Two other trees that are common in Big Sur are the Monterey pine and the Monterey cypress (see chap. 4, section on the mixed evergreen forest). These two species are native to the Monterey Peninsula, but

Figure 191.   *Danaus plexippus,* Monarch butterfly, on
blue gum

they are not believed to be native to the Big Sur region. The Monterey
cypress, in fact, was close to extinction when the Spanish arrived in
1769. At that time, there were only about 11,000 of the trees remaining
in stands that covered only about 20 ha (50 acres) near the shoreline of
the Monterey Peninsula. The Monterey cypress and Monterey pine have
since been widely planted. They were favorites of homesteaders, and
these old trees often are the only signs remaining at abandoned homestead sites. Recent settlers have continued the practice, and the trees line
the highway in many areas from Carmel to San Simeon.

RESIDENTIAL DEVELOPMENT AND ROADS

Most Big Sur residents greatly value and respect their natural surroundings, and most tend to keep them as natural as possible when they build
their homes. Trees are left standing and local building materials are
used. Nonetheless, commercial and residential development pressures
are increasing, and it is necessary to look at the adverse impacts of such
developments on Big Sur's natural features.

The most obvious impact of new homes and other buildings on the hillsides is a visual one. The Big Sur experience, more than anything else, is a visual experience. Some argue that the great scenic values for which Big Sur is so famous are being destroyed piecemeal by increased development. There are currently about 400 developed residential parcels in Big Sur. However, the recent County Land Use Plan allows for another 1000 new residences. The same plan allows for the building of 300 commercial hotel units in addition to the 170 already existing in Big Sur. Such an increase, if allowed to proceed, will undoubtedly alter Big Sur's wild and scenic character.

There are some other disturbing trends besides the building of new homes and hotel rooms. Many current homeowners, especially those directly along Highway 1, have planted lines of nonnative trees and shrubs to block their homes from view of the road. The Big Sur Coast Land Use Plan specifically calls for the use of native plants in such cases, yet many landowners either ignore or are unaware of this fact. While it may be appropriate in some cases that homes and other structures are hidden by this vegetation, the trees and shrubs also create a sort of tunnel effect along the road. North of Esalen Institute, for example, gum trees, Monterey pine, and various shrubs obscure or completely obliterate ocean and coastline vistas. As discussed earlier, such nonnative flora are also detrimental because they compete with native plants.

Increased development also puts a strain on the already limited water resources and necessitates the building of more access roads on the hillsides. Like cattle paths and hiking trails, but on a much greater scale, these roads accelerate erosion and can cause landslides. The slides are followed by soil loss and stream sedimentation.

Landslides are a natural geological occurrence. As the mountains are uplifted, slides and slumping occur where the slopes are too steep and the sediments too loose to resist gravity. The hills and cliffs are full of ancient slides that are overgrown with vegetation. But road and trail construction across a steep slope can increase the critical angle of the slope and undermine it. This also concentrates the energy of rain runoff, causing it to be more erosive.

Highway 1 is the most disruptive of all local roads in this respect. It has had a long and costly history of landslides since its construction. During the mid-1980s, there were several slides that closed the highway, the most notable of which included the Sycamore Draw slide, the J. P. Burns slide, and the Redwood Gulch slide. Cal-Trans, the California state highway maintenance department, corrected these slides by cut-

ting and bulldozing debris from the tops of the slides and moving it to
the bottoms, eventually decreasing the angle of the slopes to a less dangerous and more stable degree.

What remains, unfortunately, are massive, barren scars on the mountainside. The J. P. Burns slide, in fact, was the largest earth-moving operation in Cal-Trans history and created a scar that from air or sea is a
more visible landmark than Point Sur. These slopes are also scoured of
any soil layer and are thus ripe for increased erosion and invasion by
nonnative weeds such as pampas grass. Cal-Trans corrective operations
also thrust great quantities of sediments into the intertidal area, forming
beaches where none had existed before. Critics of Cal-Trans hope that
future repairs will minimize the alteration of Big Sur's natural landscapes even if it means more costly and time-consuming repairs.

CHANGES IN FAUNA

Extinction and depletion of animal species by humans is not just a modern phenomenon. Although archaeologists and anthropologists argue
about the specifics, there is a general belief that prehistoric human hunters may have been responsible for the extinction of several prey species
in both the New and Old Worlds. It is still unclear just how serious an
impact California's Stone Age residents had upon their nonhuman animal counterparts.

There must have been some animals, perhaps mollusks or birds from
the intertidal, that were heavily depleted. Researcher Burton Gordon
points out the presence of bones of an extinct diving duck, *Chendytes
lawi,* commonly found in middens north of Santa Cruz. This duck was
flightless, had large, goose-sized legs, and was probably easy to capture.
These bones are found in midden layers dated 5390 to 3780 B.P., and
the duck may have been overhunted by the local natives.

Changes in Big Sur's fauna were greatly accelerated with the arrival
of European settlers. The general pattern of these changes involves several phases. First was the immediate eradication of those animals that
directly compete with or endangered settlers, usually upper level carnivores such as grizzly bears, mountain lions, and wolves. Then came the
exploitation of animals for their food, sport, and commercial value,
with examples being the gray whale and sea otter. The third stage was
the depletion of certain species due to loss of habitat and direct or inci-
dental poisoning, which includes the peregrine falcon, brown pelican,
and California condor. Finally, imbalances occurred from the introduc-

tion of nonnative animals such as wild pigs, livestock, and feral dogs and housecats and the subsequent increase or decrease of certain related species.

Ironically, grizzly bears (*Ursus arctos*) at first thrived with the coming of the Spanish. Domestic cattle in the northern Santa Lucia range were so numerous in the late eighteenth and early nineteenth centuries that grizzlies had a new and plentiful food source. The bears also fed on whale remains that floated ashore as a result of the whaling industry. During this time, according to ecologist Tracy Storer, the bears of central California "multiplied as they had never done before."

Grizzlies persisted in the Santa Lucia Range until the late 1800s. Although they were hunted by the Spanish and used for sport in bear and bull fights, the grizzlies were able to survive in the more wild and unsettled parts of the range. But the homesteading era brought more settlers into the backcountry, settlers that would not tolerate the loss of their ranch animals. In 1857, a man named Jacobo Escobar was paid $70 for killing three grizzlies that were taking cattle on Rancho El Sur. Michael Pfeiffer hung strychnine rolled up in balls of fat from oak trees to kill the grizzlies in Sycamore Canyon. In 1878, the sheriff of Salinas came across a large bear near Tassajara Springs, and it was reported at the time that Pine Valley was full of grizzlies. Although the last sighting of a grizzly in California is believed to have been in the southern Sierra Nevada at Sequoia National Park in 1924, the bears in Big Sur probably did not survive into the twentieth century.

Mountain lions and wolves were similarly persecuted. Wolf numbers were probably never very high in this region, but the animals reportedly preyed upon cattle and sheep in the early 1800s. Spanish cattlemen at Monterey killed them with poison imported from Mexico. Mountain lions, however, are still regularly seen in the backcountry and on the coastal ridgetops, although nowhere near their original numbers. These animals have been hunted both for sport and by ranchers who feared they were losing too many sheep and hogs to the big cats. Arbues Boronda, a homesteader in the Big Creek area in the early 1900s, killed about thirty mountain lions a year. According to neighbor Marion Harlan, Boronda raised only hogs, of which the lions would take a significant number. So Boronda trained his dog, "a big hound dog," to hunt mountain lions. Some years he got only fifteen lions, while other years he got fifty. As the cats became more rare in Big Sur and throughout the state, the hunting bounty on the species was finally removed in 1967. In a recent and controversial move, the State Fish and Game

Commission attempted to reopen a hunting season on the lions in 1987; the proposed season is currently suspended under a court injunction.

Another aspect of Big Sur's faunal changes involved the commercial hunting of several species of marine mammals. These animals include the southern sea otter, gray and humpback whales, California sea lion, and elephant seal. Their ecology and recent history are discussed in more detail in chapter 3 in the section on marine mammals.

Tule elk (*Cervus elaphus*) and pronghorn antelope (*Antilocapra americana*) are two terrestrial species that may have once occurred in eastern parts of the region. The historical range of the elk is unclear. They were quite common in the marshy areas around Monterey Bay and the Salinas Valley, but the species may have also extended up the grassy valleys of the Santa Lucia Range. It is unlikely that they inhabited the steep, coastal areas. They survived through the Spanish, Mexican, and early American periods, but by 1875, only one pair remained in California. Since the early 1900s, the elk population has thrived under strict protection and several populations have been established throughout the state. The nearest population in Big Sur is a herd of over 100 animals at Fort Hunter–Ligget on the inland side of the Santa Lucia Range.

The pronghorn antelope did not last as long. Chroniclers of the Portola expedition remarked on the abundance of antelope in the Salinas Valley. The animals may have also inhabited the Nacimiento and San Antonio valleys, but there is no historical evidence to support this possibility. It is believed, though, that the pronghorns preferred the drier grasslands of the valley areas, while the tule elk preferred moist areas. This difference in habitat may have allowed the elk to avoid direct competition with cattle for a few decades longer than the pronghorns. The California Fish and Game Department recently reintroduced pronghorn into eastern Monterey County and plan to establish a herd at Fort Hunter Ligget in the near future.

Loss of habitat and pollution has seriously affected several bird species that historically claimed Big Sur as part of their range. The California condor, now teetering on the brink of extinction, was once considered common in Monterey County. In 1910, a rancher named Gamboa counted as many as 15 of the birds crowding around a dead cow near Big Creek. Seventeen condor eggs were taken by egg collectors in Monterey County during the latter half of the nineteenth century, perhaps accounting for the subsequent lack of a local breeding population. Nonetheless, Big Sur was still part of the species' range, with at least eight condor sightings here during the 1970s.

Like the grizzly bear, the condor may have at first enjoyed a population increase with the coming of the Spanish and Americans. Dead cows and whales were probably more plentiful than ever before. But these conditions were relatively shortlived. Burton Gordon points out that the decline of the condor in the Monterey Bay area coincides with the decline of the whaling industry and the changeover from the cattle-based economy of the Spanish period to the agriculture-based economy of the American period. The Spanish were more interested in cattle hides than meat, and they often left skinned carcasses on the range. This practice continued until the California Gold Rush of 1849, when California's increasing population created a greater demand for meat. There was a sudden decrease in food available to the condors during this changeover period. Aside from the egg collecting, the large birds were also used for target practice by hunters, and condors often fed on animals that had been killed with poison or lead shot, in turn poisoning themselves.

Peregrine falcons and brown pelicans are two more bird species found in Big Sur that have suffered a substantial decline. Both are classified as endangered species, and both are believed to owe most of their problems to the presence of DDT and other pesticides in their respective food chains. Other problems include shootings, the illegal nest robbing of peregrine eggs and chicks by falconers, and the tangling and hooking of pelicans in fishing nets and lines. Both birds have made encouraging comebacks due to the banning of DDT, and the peregrine has been further aided with a captive breeding and reestablishment plan throughout much of the state. More information on these and several other uncommon birds, such as bald and golden eagles, can be found in chapter 6 in the section on birds.

Not all native animals suffer from human disturbance. California ground squirrels, for instance, are native rodents that become extremely numerous on lands that are overgrazed; areas near Point Sur, Prewitt Ridge, and Palo Colorado Canyon have large squirrel colonies. Raccoons feed nightly at the garbage dumpsters of restaurants and campgrounds. Black-tailed deer have probably increased in numbers due in part to the eradication of predators and their favorable treatment as a game animal. They also do well in areas that are burned and logged because of the new growth that follows such disturbances.

There are several nonnative animal species living today in the Big Sur region. The wild pig and wild turkey (*Meleagris gallopavo*) were introduced for hunting purposes. The wild pig, a native of Europe, was introduced in the Carmel Valley by hunters and has since spread throughout the mountains. It is a formidable animal with curved tusks and a large head, and it has increased its influence by breeding with escaped domestic pigs. Wild pigs feed in the open woodlands, hardwood forests, and grassy meadows, digging up roots, bulbs, and tubers with their fleshy snouts. They are popular game animals, but they are considered pests since their rooting causes topsoil to erode and damages native vegetation. Backcountry areas of the Los Padres National Forest, especially the upper Carmel Valley and Arroyo Seco drainages, are the most seriously affected by the animals. In the 1960s, several problem pigs were trapped in Pfeiffer–Big Sur State Park and removed. Elsewhere in California, for example, in Marin and Santa Cruz counties, the wild pig population is so large that expensive methods have been tried to control the animals.

The European starling (*Sturnus vulgaris*) is the most significant introduced bird. It was originally released in New York's Central Park in 1890, and by 1954 it had made its way to Carmel Valley. Unfortunately, this bird is not restricted to urban environments and is becoming increasingly common in coastal and backcountry Big Sur. It is an aggressive cavity nester and often displaces other hole dwellers, such as bluebirds, woodpeckers, and purple martins, from their nests.

The presence of exotic plants and animals in agricultural, urban, and suburban areas is often tolerated and even encouraged. Interesting and colorful trees and shrubs are planted in parks, and many nonnative birds, such as the English sparrow (*Passer domesticus*), fare extremely well in settled areas and do no apparent harm. But in an area such as Big Sur, which is valued more than anything else for its wildness and unspoiled character, the increased presence of exotic plants and animals should be recognized and controlled wherever possible.

PART II

Field Guide to Big Sur Public Lands

Introduction

The Santa Lucia Range and the Big Sur coast have long been recognized and enjoyed by the public. Even before Highway 1 opened, people came here to seek solitude and grandeur. The earliest sightseeing visitors used routes developed by the pioneers, some of which followed old trading and travel routes used by the Native Americans. The Old Coast Trail traversed the coastal ridge north to south and connected various homestead sites. By the 1920s, this trail was famous among writers as one of the most spectacular in the west. Likewise, the main trading routes from east to west—from Jolon to Lucia and from Carmel Valley to Big Sur Valley—were popular but rugged routes to the coast.

With the founding of the Monterey National Forest in 1906, use of these trails increased. The 1930s and 1940s saw a rapid expansion of access trails into the Big Sur backcountry as the U.S. Forest Service began managing its lands for recreation. The coastal state parks were also formed during this time. The backcountry was used extensively by pack trains of hunters, fishermen, and recreationists, and a small wilderness tourist industry soon developed.

The network of trails in the backcountry today dates from these early periods. Some of the old trails are no longer maintained and have returned to the wild. Others are still well used, forming an extensive trail system that provides access to most parts of the backcountry. U.S. Forest Service maps, including an excellent map of the Ventana Wilderness, show this modern trail system. U.S. Geological Survey topographic maps, although often outdated, give fairly accurate details of the topography and some trails and roads. In addition, brochures on individual state parks and trail guides have been published that give extensive, detailed trail information.

We do not describe each trail in the Big Sur area step by step, nor do we provide a detailed trail map. Instead, we try to give a picture of the character of the land in all the diverse parts of the area, focusing on features of natural and historical interest. This focus will also allow the reader to anticipate what kind of environment to expect when planning an excursion. The information here is meant to complement part I so that you can go out and see, touch, and feel what makes Big Sur so unique among wild areas of the United States. In addition to the natural history of each area, we provide general information on access and facilities. Five maps are provided at the back of the book which cover the entire Big Sur region and adjacent areas (see next section).

This field guide covers the entire Big Sur area—the coastline from Garrapata State Park on the north to San Carporforo Creek on the south and the Santa Lucia Range inland from these points. The guide is divided into three major sections: coastal state parks, the coastal area of Los Padres National Forest, and the Ventana Wilderness (also in the Los Padres National Forest). In the state parks section, we describe each park individually. National Forest lands are more extensive and so we treat them a little differently. First, we describe those parts of the national forest that include coastline, primarily in the southern Big Sur area. Then we describe inland areas and the Ventana Wilderness, taking each watershed and describing it much like we would a single state park. Lands both within and out of the wilderness area are included.

In all cases, we present those features that we find outstanding and illustrative of the special natural history of the area. There is much more to this mountain range than we can cover, however, and much more to be discovered. Each new trip into the backcountry, each new day hike along a trail reveals plants unseen before, animals only glimpsed in guidebooks, rocks of unusual color, pattern, and texture, and startling vistas. We hope that this part of the book leads the reader into an exploration of the range that heightens the sense of wonder that is so intrinsic to the Big Sur area. We ask visitors to travel lightly on this fragile landscape and to observe wilderness etiquette when camping and hiking. An excellent guide to "minimum impact" camping is provided by Bruce Hampton and David Cole in their book *Soft Paths* (1988, Stackpole Boots, Harrisburg, Penn.).

MAPS OF THE BIG SUR AREA

We have provided at the back of this book five topographic maps that cover Big Sur at a sufficient scale for most hiking and driving purposes. We believe that these are the best maps available to use with this book. However, other maps are available that may be useful for some trips.

The U.S. Geological Survey publishes topographic maps at a scale of 1:24,000. The quadrangles that cover the Big Sur area include Point Sur, Mount Carmel, Carmel Valley, Big Sur, Ventana Cones, Chews Ridge, Pfeiffer Point, Partington Ridge, Tassajara Hot Springs, Junipero Serra Peak, Lopez Point, Cone Peak, Cape San Martin, Alder Peak, Villa Creek, and Burro Mountain. These maps are available from the U.S. Geological Survey, Map Sales, P.O. Box 25286, Denver, Colorado 80225 (telephone 303-236-7477). They are also available at many backpacking and camping stores in California.

The U.S. Geological Survey also publishes 1:100,000-scale metric maps that cover the area and show topography. The Point Sur and Cambria quadrangles cover all of the areas discussed in this book and a large area inland. They can also be ordered from the Survey at the same address as above.

The U.S. Forest Service publishes a map of the Los Padres National Forest, a large portion of which is south of the Big Sur region near Santa Barbara. The part of this map covering the Big Sur Ranger District includes all of the Ventana Wilderness and surrounding forest lands, but excludes some coastal parks of the Big Sur area. The scale of this map is rather small (about 1:169,000), but it shows roads in good detail. This map is available at the Big Sur Ranger Station in Big Sur, or from the Monterey District, Los Padres National Forest, 406 S. Mildred, King City, California 93930.

The U.S. Forest Service also publishes a map of the Ventana Wilderness at a scale of 1:63,360. This relatively new map (1987) is an excellent one to have for the wilderness, but it does not include all of the Big Sur area as described in this book. It is also available from the Big Sur Ranger Station in Big Sur or by writing the Monterey district at the above address.

Coastal State Parks

GARRAPATA STATE PARK

ACCESS: There is no main entrance to Garrapata State Park, but it is accessible via several highway pullouts beginning 8.7 km (5.4 mi) south of Rio Road in Carmel and extending along the coast about 3.4 km (2.1 mi) (see map 1 at the back of the book). Prominent signs beside the highway mark the northern and southern boundaries of the park. Unmarked trails to coastal bluffs, rocky coves, and a few small beaches depart from the highway pullouts. There are trail signs at Soberanes Canyon, 10.8 km (6.7 mi) from Rio Road, and at Soberanes Point, 11.4 km (7.1 mi) south of Rio Road.

INTRODUCTION

The heart of Garrapata State Park is several convoluted miles of some of the most dramatic rocky shoreline in California. The craggy coastline is backed by a marine terrace that ranges from 5 to 15 m (15 to 50 ft) high and a few meters to 300 m (10 to 1000 ft) wide. Inland from the narrow terraces, austere mountains rise to about 600 m (2000 ft) in elevation, and the park includes an extensive area of this inland ridge.

The coastal bluffs are covered with coyote bush, California coffeeberry, California sagebrush, bush lupine, blue blossom, and other coastal scrub plants. This colorful tapestry of various shades of gray and green shrubs are mingled year-round with such wildflowers as Indian paintbrush, sticky monkey flower, and California buckwheat. The scrub is low and wind pruned to smooth contours. Bright carpets of introduced ice plant (*Caprobrotus edulis*) cover a large area within the scrub along the bluffs of the park. It is the sole ground cover in many areas and seems to be spreading up the coastal slopes. Seaside aster (*Erigeron glaucus*) and succulents such as sea lettuce are common near the bluff edges, and a few scattered Monterey pines and Monterey cypresses grow near the northern end of the park. A long row of Monterey cypresses lines Highway 1 at the mouth of Soberanes Canyon, near the site of the Soberanes homestead.

The park also includes lower Soberanes Canyon, a refuge for a lush redwood forest and riparian vegetation. Spring wildflowers such as sky lupine, California poppy, owl's clover, and shooting star flood the extensive grasslands of the park in spring. A large and expanding colony of coast prickly pear cactus (*Opuntia oricola*), a Big Sur nonnative, grows on the canyon's south-facing slope near the mouth of the canyon.

This part of the Big Sur coast is composed of a type of granitic rock known as quartz diorite. The large crystals of this coarse-grained rock are prominent and glisten in the sunlight; close up, the black and white crystals give the rock a salt-and-pepper appearance. Within the surf splash zone, the overall rock is grayish in color, but higher up it is weathered to a pastel buff to orange. An intricate network of fractures criss-cross the surface of the rock; these joints formed as the rock was cooling and contracting deep beneath the surface of the earth. The numerous cracks provided an avenue for water to enter when the rocks were uplifted to the earth's surface, and much of the ruggedness of the coastline here is a result of erosion along joints and other fissures in the hard rock. Deep coves have formed along large fissures, some of which extend tens of meters into the shoreline, forming an intricate interfingering of rock and sea.

The quartz diorite here is typical of the granitic rock of the northern Santa Lucia Range. There are few places in the range where these rocks are as well exposed as here since they are laid bare by the action of the surf. This rock resembles the granodiorite of Point Lobos and the Monterey Peninsula, which have also eroded into deep, craggy coves. The only other coastal granitic rock accessible in the Big Sur area is to the south at Partington Cove (see Julia Pfeiffer-Burns State Park). These hard granitic rocks produce little sediment as they erode, and this is the primary reason for the crystal clear water along these sections of shoreline.

Thick marine terrace deposits on top of the granitic basement rocks are clearly exposed along the coastal bluffs, especially in the cut banks of Highway 1. The coarse sand of these deposits was ground from the basement rock by surf when the bluffs were lower in elevation. These deposits now form striking, crumbly cliffs that rapidly erode, and nowhere else in Big Sur are marine terrace deposits so clearly exposed.

The park property was once part of the 3568-ha (8818-acre) San Jose y Sur Chiquito land grant given by Mexican governor Juan Alvarado to Marcelino Escobar in 1839 (see chap. 7, Human History). The property stretched along the coast from the Carmel River to Palo Colorado Creek and was used for ranching. The ranch changed hands and was divided into smaller parcels, some of which were purchased by Ezekial Soberanes, Sr., and his son in 1878. The Soberanes ranch house was an adobe covered with clapboard siding that stood south of the Soberanes Creek mouth. Ezekial Soberanes is the earliest recorded European resident in the area. The land again changed hands in the 1940s, and all that remains of the old ranch is the barn and corral just east of Highway 1.

The dark, shell-flecked midden soils so common along these coastal bluffs indicate that people lived in this area long before the Spanish arrived. These people were probably members of the Rumsen subgroup of the Ohlone Indians (see chap. 7). Archaeological work done on a small portion of a midden here turned up a shell bead dated at A.D. 100–300. Animal remains indicate that the people here relied mostly on shellfish, especially mussels and abalone, as a food source. Sea lion and sea otter bones were also identified, as well as bones from land mammals such as deer, rabbits, and squirrels. The natives used plant food resources including acorns and buckeye seeds. The archaeologists studying this midden believe that this site was only used in the summer months. Such an exposed site would be cold and windy in the winter, and the mussels that seem to have been the food staple here are not edible in the winter months. Obsidian flakes from the site came from the Borax Lake area, about 290 km (180 mi) north of Big Sur in the northern Coast Range.

SOBERANES POINT TRAILS

The only clearly marked coastal trails in the park are in the vicinity of Soberanes Point. This prominent and distinctive headland extends from a large buttresslike ridge off the mountains and ends in a gently rounded, conical mound known as Whale Peak. The summit of the peak is marked with a prominent bright orange mat of ice plant. A short trail from Highway 1 ascends this low peak. A broad, sweeping marine terrace surrounds the point, and trails follow the coastline around it. A short stroll of about 1.6 km (1 mi) around this point offers some of the most dramatic coastal scenery in Big Sur.

The northern end of the trail begins at the mouth of Soberanes Canyon on Highway 1, 10.8 km (6.7 mi) south of the Rio Road intersection in Carmel. From here it cuts through coastal scrub, around a deep gully eroded into the terrace, and out to the bluffs. The cover of nonnative ice plant on and around the point is extensive, and isolated colonies of this hardy coastal plant can be seen far up the slopes of the coastal ridges. Looking back toward the mountains, another prominent nonnative, the coast prickly pear, is visible above the mouth of Soberanes Canyon.

The rocky point just west of the Soberanes Creek mouth is Pastor Point, and a branch off the main trail leads out to a promontory near the point. A small footpath descends to cross a narrow, surf-worn channel that separates the rock of the point from the mainland bluff. A venture across the channel and out to the rocks at low tide is worth the scrambling, as the promontory of rock offers superb views of the coastline north and south. The white, guano-stained mounds of Lobos Rocks are visible about 500 m (1600 ft) offshore to the northwest, and groups of barking sea lions often rest on them. The deep blue cove stretching inland to the northeast is filled with kelp beds where sea otters often feed.

Numerous small side trails continue to branch off the main trail around Soberanes Point. These lead to the edge of the coastal bluff, where it is often possible to descend to rocky coves. Many tidepools have been worn into the rock and these are treasure troves of intertidal life. Sea palms stand on the surf-battered ledges, and feather boa kelp is draped in the surging pools. A host of other marine algae cling to the rock, but there is a conspicuous scarcity of shellfish here, such as mussels, barnacles, and chitons. This may be because the coarse, crumbly surface of the rock offers little foothold for these creatures, or it could be due to extensive harvesting by humans and sea otters. Shorebirds such as black turnstones are common here fall through spring, while brown pelicans glide by or perch alongside cormorants on offshore rocks. Belted kingfishers hunt the shallows of clear water, and black phoebes snatch sand flies from rotting kelp.

The volcano-shaped cone of Point Sur is in clear view to the south from Soberanes Point, and northward, the jagged spit of Yankee Point is the most distant visible point. On exceptionally clear days it is possible to see across Monterey Bay to the north as far as Santa Cruz. Salt-laden winds are often brisk on this point and have shaped the scrub to its picturesque low form. Just south of Soberanes Point, a deep cove known as South Point Cove is cut into the rock. The clear waters of this sheltered cove are choked with dense concentrations of giant kelp and bullwhip kelp. The trail meets Highway 1 again just south of the point at a pullout marked with a coastal access sign.

OTHER COASTAL ACCESS TRAILS

All other coastal access trails in the park are unmarked as of this writing. These trails depart from highway pullouts to lead across the coastal bluffs to viewpoints and, in places, descend to rocky coves. They offer short walks, but it is possible at times of low tides and calm surf to pick a route along fairly long sections of the coastline. High surf and tides can make this a very risky venture, however, as it is possible to become trapped by waves or high tide in steep-sided coves.

INLAND TRAILS

Two trails cut inland from the coast and can be connected to form a loop. The Soberanes Canyon Trail leaves the east side of Highway 1 about 11 km (6.8 mi) south of Rio Road in Carmel. An old barn and corral stand east of the highway near the trailhead, and a topographic map showing the trails hangs on the east wall of the barn. The Soberanes Creek Trail crosses the creek and then follows it inland, while the Rocky Ridge Trail branches off and climbs the grassy ridge north of the canyon mouth.

A walk up Soberanes Canyon reveals that the barren, austere appearance of the mountains here is deceiving. The trail follows the small perennial creek through a stand of coast prickly pear, coastal scrub, and grassland for the first mile. The creek is lined with some riparian vegetation dominated by willows. But it isn't long before the trail enters a dark redwood forest. Ferns, mosses, and streamside plants grow in the humid shade only a short distance from sunny, scrub-covered slopes. The redwoods are medium sized; this narrow canyon offers few stable flats, secure from flash floods, where big redwoods tend to grow.

The trail winds along the edge of the redwoods, dropping into them in places, and eventually cuts out of the canyon to the northeast up a steep ridge. It follows this narrow, grassy ridgeline up to the summit of the coastal ridge, where it meets up with the Rocky Ridge Trail. The open ridge offers expansive views of the jagged coastline below. It is a tough climb, but few trails in Big Sur provide such ready access to dramatic coastal views. The trail skirts the 874-m (1435-ft) promontory of Rocky Ridge and then descends steeply back down to the mouth of Soberanes Canyon, passing through grassland and sparse coastal scrub the whole way. The steep slopes of Rocky Ridge drop down to Soberanes Creek on the south and to steep, short drainages on the west. The entire loop hike is about 10 km (6 mi) in length and includes an elevation gain of nearly 600 m (2000 ft).

POINT SUR LIGHTHOUSE

ACCESS: The Point Sur Lighthouse State Historic Park is located about 30 km (20 mi) south of the Highway 1 and Rio Road junction in Carmel; it is just to the north of Andrew Molera State Park (see map 1). The park is only open for guided tours on weekends, but this schedule will probably change in the future as visitor use increases. Inquire at Pfeiffer–Big Sur State Park for updated tour information and fees.

Point Sur is one of Big Sur's most distinctive landmarks. Locally referred to as "the rock," it rises 110 m (360 ft) above sea level and is about 0.4 km (0.26 mi) in diameter at its widest point. It protrudes from the surrounding terraces and, at first glance, looks like a mysterious nearshore island, but it is actually connected to the mainland by a low-lying plain covered with shifting sand dunes. The gray stone buildings and lighthouse atop the rock augment Point Sur's mysterious aura, and it is one of the oldest and most complete light stations remaining on the California coast.

Point Sur has long threatened sailors and their ships, and several shipwrecks have occurred in the area. The northwest winds are often quite fierce here and have literally pushed ships, especially sailing vessels, onto the rocks that sit just offshore. The light was placed atop the point in 1887 to warn sailors away from these rocks.

The primary attraction of the park is the unusual history and impressive architecture of the light station. Construction began in 1887, a full 50 years prior to the completion of Highway 1, and access to and maintenance of this remote outpost was never easy. State park docents lead tours around the light station and give a complete history of these and related events.

The view from the top of the rock is superb in all directions. "False Point Sur" is the tree-covered knob that rises above the marine terraces south of the Navy base. Beyond it are the broad terraces of El Sur Ranch and Andrew Molera State Park, and beyond these is the Big Sur River Valley. Pico Blanco, a white mountain of marble, rises to the east behind the grassy ridges of El Sur Ranch. The Little Sur River mouth and Hurricane Point are along the coast to the north, and it is possible on clear days to see most of the points of the north coast, the Monterey Peninsula, and across Monterey Bay to Santa Cruz.

Point Sur is located west of the Sur fault and is composed entirely of rocks from the Franciscan Complex (see chap. 1, Big Sur Geology). The fault trends down the length of Big Sur Valley, then cuts behind the ridges directly east of Point Sur and comes into view again near Hurricane Point, where it trends offshore. A dark green metamorphosed lava known as greenstone is Point Sur's most prevalent rock, but some altered gabbro crops out on the north side of the point and some sandstone is scattered around. Gabbro is a dark volcanic rock that is extremely tough, and Point Sur's steep relief is a result of the resistance to erosion of both greenstone and gabbro.

On the landward side of the point is a large area covered with sand dunes. Many of the dunes are stabilized with dune grasses, but others are still moving southeastward as the prevailing winds push them along. The grasses stabilizing the dunes are a relatively recent phenomenon. Remond Richardson, a young geologist from Stanford University, visited the Point Sur area in the early 1920s and described the local features for his Master's thesis. He found these dunes to be the most actively migrating dunes along the entire Big Sur coast. He noticed the incessant northwesterly wind pushing the sand across the narrow neck of the point from the north side to the south side. This action is clearly visible today where the sand spills across the paved access road, but it was much more active in Richardson's day prior to the establishment of the dune grasses.

Richardson believed that thousands of years ago the Big Sur River may have flowed out to the ocean north of Point Sur instead of at its present mouth a few miles to the south. He traced a river course that led farther north along the terrace. False Point Sur and Point Sur were apparently on the west bank of the ancient river, and its mouth was at the beach on the north side of the point. The river later cut its present course to Molera Point as the entire area was slowly uplifted.

Point Sur is an important boundary in many ways. The point is believed to have marked the coastal border shared by the Ohlone and Esselen Indians. It is the westernmost point along this section of coast, sticking out into the ocean and deflecting northwesterly winds and fog.

The areas north of the point are usually more foggy and windy than those to the immediate south.

This phenomenon may help to explain why the Point Sur region is generally regarded as the southern boundary of California's northern coastal scrub plant community. The stabilized dunes and bluffs support typical coastal scrub, and the most common plants are lizardtail, yellow bush lupine, California sagebrush, and Indian paintbrush. This area along the access road to the lighthouse is also part of the El Sur Ranch and is heavily grazed by cattle. Milk thistle, which is a persistent exotic weed, has made disturbing inroads into the scrub and threatens to crowd out the lupines and other native vegetation.

The vegetation on Point Sur is strongly affected by the northwesterly winds. Windy days are the rule at Point Sur, and almost all of the plants exhibit low-growing forms. Poison oak, beach sagewort, California sagebrush, bush lupine, and lizardtail grow in wind-pruned fashion up on the exposed parts of the rock. Many colorful flowers are also found along the road and buildings at the top of the point: California poppy, beach evening primrose (*Camissonia cheiranthifolia*), common yarrow, several types of buckwheat (*Eriogonum* spp.), seaside aster, and powdery dudleya (*Dudleya farinosa*). Ice plant and New Zealand spinach (*Tetragonia tetragonioides*) are common nonnative plants that were probably introduced by the lighthouse keepers.

Point Sur also has some impressive offshore vegetation. Massive beds of bullwhip and giant kelps extend far offshore south of the point and support one of the richest concentrations of marine life in Big Sur. Brown pelicans, cormorants, black oystercatchers, and many other birds are common on the steep flanks of Point Sur and neighboring rocks. Harbor seals are seen regularly on offshore rocks, and sea otters feed on the plentiful shellfish between Point Sur and Molera Point. Whales are seen from the point, especially gray whales as they pass close to shore during their migration. Humpback, blue, and fin whales are much less common, but in 1986, a young male blue whale over 18 m (60 ft) long washed up on the beach just south of False Point Sur.

The tidal flats between Point Sur and False Point Sur are probably the best developed intertidal habitat in Big Sur. The area is relatively flat, composed of Franciscan sandstone, and is protected from the full brunt of the waves by Point Sur and smaller offshore rocks. Abalones, chitons, seastars, snails, limpets, and crabs are easily seen during medium and low tides. Sea otters and many types of birds and mammals forage in this area, and it is not uncommon to surprise a great blue heron or a raccoon during the early morning. This area is not part of the state park; property above the mean high tide line belongs to either the El Sur Ranch or the U.S. Navy and access is thus limited.

ANDREW MOLERA STATE PARK

ACCESS: Andrew Molera State Park is located on Highway 1 35 km (22 mi) south of the Rio Road junction in Carmel and 6.4 km (4 mi) north of Pfeiffer–Big Sur Park (see map 1). The main park entrance and parking lot is on the west side of the highway, and a number of other less conspicuous entrance gates exist along the road both north and south of the main entrance.

INTRODUCTION

Andrew Molera State Park is the largest state park on the Big Sur coast. Its 1920 ha (4800 acres) include long stretches of windswept beach, redwood-shaded rivers, and high elevation ridgetops that offer views to the ocean as well as into the backcountry. The park also covers a broad range of geological features, plant communities, and wildlife. There are excellent exposures of the Franciscan complex along the beach cliffs, and portions of the Sur and Sur–Hill faults are located on the east side of the park. Classic examples of marine terrace formations are also found along the coastal part of the park.

The coastal areas are covered with expansive stands of coastal scrub, while the Big Sur River, which cuts the park in half, is lined with riparian woodland that offers some of the best birdwatching in Monterey County. Large redwood and hardwood forests grow along tributary creeks and in side canyons. The steep ridges on the east side of the park support rolling grasslands and some coast live oak woodlands.

MOLERA BEACH

Molera Beach stretches about 3.7 km (2.5 mi) south from the Big Sur River mouth to Cooper Point. It forms the base of a long marine terrace and is one of the most beautiful beaches on the entire Big Sur coast. Long, sandy stretches broken by wave-swept points give way to cobble-covered flats that rumble as the waves recede. Plants of the coastal bluff scrub cover the cliffs and are in bright bloom for much of the spring and summer, and colorful and complex exposures of the Franciscan Formation are found along the cliffs.

The exposed rocks along most of the beach are gray, tan, and brown sandstone and shale. Much of the sandstone here is known as *gray-wacke* and is dark gray and brown in color. Pink garnets have eroded out of some of the sandstone and given much of the beach sand a reddish or purple hue. Interbedded with the sandstone are shale layers of a dark, almost blue-gray color. There are also thin bands of gray limestone sometimes associated with the shale. Some brilliant red and blue cherts, cut by thin white veins of quartz and calcite, outcrop in places. Nearby, a dark green igneous rock known as *greenstone* also has white veins running through it. About halfway along the beach south from the river mouth is a spectacular exposure known as the "Franciscan Rocks." Layer upon layer of colorful sedimentary rocks, many just a few centimeters thick, are folded and offset here.

The vegetation along these cliffs is typical of Big Sur's coastal bluff scrub. Growing on the cliffs and debris are colorful plants, many of which flower yellow: bush lupine, lizardtail, sedums and dudleyas, Hooker's evening primrose (*Oenothera hookeri*), and yellow sand verbena (*Abronia latifolia*). Seaside daisy (*Erigeron glaucus*), black sage, and California sagebrush are also common. Common monkey flower grows with horsetail rushes and arroyo willow along the many springs and small coastal streams coming off Pfeiffer Ridge.

Hiking around these points can be quite dangerous if tides are up and it is a windy day. Strong northwesterly winds—the rule rather than the exception along this beach—drive stinging sands that can be blinding. It is often easier to hike south along the beach, with the wind at your back, and then cut up to the Bluff Trail via the Spring Trail and return to the river mouth this way where winds and flying sands are less intense.

COASTAL TRAILS

A good network of well-graded and maintained trails is found along the coastal bluffs and ridges above Molera Beach. Both the Bluff Trail and the Ridge Trail originate at the same point on the south side of the river mouth. The Bluff Trail, which is less than 3 km (2 mi) long, stays to the right and is an almost level stroll along the elevated marine terrace at the western foot of Pfeiffer Ridge. The vegetation is coastal scrub with grassy openings. Coyote bush, bush lupine, and lizardtail are the dominant shrubs, and lizardtail grows in unbroken waist-high stands that cloak the terrace in yellow when the flowers bloom in summer. Look here for the coastal scrub birds described in chapter 4.

An area of stabilized sand dunes toward the end of the Bluff Trail supports some vegetation that is different from that of the surrounding coastal scrub. In addition to the more common shrubs, there are several dune plants that are not very common in Big Sur: mock heather (*Haplopappus ericoides*), a shrub with tiny needlelike leaves; beach sagewort (*Artemisia pycnocephala*), which is similar to California sagebrush; beach evening primrose (*Camissonia cheiranthifolia*), a small prostrate plant with yellow, four-petaled flowers; beach strawberry (*Fragaria chiloensis*), a low-growing strawberry plant with white, five-petaled flowers and serrated three-lobed leaves; and Hooker's primrose, a tall stalk with large yellow flowers. A great variety of plants grows on the landward side of this dune, including California coffeeberry, black sage, Monterey paintbrush (*Castilleja latifolia*), and sticky monkey flower.

The trail ends beyond the dune area and joins the Rattlesnake Trail and the Spring Trail, the latter of which leads down around the dune to Molera Beach. The Rattlesnake Trail climbs up Pfeiffer Ridge to a junction with the Ridge Trail. This is one of the best areas in Big Sur to see bobcats, and their droppings litter the trail. The ascent is a well-graded climb through coyote bush scrub and grassy clearings. In late spring, these drier open areas are covered with ruby chalice clarkia (*Clarkia rubicunda*), a four-petaled pink flower with a distinct reddish area at the base of the flower cup. These flowers contrast with the orange poppies and the yellow paintbrushes and dudleyas.

The Rattlesnake Trail also passes alongside some interesting wind-pruned redwoods. The winds are fierce here, and it is remarkable that the redwoods can grow at all. The trees look like a manicured hedge and have a low-lying contour that parallels the slope of the hill. Near the top of the ridge, taller redwoods grow in the protected flanks of side canyons. Above these are some excellent vistas north to Point Sur.

The Ridge Trail is an old road that is cut along the spine of Pfeiffer Ridge. It leaves the river mouth from the same spot as the Bluff Trail, heading instead to the left and uphill through coyote bush scrub. The trail affords good views to the east, north, and west along its entire length. Across the river valley to the east is the Sur fault zone, which is located near the sloping terraces cut into the side of the steep ridge. Beyond this ridge is Pico Blanco, and south along the ridge's spine is Post Summit and Mount Manuel. Below them are the steep drainages of Pheneger Creek and Juan Higuera Creek.

Toward the top of the Ridge Trail is a beautiful variety of woods and

open scrub. Yellow mariposa lily (*Calochortus luteus*), a bright yellow
flower that blooms in May and June, is commonly scattered with English plantain and wild oats throughout the clearings along the trail.
The scrub gives way to an enchanting forest of coast live oak. The twisting oak limbs are draped with lichens, and the understory is thick with
poison oak, hedge nettle, and California coffeeberry. Thimbleberry
plants, with their large maple-shaped leaves, grow thick in sunny yet
moist clearings. Some surprisingly large redwood and tanoak trees can
also be found along the trail near where it meets the Rattlesnake Trail
at the south end of the park. There is access from the Ridge Trail into
the river valley along the Hidden Trail and the South Boundary Trail.

RIVER TRAILS

The Big Sur River is accessible along its entire length within Andrew
Molera State Park. It flows down a relatively gentle grade after emerging
from the gorge in Pfeiffer–Big Sur State Park, and it stays to the western
edge of the valley near the base of Pfeiffer Ridge. There is a network of
trails on both sides of the river and over a dozen entrance gates along
the highway. The Bobcat Trail parallels the river along its eastern bank,
stretching from the parking area almost to the southern boundary of
the park; most highway entrance gates are along this trail. The River
Trail runs along the west bank of the river from the Creamery Meadow,
near the river mouth, upstream to Coyote Flats. Several short trails also
leave the highway near the northern park boundary and cross the flats
near the park campground to connect with the trail to the river mouth.

The recent geology along the stream channel is particularly interesting. The river flats and meadows are composed of river gravel and alluvium and are formed by occasional flooding and deposition as the
river loops back and forth on its way to the ocean. The river has cut
through its own deposits as the area was uplifted, and as a result the
floodplain is lower than the marine terraces on both sides of the river.
The marine terraces are made primarily of alluvium that washed down
from the mountains and was sorted by wave action. The terraces were
then raised above sea level as the mountains underwent another period
of uplift. These landforms and the history they represent are easily view-
able from Old Coast road, which is located across the highway from
the main entrance to the park.

A varied riparian vegetation and a mix of birds and mammals are
attracted to the river channel area. The riparian woodland along the Big

Sur River undergoes a gradual change as it nears the ocean. Several miles upstream from the river mouth, near the south park boundary, there is a mature woodland of large redwoods, western sycamores, black cottonwoods, bigleaf maples, and alders. East of the river and the highway are small tributaries with well-developed redwood forests, while west of the highway are flat grassy meadows dotted with redwoods and sycamores. Isolated, sunny river flats with sandy soil support a much drier plant community that includes yuccas, sagebrush, and coyote bush. This vegetation is protected from the ocean winds by the foot of Pfeiffer Ridge and the Franciscan cliffs along the western edge of the river flats.

Near the parking area, however, the river turns abruptly to the west. The riparian woodland is noticeably different here. There are still some large black cottonwoods and alders, but the redwoods have disappeared or are hidden from the salty wind within the protective covering of the alders. Large sycamores grow in Creamery Meadow and the campground. Willows and alders have the upper hand in the more exposed area closer to the ocean.

The river trails wind through this dark willow and alder forest. The willows grow especially dense, leaning on and intertwining with one another. The northwesterly wind is often raging above these trees, yet beneath the canopy, it is still and quiet except for the creaking of rubbing tree limbs. Poison oak and blackberry brambles form dense thickets, while mugwort, horsetail rushes, tule reeds, and Pacific silverweed (*Potentilla pacifica*) line the riverbanks and marshy areas that flood every winter.

The lower Big Sur River, especially the willow forest, is home to an array of small insectivorous songbirds. Chestnut-backed chickadees, bushtits, and several types of warblers are often seen here as they flit from twig to twig in search of their prey. Ornithologist Don Roberson described the Big Sur River mouth area as one of the best birding spots in Monterey County, and we support his claim. Belted kingfishers and red-shouldered hawks are sometimes seen or heard over the river, while black-shouldered kites, American kestrels, and turkey vultures are common on the marine terraces. Migrating raptors such as golden eagles and rough-legged hawks are rare but regular visitors to these terraces.

There is also a small lagoon where a sandbar closes off the river mouth in summer and fall. This is a rare feature along the Big Sur coast and attracts ducks and other waterbirds. Just offshore are several seastacks that are often occupied by nesting western gulls, roosting cormorants, and brown pelicans. Sanderlings, willets, and marbled godwits occupy the sandy beaches to the north of the Headland Trail, while black oystercatchers and black turnstones probe the rocky areas. This entire area is excellent for birdwatching. The river mouth area is also the site of an Esselen midden and possible village.

North of the river mouth and on the south side of Point Sur is a group of offshore rocks known as the "Sur Breakers." The water is relatively shallow, and large kelp beds extend father off the coast here than they do elsewhere. This area is rich in sea otters and harbor seals. The seals often rest on low nearshore rocks that are accessible at low tide.

COOPER CABIN AND LOCAL HISTORY

The Cooper Cabin is located just west of the campground on the north side of the river. It is considered to be the oldest standing structure in Big Sur and was built sometime in the mid-1800s. In 1834, the governor of Alta California, which at that time was still part of Mexico, granted the El Sur area to Juan Bautista Alvarado. Six years later, Juan Bautista Rogers Cooper acquired the land grant from Alvarado and used the land to graze livestock.

Over the years, Cooper leased portions of the ranch to other people, and in 1891 Eusebius Molera took over half the El Sur and attempted to breed buffalo with cattle. The experiment was shortlived because the "beeffalo" offspring were so odd-shaped that females often died while giving birth. In 1899, Cooper's wife Martha inherited one-third of the ranch and ran it herself. She stocked it with 1000 head of cattle, half of which were dairy cattle, and she grew hay and vegetables in the flat terraces on both sides of the river. In 1915, Andrew Molera took over operation of the ranch and ran it until he died in 1931; he was such a large man that a special coffin had to be built to fit him. Frances M. Molera, his son, died in 1968 at the age of 88 and left the land that now comprises the park.

The Cooper Cabin is surrounded today by many large blue gum trees that are believed to have been planted when the cabin was built. In 1986, state park workers started removing some of the younger trees. As mentioned in chapter 8, officials are concerned that the exotic trees are encroaching on and crowding out the native willows and alders, thus affecting the native wildlife. Certain groups, however, are opposed to the cutting. Biologists fear that the loss of trees would adversely affect the monarch butterflies that use the area as a roosting site while migrating. Some local residents also feel the trees are of historical value and should not be treated as a common exotic weed. The removal program continues as of this writing.

EAST MOLERA TRAIL

The East Molera Trail (gate C) is probably one of the least visited areas in the park. It departs from the east side of the highway about 0.4 km (0.25 mi) south of the main park entrance. The trail begins at an old wooden cattle ramp, climbs up to a roadcut and cement watertank, and continues uphill along an overgrown dirt road. It passes through a forest of coast live oak with an understory of sticky monkey flower, hedge nettle, and poison oak.

The trail leaves the forest and passes through a large field lying at the base of a ridge to the east. This sloping area, which is the size of several football fields, is covered with an impenetrable stand of milk thistle. Milk thistle usually takes hold in areas that were heavily grazed or were otherwise disturbed, and this field is probably the largest contiguous stand of the exotic weed in Big Sur. Other areas within the park also have extensive thistle growth, which does support some wildlife. Insects and butterflies feed on the flowers, and several species of swallows come to the field to hunt. House finches (*Carpodacus mexicanus*) and other seed-eating birds feast in the summer when the plants set seed.

This field is underlain by ancient landslide debris that came down from the steep mountain above. The area was uplifted along the Sur fault, and the trail crosses the fault as it leaves the field and begins to climb up the ridge. The trail leaves the metamorphosed Franciscan rocks southwest of the fault, passes through a band of sedimentary rocks as it climbs the old road up the ridge, and crosses the Sur–Hill fault. The sedimentary rocks at the ridgetop give way to metamorphic rocks of the Salinian block, and some outcrops of marble dot the grassy knolls.

The climb offers an interesting variety of vegetation. The lower ridge face is covered with coastal scrub dominated by California sagebrush, coyote bush, sticky monkey flower, and lizardtail. The slopes a bit higher up support open grassland made up primarily of wild oats, while some coast live oak and California bay grow in the shallow folds of the slope. The grasses continue up to the ridge summit and grow beneath handsome stands of redwoods and old, lichen-encrusted coast live oaks. The redwoods are tall, but their limbs appear to be shortened. Much of their foliage grows close to the trunk, which is probably a result of recent fires or the dry, windy conditions along the ridgetop. Milk thistle has also reached the summit and is thick in many parts of these once open meadows.

There are great vistas inland and oceanward from the high point of the trail. Pico Blanco stands across the canyon, and the Pico Blanco Trail and the mining roads are all in clear view. The park property extends east down to the South Fork of the Little Sur River but no trails enter this area. A roadcut continues to climb up this grassy ridge, and it is possible to hike clear to Post Summit and beyond to Mount Manuel.

WATERFALL TRAIL

The Waterfall Trail (gate F) leads to a thin falls that is hidden below tall redwoods. The trailhead is easy to miss on the east side of the highway. It is a few hundred meters south of the main park entrance, so look for gates 9 and 10 on the west side of the road. The trailhead is near these gates, so you can park here. Cross the highway and follow the trail (which is actually an old road) up a few hundred feet and look for a narrow path forking off to the right. The falls are just ahead.

Just west of the falls is a spring draining down from a slide area on the north side of the creek. Tufa deposits occur on the dead wood and tree roots near where the spring bubbles forth from the ground. Tufa is a porous, often crumbly form of limestone that is usually deposited by spring water on twigs and debris. The location of the falls and spring here may be due to the presence of the Sur fault just upstream. It is interesting to note that other falls of approximately the same size are also found along the Juan Higuera and Pfeiffer Redwood creeks along the Sur fault.

Beyond the falls and spring are the remnants of several paths and an old logging road. Several of the largest redwoods were cut a long time ago, but their offspring have quickly filled the gaps in the canopy. Many virgin redwoods were left standing, and these groves are some of the most picturesque in Big Sur. Redwood sorrel and sword ferns carpet the sloping forest floor. The sorrel cover is so dense that it extends into the adjoining bay forests and up the steep hillsides. There are a few tanoaks and bigleaf maples along the creek, but redwood and bay are the dominant trees along most of the creek.

The paths continue upstream in an intermittent fashion and force hikers to improvise to avoid deadfalls and recent slides. It appears that much of the forest actually grows on old mudflow and landslide debris. The stream has cut a relatively recent channel with steep walls through these loose deposits. The hummocky terrace directly above the stream bed is covered with boulders and cobbles of limestone, sandstone, and other rocks that were probably dropped by a mudflow. The forest trees atop these deposits grew after these materials slid down from the slopes above or were deposited by a flooding stream.

This creek, named Highbridge Creek according to local resident Hans Ewoldsen, was one of four major tributaries of the Big Sur River to experience mudflows after the Molera fire of 1972. Geologist Lionel Jackson used redwood root development and aging techniques to estimate dates of ancient mudflow occurrences along nearby Pfeiffer Redwood Creek; his work is discussed in the section describing Pfeiffer–Big Sur State Park.

The paths eventually die out as the canyon becomes more narrow and steep. One can hike up the canyon on the south side of the stream, leave the forest, and emerge onto a grassy clearing. The rest of the area above the redwood forest is a mixed hardwood forest occasionally dominated by bay. Douglas' iris, hedge nettle, and poison oak are the most common understory plants. This trail is particularly beautiful in spring when both the sorrel and the iris are in bloom. The redwood–bay forest floor is covered with green leaves and white flowers, while the hardwood forest floor is dotted with purple iris blossoms.

PFEIFFER–BIG SUR STATE PARK

ACCESS: Pfeiffer–Big Sur State Park is located 39 km (26 mi) south of Rio Road in Carmel (see map 1). There is a day use fee, and reservations are necessary for overnight camping. The park is extremely popular in the summer, and camping tickets can be purchased through the computerized ticketing agencies found throughout California.

INTRODUCTION

Pfeiffer–Big Sur State Park is often referred to as "the" state park in Big Sur. With its 323 ha (807 acres), it is not the largest of Big Sur's state parks, but it is the oldest and most well known. The park is famous for its narrow gorge carved by the Big Sur River and the old-growth redwoods that line the river and several of its tributaries. It was founded in

1933 when John and Florence Pfeiffer sold and donated much of their family's homestead land to the State Park Commission. Since that time, it has become one of the most popular state parks in California.

This park is more family oriented and more developed than are the other state park and National Forest lands in Big Sur. Over 200 drive-in campsites with tables and stoves are tucked beneath the redwoods and oaks. Restrooms and hot showers are conveniently located. There are two grocery stores, a laundromat, large group camps, and a "campfire center" where presentations on local natural history are given. An interpretive nature center is also being built. People return year after year to swim, hike, and relax, and the campground fills up every summer and on holidays.

Although often crowded during the summer, the park still offers some rewarding day hikes. The following description has broken the park down into four main areas: the river and gorge; Pfeiffer Redwood Creek and the Pfeiffer Falls Trail; the Oak Grove Trail; and the Buzzards' Roost Trail to Pfeiffer Ridge. Each of these areas, although close to one another, differs dramatically in terms of vegetation and geological history.

BIG SUR RIVER AND GORGE

It is best to look at a bit of regional geology to understand the course of the Big Sur River and the gorge and valley through which it flows. Gordon Oakeshott gives a good if somewhat dated description of the river's geological history in his *Guide to the Geology of Pfeiffer–Big Sur State Park*.

The river drains a total area of about 160 km² (62 mi²). Its headwaters are in the Ventana Wilderness on the upper slopes of the Coast Ridge and the Ventana Cones. Before entering Pfeiffer–Big Sur State Park, the river first flows in a northwesterly direction and follows the general trend of most of the faults in the area. It turns to the west as it nears the gorge. Once through the gorge, it makes a sharp ninety degree turn back to the northwest where it crosses the Sur and Sur–Hill faults. It flows in this direction along the more easily eroded rock of the fault zone, much of which is crushed and broken and thus less resistant than other rocks. The river then meanders through the relatively broad Big Sur Valley on its way to the Pacific.

The gorge was cut as the Santa Lucias rose during the most recent periods of uplift. The river's gradient was increased by this uplift, giving it greater power to slice through the hard crystalline rocks of the Salinian block. These metamorphic rocks, which are mostly gneiss, are described in chapter 1, Big Sur Geology. The gorge is littered with massive gneiss boulders that fell from the slopes above as the river deepened its course. Many of these boulders, along with gravels and sands, were carried by the river out of the gorge and deposited along its banks. Many deep pools and waterfalls are found here.

The stream-deposited materials, or *alluvium,* carried by the river illustrate the recent uplift of the area. Alluvium is dropped by a river in broad, gently sloping flats along its course. The Big Sur River deposits its load upon leaving the steep gorge and entering the more level valley. As this area was uplifted, many of these alluvial flats were elevated and the river was forced to cut deeper into its older channel deposits. Terraces and benches made of these older alluvial deposits lay as much as 90 m (300 ft) above the present river level and represent the historical river course. Prominent terraces are found throughout the area, such as along the Oak Grove Trail near its junction with the Mount Manuel Trail, near the Homestead Cabin, and at the broad flat that is the site of the U.S. Forest Service Big Sur Station.

Many of the terraces are covered with interior and coast live oaks, which also grow on some of the ridge spurs and with California bay in most of the draws. The north-facing slopes and valley floor support redwood and mixed hardwood forests. The south-facing slopes above the gorge and valley are covered with dense scrub dominated by black sage and California sagebrush.

The streamside vegetation consists of riparian trees and undergrowth, but sunny river flats and grassy clearings also support many drier shrubs such as coyote bush, sticky monkey flower, sagebrush, and sage. The riparian trees include redwoods, western sycamores, red and white alders, bigleaf maples, and some large black cottonwoods. Willows also grow tall in places. The understory is mostly dense brambles of poison oak, blackberry, and hedge nettle.

Many riparian and forest animals live along the river. The campgrounds attract large numbers of common crows, Steller's jays, Brewer's blackbirds, western gray squirrels, and Merriam's chipmunks. We have watched these animals attack and destroy a nicely set picnic lunch that was left unattended for a few minutes too long. These animals, especially the birds, move boldly about from site to site, raiding tables, food coolers, trash bags, and so on. They make for an interesting if not quite traditional wildlife display.

Some of the more secretive animals that are drawn to the riparian area include skunks, black-tailed deer, raccoons (although these, too, can be quite bold), and gray foxes. Red-shouldered hawks are heard calling to one another up and down the valley; they often perch in a sycamore or black cottonwood that is directly over the stream. Dippers and belted kingfishers fly up and down the stream corridor. Small warblers and chickadees frequent the dense undergrowth, while flycatchers hunt flying insects over pools.

PFEIFFER FALLS TRAIL

Pfeiffer Redwood Creek spills down the steep west face of Mount Manuel and joins the river just below the Big Sur Lodge. The short trail to Pfeiffer Falls follows the creek upstream for about 1 km (0.6 mi) through a dark redwood forest. A few tanoaks, bays, and bigleaf maples struggle beneath the dense redwood canopy, and the understory is primarily redwood sorrel, hedge nettle, and sword ferns.

From the trail it is easy to see where the creek is cutting through recent alluvial deposits. Small cobbles layered with silt are exposed in the stream channel walls near the junction of the Pfeiffer Falls and Oak Grove trails. These materials were deposited during mudflows and floods that periodically occur during heavy winter rains. A *mudflow* is a mixture of soil, sand, rocks, and water that is usually born by heavy rains in areas of steep topography. Such flows can travel as fast as 80 km/hr (50 mi/hr) and can move huge boulders, cars, and buildings along in their path.

This part of the Big Sur Valley experienced destructive mudflows during the winter of 1972–1973. The watersheds of four tributaries of the Big Sur River, including Pfeiffer Redwood creek and the three major creeks to the north, were denuded by the Molera fire in summer and then pounded by heavy rains the following winter. Homes and businesses were smashed to pieces or inundated with tons of mud. Cars and trucks were carried into the river and swept downstream, one as far as 3.2 km (2 mi).

These most recent mudflows were found to have been deposited atop older mudflows. Looking for patterns of mudflow occurrence, geologist Lionel Jackson studied the redwoods that grow atop these deposits and noticed that their root systems act as "bedding markers" along the tops and bottoms of the ancient mudflows. When a redwood tree's base is buried, it sprouts new roots from the base near the surface. By excavating and dating these root layers, some of which are visible poking out from the stream channel wall, he then established a rough chronology of past mudflows. His results suggest that at least three periods, and maybe more, of mudflow activity occurred along Pfeiffer Redwood Creek between A.D. 1370 and 1800. He further concluded that mudflows have long been a natural phenomenon in the Santa Lucia Range, especially where steep slopes are periodically denuded by fires and heavy winter rains are common.

Pfeiffer Falls is just upstream from these deposits. The falls are about 12 m (40 ft) high and have worn a thin channel into the gneiss of the Salinian block. The falls were formed as the stream flowed over the hard gneiss and then encountered the less resistant Santa Margarita Sandstone at the Sur–Hill fault. The sandstone was more easily eroded than the gneiss, and the falls were left as the softer rock was worn away.

The sandstone is well exposed downstream from the falls near the footbridges that cross a small tributary on the north side of Pfeiffer Redwood Creek. These bridges are part of the loop trail to Valley View, and they pass over crushed and broken rocks of the fault zone. The trail climbs out of the narrow canyon, leaves the redwood forest and enters a mixed hardwood forest of California bay, coast live oak, and tanoak. The influence of microclimates is evident here as small patches of black sage scrub and coyote bush occur on warmer slopes between the hardwoods. Scattered outcrops of limestone also occur along the trail, which ends at Valley View. There are vistas down the length of the valley to Point Sur.

OAK GROVE TRAIL

The Oak Grove Trail is about 2.4 km (1.5 mi) long. It leads from the Pfeiffer Falls Trail to the Gorge Trail, and it also connects with the Mount Manuel Trail leading into the Los Padres National Forest. The vegetation is mostly a mixed hardwood forest of coast live oak, tanoak, and bay with an understory of Douglas' iris, rattlesnake grass, sticky monkey flower, poison oak, and vetch. There are southwestern slope exposures, especially above the forest, that are covered with black sage, coyote bush, sticky monkey flower, California sagebrush, and bush lupine.

The trail primarily stays within the thin zone of Santa Margarita Sandstone between the Sur and Sur–Hill faults. Near the Homestead Cabin are some old uplifted terraces laid down by the Big Sur River.

These terraces are not cut or displaced by the faults, indicating that little or no recent lateral movement has occurred along the faults since the terraces were formed. The road cut below the cabin has exposed a contact zone where terrace deposits lay atop the sandstone.

The cabin was built by John Pfeiffer when he homesteaded these lands in the late 1800s. John was seven years old when his family, led by his father Michael Pfeiffer, first arrived in Big Sur in 1869. They settled at the mouth of Sycamore Canyon, near Pfeiffer Beach. Before they arrived, however, a man named George Davis had become the first white settler in the Big Sur Valley. In 1853 he claimed a tract along the Big Sur River and built a cabin near where the Mount Manuel Trail begins, just above the Pfeiffer cabin site. In 1868, Manual and Florence Innocenti purchased Davis's cabin and land for fifty dollars. Florence and seven of her children are buried in a cemetery near John Pfeiffer's homestead cabin.

Decades later, when he was a grown man, John Pfeiffer homesteaded several claims in the park area and purchased additional lands. By the turn of the century, the Pfeiffers were running a sawmill and a boarding house on their property. In 1933, Pfeiffer sold most of the land that forms the park to the state. John was a naturalist and conservationist, and he and his wife stipulated that it be preserved as a park.

BUZZARDS ROOST TRAIL

The Buzzards Roost Trail follows the south bank of the Big Sur River from the west side of the Highway 1 bridge. It heads toward the group camp area, then turns uphill and begins climbing Pfeiffer Ridge. The riparian woodland quickly gives way to a redwood–mixed hardwood forest. The trail forks where a sign marks the Buzzards Roost loop; it heads off to the right, climbs to the summit, and then returns from the south.

The forest, which is dark and has little understory here, gets increasingly dwarfed as the trail approaches the summit. The redwoods and bays are the most noticeably stunted, and it is hard to tell whether it is soil nutrient deficiencies, slope aspect, lack of moisture, or past fires that has caused this curious condition. Nothing except redwood or bay seedlings grows in the darkened understory, and small adult trees form almost impenetrable thickets in places.

The trail reaches the ridgeline and leads to another interesting vegetative phenomenon—redwoods growing side by side with chaparral plants. This is an example of sudden microclimate variation as the cool northeast-facing slope gives way to the hot, exposed ridgetop. Manzanitas, chamise, wartleaf ceanothus, and yerba santa grow along the ridgeline with the dwarf redwoods and interior live oaks. The dry Franciscan soil of this area is derived from sandstone and shale and is probably one reason the chaparral plants dominate here.

The trail continues past the summit of Pfeiffer Ridge, where there are views of Sycamore Canyon and the ocean beyond, and then drops back down into the forest. There are larger redwoods on the moist side of the ridge, several of which are used as a roosting site by turkey vultures. Many of the tanoak and bay trees along this part of the trail are mature stump sprouts and indicate that the area probably burned some years ago. There are a few buckeye trees that grow in ravines within this forest.

The trail soon returns to the loop junction, and it is a short walk back down to the river. The entire hike is a little over 4.8 km (3 mi) with an elevation gain of almost 240 m (800 ft). The trail is well graded and maintained, and our only complaint is with the traffic noise. As on the Oak Grove Trail across the valley, noise from vehicles on Highway 1 seems to be amplified at higher elevations.

JULIA PFEIFFER-BURNS STATE PARK

ACCESS: The main entrance to Julia Pfeiffer-Burns State Park is located on Highway 1 about 59 km (37 mi) south of Rio Road in Carmel, and 18 km (11 mi) south of Pfeiffer–Big Sur State Park (see map 3). This entrance leads to a parking lot with restrooms and to trailheads that provide access inland and to the coast. An alternate entrance to the park is 3 km (2 mi) to the north at Partington Canyon where trails depart to Partington Cove on the coast and inland to the Tin House.

INTRODUCTION

Founded in 1961, Julia Pfeiffer-Burns State Park covers 753 ha (1860 acres) of diverse, rugged terrain. The lower portions of two major coastal watersheds—Partington Creek and McWay Creek—are included within the park. A waterfall that plunges to the surf at the mouth of McWay Canyon is the focus of most visitor use in the park. The rocky enclaves of Partington Cove are also well known. The less visited upland areas of the park contain a variety of plant communities, including stands of large, virgin redwoods, mixed evergreen forests, grasslands, coastal scrub, and chaparral. About 10 km (7 mi) of coastline (most of it inaccessible) are also included within the park, and an underwater park of 680 ha (1680 acres) was added to the park in 1970.

The park straddles a geologically complex area. The McWay thrust fault, a branch of the Sur–Nacimiento fault, trends offshore at the mouth of McWay Canyon. The fault juxtaposes a long sliver of Cretaceous conglomeratic rocks against crystalline metamorphic rocks of the Salinian block, which underlies much of the upland area of the park. Saddle Rock and nearby offshore rocks are composed of the conglomerates, while north of the creek mouth, a large body of Salinian granitic rock extends along the coast for several kilometers. This is the only extensive coastal granitic rock in the Big Sur area south of Point Sur. Partington Cove and nearby rocky coves were formed by the erosion of this hard, crystalline granite. Thus, three of the major rock assemblages of the region are included within the park. They are most visible along the coastal cliffs and offshore rocks.

The park also has a number of features of historical interest. The lower McWay Canyon area was originally settled by Christopher McWay in 1887, although he did not patent the land until 1894. The original barn from the homestead still stands near the park entrance, but it is rapidly deteriorating. Christopher and his wife Rachel are buried near the barn. In 1900 and 1901, John Waters acquired the McWay holdings and built his cabin up the north fork.

The McWay properties went through several owners before Lathrop and Helen Brown bought them in 1924. Lathrop Brown was a politician who served in Congress and the Department of the Interior. The Browns called their new property the Saddle Rock Ranch because of the saddle-shaped rock near the falls. The ranch extended to Partington Creek, with houses near the park entrance as well as the Tin House on the ridgetop above Partington Canyon. (The Tin House is a famous abandoned structure made of tin scavenged from abandoned gas stations during World War II.) The ranch was a summer home for the Browns. The main house was destroyed at the wish of the owners when they gave their land to the park system. A wooden waterwheel for hydroelectric power was built on McWay Creek by the ranch foreman Hans Ewoldsen and still stands; this waterwheel generated the first electrical power used in Big Sur.

Julia Pfeiffer-Burns was a Big Sur native who befriended Helen Brown when she arrived in Big Sur. The Browns deeded their property to the state park system in 1961. So taken was Helen Brown with Julia's character and spirit that she arranged that the park be dedicated to Julia Pfeiffer-Burns, "a true pioneer."

Partington Canyon also has an interesting history. John Partington arrived there with his wife and five children in 1874 and founded a tanbark harvesting operation. In one year alone (1902), Sam Trotter and forty men took 10,000 cords of tanbark out of Partington Canyon. The cove at the mouth of the canyon is well known for the landing built there to load the tanbark onto ships (see chap. 7, Human History). Local legend says that this landing was used in the 1920s to export moonshine from distilleries in the Partington area. The Trotter brothers, Frank and Walter, rebuilt the boat launch to lower their small fishing boat into the cove. The large tripod used for lifting the boat still stands at the landing.

WATERFALL TRAIL

This 0.5-km (0.3-mi) trail is the most popular trail in the park. It starts at the parking area at the main entrance and leads toward the coast through a tunnel beneath the highway. Lush coastal scrub lines the trail and continues up the steep hillsides on both sides of the canyon. The numerous nonnative plants around the main entrance and cove, including large blue gum trees, Monterey pines and cypresses, acacias, and a number of exotic garden plants such as calla lilies, testify to the human occupation of the area. In fact, the Browns maintained a garden full of exotic plants at their Waterfall House and many of these remain in the area.

In spring, flowers such as sticky monkey flower, Indian paintbrush, common yarrow, blue blossom, and coast morning glory are common in the scrub. The creek in this lower section is bordered by willows, alders, and other riparian plants including western coltsfoot and elk clover. A few redwoods grow here as well. They are much smaller than those upstream, and their foliage is brown, perhaps due to damage from salt spray on the ocean winds.

From the tunnel mouth, the trail traverses the slope northward to arrive at an overlook of McWay Falls. (The trail once continued to the site of the Browns' Waterfall House but was washed out by a landslide in 1983.) Some of the rock outcrops along the east side of the trail are marked with *slickensides,* shallow grooves and polished surfaces worn in the rocks where they have slid past each other. Slickensides are an indication of faulting activity, and these are probably a consequence of movements on the McWay fault.

The McWay Falls spills over a narrow notch in hard metamorphic rocks very near the McWay fault line. It is probably no coincidence that the falls is located on the fault; it marks the edge between the hard Salinian rocks and the softer conglomerate rock. The water has cut more deeply into the softer rock, resulting in the sharp break at the falls. The deep cove at the base of the falls also coincides with the fault line. There, the crushed rock of the fault zone has been cut away by the surf to form the cove. Saddle Rock is composed of the conglomerate, while the rocks near the viewpoint are Salinian granites.

This waterfall once had the distinction of being the only falls on the west coast to cascade directly into the ocean. However, the repair of the landslide on Highway 1 just north of the park entrance in 1983 changed this. The sediments dumped into the ocean by bulldozers repairing the slide caused many beaches to form to the south. One of these formed at the foot of the falls, so that now the falls spills onto a sandy beach rather than into the ocean. The beach may eventually erode, however, and the falls will land in the ocean once again.

There is an extensive grove of Monterey cypresses above the falls and a few picturesque trees out on Saddle Rock. Like all the cypresses and pines in the area, the trees are not native but were planted. The cypresses and the craggy rocks make this small cove reminiscent of Point Lobos. The surf rolls spectacularly into the cove in winter, sometimes washing completely over Saddle Rock. A low carpet of coastal bluff scrub that includes sea lettuce, California sagebrush, and introduced ice plant clings to the rocks and coastal cliffs.

A different perspective of this cove is available from the other side of the falls. If you turn left when exiting the tunnel on the Falls Trail, the path will lead to two campsites and to overlooks on the cove and Saddle Rock. This area is known as the South Gardens. Pieces of weathered concrete and rusted steel bars cling to the rock, the remnants of a concrete path built in 1941. The path included a section of ladder that was built to provide access out to Saddle Rock. Erosion has made it impossible to cross the narrow ridge to the rock and has all but destroyed the last remnants of the walkway.

The bouldery mass of conglomeratic rocks that make up Saddle Rock is clearly visible from the South Gardens. Esselen Indians used this nearly level place as a camp or village site, as evidenced by the scattered shell fragments in the soil here. Shorebirds such as western gulls and black oystercatchers nest on Saddle Rock, and pigeon guillemots roost on the cliff faces. Cormorants and brown pelicans often perch on the rocks. This is also a good vantage point for seeing sea otters, sea lions, harbor seals, and passing gray whales, and it affords a view northward along the coast to the spectacular McWay Rocks offshore.

MCWAY CANYON TRAILS

A number of unnamed trails follow the forks of McWay Creek a short distance up the canyon from the main parking area. The trails are un-marked and lead past the old homestead barn through dense redwood groves. The creek flows over a gentle grade for the first few hundred yards above the parking area. The streamsides are littered with de-bris—logs, boulders, and hummocks of mudflow deposits—from the massive flooding that followed the Rat Creek fire in 1985. The vegeta-tion in both these lower canyon bottoms is predominantly redwood for-est that includes some hardwoods. The redwoods here are big, but they are not as large as those farther up the creek on the Ewoldsen Trail.

Steep cliffs rise abruptly just upstream of the confluence of the creek's two forks. Waterfalls tumble down the cliffs on each fork. The falls on the north fork are larger and steeper, falling about 10 m (30 ft) down steep granitic rock faces in a few short falls. The falls have carved smooth troughs in the hard granitic rock, and old, worn grooves from past falls are visible on cliff faces far from the site of the present falls, perhaps indicating that some rock movement has occurred. The cliffs are coated with mud from the floods, and these channels must have flowed spectacularly following the Rat Creek fire.

There are taller falls upstream on the North Fork. It is possible to climb past the South Fork's falls and follow the creek up to its junction with the Ewoldsen Trail. The climb up beside the falls is dangerous, however, and not recommended. Upstream from the Ewoldsen Trail, yet another steep waterfall occurs on the South Fork.

EWOLDSEN TRAIL

The Ewoldsen Trail was closed after the Rat Creek fire burned most of the park in 1985, but is now partially rebuilt or reopened. The trail provides access to the spectacular and diverse uplands of the park. When complete, it will connect with the Tanbark Trail in Partington Canyon, making a long loop hike through the park possible.

The Ewoldsen Trail is named after the former ranch foreman, Hans Ewoldsen, who still lives in Big Sur. He rebuilt the original trail from a logging trail in 1933. It begins just upstream from the parking area at the main entrance. Signs point the way as it crosses the creek and angles up the north-facing slope through burned redwoods. Oak and bay trees mingle with redwoods, and the understory includes sword ferns, gooseberry, western wake-robin, and carpets of redwood sorrel. Higher up the steep slope, the forest opens to clearings where hedge nettle, bracken fern, and wild iris grow beneath scattered coast live oaks and bay trees. This undergrowth was particularly lush in the wake of the Rat Creek fire, when fire-following short-lobed phacelia (*Phacelia brachyloba*) formed a dense cover. Most of the trees are still sprouting profusely, and redwood sprouts are so dense they obscure the trail in places. Some redwood stumps on this slope are little more than blackened slabs of charred wood that have burned many times, attesting to the history of fire in this area.

"Cat eyes" are common on the redwoods along this stretch of trail. These are hollows in tree trunks, usually on the uphill side, that are a result of repeated fires. They are caused by the trunks damming debris such as sticks, needles, and logs on their uphill side. The debris accumulates over the course of many years, and this pile of fuel burns hotly and scars the uphill side of the tree when fire sweeps through. The trunk is eventually hollowed out as this process repeats itself. After many fires, a redwood may become so hollowed out that it can no longer stand. Some trees along the Ewoldsen Trail reached this point and toppled during the Rat Creek fire. The fallen giants laying beside their burned, thin bases can be seen here and there. It seems that more redwoods are killed by this mechanism than are killed directly by the heat of fire.

The trail follows a border between forest and grassland, drops into the redwoods along the south fork of McWay Creek, then climbs up the ridge between the north and south forks. Huge, flat-topped stumps testify to the logging that took place in this drainage area. There are some nice views down McWay Canyon to the ocean from a grassy clearing along the trail as it winds into the north fork canyon. Larger redwoods grow near the creek. Deep banks of sand, mud, and cobbles remain from the flooding that followed the Rat Creek fire. As in the lower parts of most coastal creeks, the redwoods here have probably had to contend with many such fire-caused mudflows.

The north fork canyon widens and flattens out as the trail follows it upstream. Very large redwoods grow here. Hans Ewoldsen believes that the largest redwood in Big Sur stands here, and we have seen none larger. The trail climbs up from the stream into an open forest of live oak and tanoak with a grassy understory. Bird life becomes noticeably more plentiful as this transition takes place. We have seen acorn and hairy woodpeckers, black-headed grosbeaks, plain titmice, scrub jays, goldfinches, and other birds in this area. An old picket fenceline remains from the John Waters homestead, which once stood at the upper end of a clearing here. The trail traverses uphill and enters a small tributary canyon where small redwoods grow, then follows an oak-lined gully up to the ridgecrest.

The trail breaks out onto the coastal ridge above Highway 1. The contrast from the quiet, closed forests of McWay Canyon to the open expanse of the grassy ridges and ocean is dramatic. There are wonderful views north and south on the coast from Pfeiffer Point to Lopez Point and down to the guano-covered McWay Rocks breaking the swells offshore. Unfortunately, the scar from the repair of the giant 1983 landslide dominates the foreground view. This scar is many times the size of the landslide that it repaired and is practically barren of plant life, despite extensive reseeding efforts.

The steep trail climbs along the ridgecrest beneath coast live oaks. The vegetation becomes noticeably drier with increasing elevation, and the first chamise plants appear at about 550 m (1800 ft). The trail leaves the ridgecrest and contours along the southwest face of the coastal ridge to come abruptly upon a spring bubbling from beneath the roots of a large live oak. This is the Jim House spring, and the broad path leading to it is the remnant of a path for a water sluice. According to nearby resident Jeff Norman, John Waters built the sluice to divert water to his homestead below. As of this writing, the trail has not been repaired beyond this point.

The old trail becomes obscure beyond the spring. It follows a rough contour in and out of several steep, brushy ravines along the flank of the ridge. A few Coulter pines grow on the upper slopes of the ridge above 600 m (2000 ft). The trail eventually arrives at the Tin House on the ridge above Partington Canyon (discussed in the Tanbark Trail description that follows). From here, it is possible to follow the Tanbark Trail down into Partington Canyon and back to Highway 1, a walk of about 5.3 km (3.3 mi). It is 3 km (2 mi) along the highway back to the main parking area from the terminus of the Tanbark Trail. This loop is a rewarding but long day hike for an experienced hiker.

TANBARK TRAIL

The Tanbark Trail starts at the hairpin turn in Partington Canyon, 3 km (2 mi) north of the main park entrance. After passing through a short section of coastal scrub, the trail crosses a footbridge over Partington Creek. The trail then enters a lush redwood–riparian forest alongside the creek. This drainage was not burned in the Rat Creek fire, and evidence of fire is much fainter here than in McWay Canyon. The trail follows along the south fork for a short distance and then begins a long series of switchbacks up the north-facing slope.

The redwoods in this canyon are some of the most beautiful on the Big Sur coast. As in McWay Canyon, extensive redwood logging has taken place in the lower creek, but there are many virgin trees higher up. Interestingly, it seems that the remaining old-growth trees in this lower part of the canyon are specimens that are unsuitable for lumber; most are twisted or bent. Many of the redwood stumps have square openings cut into their downhill sides. These notches supported platforms upon which sawyers stood to cut the trees; on such steep slopes it was necessary to build these platforms to achieve a horizontal cut through the trees. Also, the lumberjacks stood on the platforms to get above the gnarled basal burls of the trees, which were unsuitable for lumber and difficult to cut.

Tanoaks were also extensively harvested in this canyon early on in Big Sur's pioneer history (see chap. 7). The remains of the tanoak stumps have long since rotted in contrast to the rot-resistant redwood stumps. A more subtle reminder of the tanbark harvest is that most of the tanoaks are of the same young age since they all sprouted at the same time following the logging.

The long climb up the ridge stays almost entirely within this redwood–tanoak forest, occasionally breaking out into coastal scrub clearings with fringes of live oaks. From these clearings, there are views down to the ocean and across the canyon to the houses on Partington Ridge, one of the main centers of population on the Big Sur coast. The forested expanse of Partington Canyon, one of the larger canyons along this section of coast, comes partially into view.

Numerous side trails branch off the main trail. Most of these are remnants of trails used to haul out tanbark, and in many places they and the main trail are shored-up extensively with redwood cribbing. A portion of the Old Coast Trail also winds through Partington Canyon, briefly coinciding with the Tanbark Trail. There is elaborate stonework along the trail near Swiss Camp, where springs emerge and flow down the slope. This is the work of Gunder Bergstrom, a Swede who lived in the area in the 1920s. The main trail remains well marked in this maze of trails as it climbs up to the Tin House.

The Tin House sits on a small flat area on the ridgecrest at 597 m (1960 ft) elevation. It has a commanding view of the coastline and a somewhat obscure history. Local legend has it that Lathrop Brown built it as a guest home for his friend Franklin D. Roosevelt, a college classmate. Hans Ewoldsen disputes this, however, and says it was built as a second home for the Browns and that Roosevelt never visited it. It was built from tin scavenged from an out-of-business gas station during World War II. It is remarkable that so much tin went into the construction of the house at a time when tin was a tightly controlled war material.

The house has distinctive lines and bold trim. It has several rooms and quarters for a live-in maid. A wire was laid around the perimeter of the roof to divert lightning to the ground. Large picture windows open to the north and south in the large main living room, but the view westward to the ocean is blocked by a solid wall. Hans Ewoldsen explains that it was designed this way to avoid having the afternoon glare off the ocean shine into the house. The Tin House was fairly intact fifteen years ago, according to long-time resident Jeff Norman, but it is rapidly decaying. The roof leaks and the plasterboard walls are rotting. The house will probably collapse in the near future.

The Ewoldsen Trail, when complete, will continue from the Tin House down into McWay Canyon and the main entrance to the park. The Tin House road leads from the Tin House to meet Highway 1 at a scenic turnout south of the Tanbark Trailhead. Most of the road goes through grassland and coastal scrub as it cuts steeply downhill. This is a good place to see spring wildflowers such as sky lupine, California poppy, shooting star, and other grassland species.

PARTINGTON COVE

Partington Cove is a small indentation in the rocky shoreline, but it is one of the most dramatic bits of coastline accessible along the Big Sur coast south of Point Sur. The rocky shoreline here is reminiscent of Garrapata State Park, another stretch of granitic coast 47 km (29 mi) to the north. On the hairpin curve on Highway 1 about 3 km (2 mi) north of the main entrance, a cattle gate on the ocean side of the highway marks the beginning of the route to Partington Cove.

From the cattle gate, a dirt road curves down a steep grade through granitic rock with a sparse cover of coastal scrub. Partington Creek emerges from a culvert through highway fill and is lined with riparian vegetation and small redwoods. The road ends after 0.8 km (0.5 mi), and a trail crosses a bridge over the creek and enters a tunnel through a rock promontory. The tunnel was made with handsplit redwood by John Partington and a few neighboring homesteaders in the 1870s and is beautifully and sturdily crafted.

Through the tunnel is the cove and the landing where tanbark was loaded onto boats (see chap. 7). Deep, blue-green water washes into the cove through a long, narrow channel incised into the weakened rock along a small fault. Long strands of giant kelp swirl in the clear water, and feather boa kelp hangs from the rock faces below the low tide line. The jagged coastline in both directions is composed of the same erosion-resistant rock and includes many small coves of deep, clear water. The clearness of the water is a consequence of the hardness of the granitic rock; little sediment erodes from this rock to cloud the water. This water clarity is part of the reason an underwater park was designated offshore.

It is tempting to climb out on the rocks beyond the landing and watch the surf crash below. This is a dangerous venture, however, as large waves occasionally sweep people off the rocks. Sea otters and harbor seals can often be seen offshore in kelp beds. California sea lions pass by frequently, venturing from their large rookery beach a few kilometers to the north at Grimes Point.

Los Padres National Forest: Coastal Areas

PFEIFFER BEACH

ACCESS: The road to Pfeiffer Beach begins on the west side of Highway 1 1.7 km (1.1 mi) south of the entrance to Pfeiffer–Big Sur State Park (see map 1). Known as Sycamore Canyon Road, it is 3.4 km (2.2 mi) in length before ending at the parking lot for Pfeiffer Beach. The beach is owned by the U.S. Forest Service and is not part of Pfeiffer–Big Sur State Park.

INTRODUCTION

Sycamore Canyon Road follows Sycamore Creek down to the ocean. Redwood, bay, and buckeye trees line the stream but soon give way to a thin stand of wind-pruned western sycamores near the ocean. These stunted trees, for which Sycamore Canyon gets its name, are remarkable examples of the influence that insistent ocean winds have on vegetation. Other sycamores grow tall and straight in the protective canyon just a few meters away.

Michael and Barbara Pfeiffer and their children, Charles and John, arrived in Big Sur in 1869 and settled in Sycamore Canyon. Their homestead, which is on private property, is located at the end of the canyon. An Esselen midden site is also nearby.

Pfeiffer Beach is perhaps the most famous of Big Sur's beaches. Several Hollywood movies have used the spectacular landscape as a backdrop for scenes. Waves crash through two natural arches and pound the many offshore rocks, and the windswept beach stretches for almost a mile to the north. Steep, loosely consolidated cliffs and sand dunes rise abruptly from the beach and are covered with a colorful scrub of bush lupines, lizardtail, California sagebrush, and coast buckwheat.

The rocks of this area have been designated by most geologists as part of the Franciscan complex. They include the typical Franciscan sandstone, siltstone, greenstone, and chert. But geologist Michael Underwood, who has studied Pfeiffer Beach, proposes that this area has experienced a different geological history than have most other Franciscan rocks. He points out that the Pfeiffer Beach rocks, in contrast to most Franciscan rocks in central California, are relatively unaltered by geological movement and are only mildly metamorphosed. He therefore refers to these rocks as the "Pfeiffer Beach Slab" to distinguish them from the more typical Franciscan rock types.

The predominant rock type along Pfeiffer Beach is sandstone. It ranges in color from tan to brown to dark gray. The sandstone is bedded in some places in very thin layers and in others is exposed as the remnants of massive (unlayered) beds. The natural arches are examples of the massive sandstone. Other rock types found adjacent to the sandstone include conglomerate, greenstone, chert, and diamictite. *Diamictite* is a chaotic mixture of rock fragments derived from local rocks.

North of Sycamore Canyon is another, smaller creek mouth, and on the north side of this creek mouth is an exposure of bedded sandstone and siltstone. These beds are folded and curved in places. Beyond these exposures, the sandy beach gives way to a boulder field where all of the local rocks are represented. Large rocks of greenstone and red chert, both shot through with white veins of quartzite and calcite, lay side by side with blocks of sandstone and siltstone. Many of the sandstone blocks are rectangular in shape and broke off from the cliffs above; their edges are rounded by wave action. Diamictite is exposed north of the boulder field near the point.

Most of the larger offshore rocks are also composed of sandstone and are approachable during the lowest of tides. The most common marine algae in these rocky areas are rockweeds, bushy clumps of *Endocladia muricata,* and the dark red *Gigartina papillata.* The rocks here are often frequented by black oystercatchers, brown pelicans, cormorants, and other marine birds. Sea otters also feed on or around these rocks.

Beyond the northern point, which is one of the windiest spots in Big Sur, is Cooper Point and the southern end of Andrew Molera State Park. It is possible for experienced beachcombers and cliff climbers to go past Cooper Point and hike from Pfeiffer Beach to Molera Beach. Watch out for large waves and crumbling rocks. Many visitors also swim at Pfeiffer Beach, but bathers should be aware of the strong currents and waves and perhaps limit their swimming to calm days.

PACIFIC VALLEY AREA

ACCESS: Pacific Valley is accessible via several highway pullouts beginning just north of the Pacific Valley Center, 90 km (56 mi) south of Rio Road in Carmel (see map 5). Several short trails cross the coastal bluff along this stretch, leading to sea cliff overlooks and some small beaches. Sand Dollar Beach, located near the southern end of the Pacific Valley marine terrace, is one of the largest and most accessible beaches along the entire Big Sur coast. Jade Cove is also at the southern end of this 5-km- (3-mi-) long terrace.

PACIFIC VALLEY

The flat coastlands at Pacific Valley are not part of a valley at all. Rather, the coastal bluff here is one of the most well-developed marine terraces along the Big Sur coast. This expanse of flat land represents a marked change from most of Big Sur's coastal slopes, which drop steeply to the ocean. As such, it provides some of the longest level walking in Big Sur. The coastal views are excellent all along the terrace. The sharp point of Cone Peak towers over the coast behind the terrace to the northeast. Its coastward side drops along the rocky spines of ridges above Limekiln Creek, and this jagged line is the steepest coastal slope in the lower forty-eight states.

The top of the terrace is covered mostly with grassland and some large patches of coyote bush scrub, while its edge and the crumbly slopes and sea cliffs are covered with a low growth of coastal bluff scrub. Coast buckwheat is common, along with lizardtail, poison oak, California sagebrush, and succulents such as sea lettuce. Most of the grassland is composed of introduced annual grasses, but in some areas, native perennial grasses have taken hold. Weeds such as milk thistle are widespread.

The soils here are thin and rest on shallow marine terrace deposits. In winter and spring, large areas on the terrace become waterlogged because the bedrock is so near the ground surface. Buttercups and bullrushes are common in these low, waterlogged areas, although the spring wildflower bloom is lessened by the impact of cattle. All of the Pacific Valley terrace is public land managed by the U.S. Forest Service and has been grazed extensively for decades.

The most interesting and attractive part of the terrace is the coastal cliff. Walking along the bluff edge leads to several promontories with excellent views of rocky shoreline. There are also a few beaches tucked below the cliff, accessible via short trails down the cliff.

A clear cross section of the marine terrace is visible in the coastal cliffs. The exposed sea cliff is made of sandstone and shale with some large outcrops and boulders of chert. These rocks are all part of the Nacimiento block of the Franciscan Complex. The layering in these rocks is sometimes apparent and is often twisted and convoluted into extremely deformed shapes. Deep layers of marine terrace deposits lay on top of the Franciscan rocks. Springs often emerge at the boundary of the terrace bedrock and the overlying deposits.

The northern one-third of the Pacific Valley terrace is about 4.5–6 m (15–20 ft) high and falls to a series of small beaches separated by rocky spits. Farther south, the terrace becomes increasingly higher (to a height of about 12–15 m, or 40–50 ft) and narrower, and the beaches are replaced by a boulder-strewn, rocky shoreline. The rocks that line the shore are angular and barely worn, indicating that they have fallen relatively recently. Very little algae covers them. These jagged rocks bear the full force of the surf and are rolled about, which tears off any algae that might get established in the calm summer season. Some low-growing algae, along with beds of mussels and barnacles, cover the lower portions of vertical rock faces.

Widely spaced rocks trail offshore into the ocean. These rocks break the surf, and some lone rocks are quite large and high. The isolated boulders and low mounds on top of the marine terrace were probably once offshore rocks similar to the ones now offshore.

SAND DOLLAR BEACH

About 1 km (0.6 mi) south of the Pacific Valley Center the coast swings deeply inland in a horseshoe-shaped embayment backed by a wide, long beach. This is Sand Dollar Beach, one of the largest beaches in Big Sur. The terrace is 18–30 m (60–100 ft) high here and is composed of crumbly schist and shale. The surf often breaks into a series of two or three breakers as it rolls onto Sand Dollar Beach, and this is a favorite spot for surfers and swimmers.

Plaskett Creek cuts across the terrace and meets the ocean south of Sand Dollar Beach. Beyond this creek, the bluff swings seaward toward Plaskett Point. This point offers dramatic ocean views and is a good spot from which to watch sea otters and passing whales. Jade Cove is about 0.8 km (0.5 mi) farther south along the terrace.

JADE COVE

The trail to Jade Cove begins at a marked pullout on Highway 1 about 15 km (9 mi) south of Lucia or 5 km (3 mi) north of Gorda. Wooden steps cross up and over the fence and lead to a well-worn trail that traverses the bluff and descends steeply to reach the cove 30 m (100 ft) below. The first part of the trail is well maintained, while the last section is rougher but easily negotiable.

There is hardly any beach at Jade Cove. The cliff ends in a jumble of green, gray, and white boulders that spill directly into the surf. These rocks are all part of the Franciscan Complex. Most onshore jade is found on the tiny cobble beach in the middle of the jumble.

Schist and serpentine are the dominant rock types at Jade Cove. There are fine fibers of white rock in the green serpentine that split off easily in long brittle threads. This fibrous rock is asbestos, a fibrous form of serpentine. Nephrite jade, found here and at Willow Creek, also has an asbestos form that is identical in chemical composition to the nonfibrous form. The difference is that the crystals in jade are arranged in a random, "felted" pattern, whereas the minerals in asbestos are aligned into long strands. The criss-crossing, felted microstructure of the nephrite jade makes it harder than some types of steel. Jade can come in many colors: green, blue, black, red, and all shades in between. Dark green is the most common. Light green, translucent jade is the most valuable to the Chinese, who compare its color to that of young bamboo shoots.

Jade is actually the common name for two different rock types—jadeite and nephrite. The two are difficult to distinguish with the naked eye, but jadeite tends to have a brighter green color. Jadeite, a silicate of sodium and aluminum, is rarer and is mined in quantity mainly in Burma, Guatemala, and Russia. Small amounts of jadeite have been found in San Benito County, California. Nephrite jade, a silicate of calcium and magnesium, is more common, but is not necessarily inferior in appearance or hardness. It was used in Chinese art for 5000 years before jadeite became available. The largest deposits of nephrite in the world are in British Columbia, where a 150-ton boulder has been mined, and in South Australia. Big Sur divers have claimed 2-ton nephrite boulders just offshore from Jade Cove.

Prehistoric people in many parts of the world used jade to fashion tools because of its hardness. The Chinese venerated jade like no other stone, and jade carving reached its greatest development in China. Ancient civilizations in Meso-America held their jade in similar regard. It is said that Moctezuma, after meeting with Cortez, was relieved that the Spanish conquistadors were only after gold and silver and were ignorant of jade. Ancient jade artifacts are extremely rare in the United States, and the few artifacts that have been found here were probably imported from Meso-America.

Jade forms as the minerals in sedimentary rock are gradually replaced by other minerals under extreme pressure beneath thousands of feet of rock. In the case of the Willow Creek and Jade Cove jade, the original rock was probably sandstone. Water percolating through serpentine supplies some of the necessary minerals, especially magnesium, for this replacement process. Thus, serpentine is often found near jade, but jade is not merely hardened serpentine.

Several blocks of jade outcrop in the bedrock in Jade Cove, but are mostly of poor quality. The best pieces are gathered from the cobble beach. The bits of jade found here have been eroded from outcrops underwater and have been tumbled and polished by the surf. Each wave mixes the cobbles, polishing them and perhaps bringing in more jade.

By clambering over blocks of colorful rock, it is possible to go a few hundred meters north of the cobble beach. The jagged ledges of a serpentine cliff block passage farther north. It is worth the effort to climb the slippery shelves of serpentine to this promontory. The waves break directly below, and it is a good spot for watching otters, seals, and whales. High tide or large waves can make it difficult to get to the point, though, or to get back to the main trail. An alternative trail, rough and not maintained, ascends the coastal bluff just south of the point.

WILLOW CREEK BEACH

ACCESS: Turn west off of Highway 1 18 km (11 mi) south of Lucia (see map 5). A narrow paved road winds steeply beneath the Willow Creek bridge to a paved parking area.

The beach at Willow Creek, like nearby Jade Cove, is a favorite for jade hunters. The nephrite jade scattered here is found in the United

States only in small areas in California, Wyoming, and Alaska. Most of the jade is found south of the mouth of Willow Creek, which flows out into the ocean just below the parking area.

A striking 100-m (330-ft) cliff towers over the north side of Willow Creek as it rushes over cobbles and into the surf. The hard, gray rock here, layered horizontally, is relatively uncommon on the Big Sur coast but is plentiful for a few miles north and south of Willow Creek. It is a metamorphic rock called *schist,* which is formed by the transformation of shale and sandstone under heat and pressure.

The clear water of the creek reflects the gray-green colors of the schist, and western gulls commonly gather here to drink and bathe in the freshwater. North of the creek mouth around the end of the cliff, a narrow, sandy beach curves for 0.8 km (0.5 mi) to the next cliff and bars further passage. This beach is often washed by waves, even at low tide.

South of the creek mouth, a broad boulder field spans the 100 m (330 ft) between the coastal cliff and the ocean. The cliff is ragged, its sheared and crushed Franciscan schist continually crumbling. The rocks are shot through with cracks, and their layers are tilted at all angles. Landslides have recently slid down to the beach in several places. Vegetation is very sparse on the unstable cliff—a few tufts of coast buckwheat and sea lettuce hang on in a few places. The gray schist is interrupted by white to green outcrops of serpentine.

Blocks of serpentine and schist are also common in the boulder field. At low tide, the lower parts of the boulder field are widely exposed, revealing a rich intertidal area. Feather boa kelp and a jungle of other marine algae drape the rounded boulders. Crabs scurry for the cool crevices between rocks. Limpets and snails abound, huddled in their home crevices when exposed at low tide. The lowest parts of the boulder field are covered with mussels and barnacles, and tidepools fill spaces between the rocks.

This boulder field is unusual for the Big Sur coast because the boulders here are not as severely beaten by waves as they are elsewhere. A submarine shelf of rock apparently extends for some distance offshore. Waves break offshore where they encounter the shallow water of the shelf and lose much of their energy before washing over the boulder field. This greatly lessens the wave shock that the algae, snails, crabs, and other intertidal organisms have to contend with and is the reason for their abundance here.

If the Santa Lucia Range continues to uplift, this offshore shelf may one day be exposed above water to become a marine terrace like the bluff in back of the beach. Near the top of this bluff, the cobbles of another ancient beach can be seen.

People search for jade on the cobble beaches near the southern end of the boulder field. Small rounded and polished pieces are common here. Occasional larger pieces keep professional jade hunters in business, who camp and live near the beach. Most of the jade is a dull green color, but it takes on a characteristic gloss when rubbed with a little oil (a dab of facial oil will do). Small pieces of surf-polished serpentine are often mistaken for jade, but jade is much harder and is rarely the same bright color as serpentine.

Jagged slabs and blocks of the sea cliff have fallen into the surf zone south of the cobble beaches. Waves crash and explode onto these blocks in spectacular plumes of spray. It is possible to climb over and through them for about 200 m (650 ft), but the massive cliffs of Cape San Martin block access farther south.

CAPE SAN MARTIN

Cape San Martin was named by Juan Rodriguez Cabrillo in 1542, and in spite of his many months of exploration of the California coast, it is probably the only place name he gave that persists today. He described "Cabo de San Martin" and named the mountains behind it the "Sierra Nevada" because they were covered with snow. Sebastian Vizcaino came along later and renamed the range and many other features of the coast.

Cape San Martin is a dominant landmark on the coast. Its massive nearshore seastack, rising 60 m (190 ft) above the ocean in a broad cone, is visible for many miles in either direction. Off the big seastack, two smaller pointed rocks protrude from the ocean 1 km (0.6 mi) westward, both composed of the same hard, gray schist as the coastal cliffs.

Scores of Brandt's cormorants nest on the north face of Cape San Martin. Western gulls and black oystercatchers also nest on the rock, relying on its inaccessibility for protection from predators such as coyotes, bobcats, and raccoons. It is possible to get to the cliffs of the cape from Highway 1 on an old dirt road. The road, which leaves the highway just 300 m (1000 ft) south of the Willow Creek Beach turnoff, once led to a light tower whose foundations are still present. The road now ends at a small dirt parking area just off the highway. A trail spans the remaining 200 m (650 ft) to a spectacular sea cliff view. This is a good vantage point from which to view the impressive mass of the offshore rock and its seabirds.

A second trail, steep and rough, descends toward the south from the parking area to reach a small cove. Massive boulders lay behind a cobble beach, and cliffs of slippery serpentine and schist bar passage farther south.

Los Padres National Forest: Ventana Wilderness

BIG SUR RIVER WATERSHED

ACCESS: Access into the Big Sur drainage is easiest via the Pine Ridge Trail, which crosses the mountain range from west to east from the Big Sur Valley to China Camp in the Carmel River watershed (see maps 1 and 2). The trail begins just south of Pfeiffer–Big Sur State Park at the U.S. Forest Service Ranger Station. Access from the Jamesburg–Tassajara Road begins at the eastern terminus of the Pine Ridge Trail at China Camp. This trailhead is located approximately 19 km (12 mi) from Carmel Valley Road.

TOPOGRAPHY AND GEOLOGY

The Big Sur watershed is the largest coastal drainage in the Big Sur area, draining about 160 km² (60 mi²) of rugged terrain in the heart of the north-central mountains. The watershed is largely defined by two major northwest-trending ridges. At its western edge is the steep wall of the Coast Ridge. Along its northern and eastern boundary is the spectacular scarp of the Ventana Cones—from Mount Manuel through Ventana Double Cone, Ventana Cone, Pine Ridge, South Ventana Cone, and Black Cone. On the south, a narrow ridge near Strawberry Camp separates the Big Sur River watershed from the Arroyo Seco watershed.

Elevations in the watershed range from sea level at the river mouth to nearly 1500 m (5000 ft) on top of South Ventana Cone. The North and South forks of the Big Sur River cut two of the deepest coastal canyons in the Santa Lucia Range and are the main streams of the watershed. The two forks run roughly parallel in a northwesterly direction before merging, turning west, and flowing through the Big Sur gorge out into the Big Sur Valley. The lower stretches of the river follow the Sur thrust fault northwest through Pfeiffer–Big Sur State Park and Andrew Molera State Park much of the way to the river mouth, just south of Point Sur. The portion of the watershed from the Big Sur Valley to the ocean was discussed in the sections on Pfeiffer–Big Sur State Park and Andrew Molera State Park. We concentrate here on the wilderness portion of the drainage.

The Big Sur River is a long, relatively gentle watercourse in spite of the fact that it cuts through very rugged terrain. Many tributary streams flow into the Big Sur, the largest of which are Pick Creek and Mocho Creek on the South Fork and Redwood Creek and Cienega Creek on the North Fork. Logwood Creek, Ventana Creek, and Terrace Creek are the major tributaries that feed into the Big Sur below the confluence of the forks.

Most of the Big Sur drainage is underlain by rocks of the Salinian block. Outcrops are most common in streambeds and on the higher slopes of ridges and peaks. Metamorphic rocks such as gneiss and schist are the most common types, but erosion-resistant granitic rocks also underlay an extensive area and compose the summits of Double Cone, Ventana Cone, and South Ventana Cone. Limestone is not as common in this drainage as it is in some other areas of the Salinian block. Very little limestone crops out in the Big Sur drainage, while the Little Sur drainage to the north has many large limestone outcrops. Sedimentary rocks of the Cretaceous age (65–130 million years old) lie near the western edge of the watershed in a broad band along the Coast Ridge. Buff-colored sandstones from these sedimentary deposits are especially noticeable in the sandy terrain just east of Micheal's Hill, where they form a dry, desertlike terrain. More recent Paleocene marine sedimentary rocks (60 million years old) lay near the headwaters of the South Fork and extend into the Higgins Creek area.

A few small patches of orange sandstone in the drainage have been tentatively identified as lower Miocene marine deposits, about 15–20 million years old. The Pine Ridge Trail cuts through these sandstone deposits just west of Redwood Creek. Such isolated marine sedimentary rocks suggest to geologists that the Santa Lucias were once a chain of islands. The sediments were apparently laid down on an ancient ocean floor and on submerged parts of the island mountains. Today, the sediments remain on the periphery of the uplifted range and in isolated locations within the range.

The major fault of the Big Sur drainage is the Sur thrust fault, which had determined the direction of the lower Big Sur River. The North Fork fault defines the North Fork's course in a similar fashion, and the Coast Ridge fault borders the watershed at its western edge. The Pick Creek fault parallels the Coast Ridge fault and has influenced the formation of the broad, straight Pick Valley.

VEGETATION

The upper slopes of the Big Sur watershed are blanketed with extensive stands of dense chaparral dominated variously by chamise, bigberry and Eastwood manzanita, and scrub oaks. A sparser growth of chaparral plants clings to rocky slopes. North-facing slopes shelter mixed evergreen forests, while well-developed riparian woodland follows the streamcourses. Redwoods grow in the North and South Fork canyons, and fingers of redwood forest continue up tributaries into very dry terrain. Grassland covers relatively small areas along ridgecrests below 1200 m (3900 ft) and intermingles with the chaparral on south-facing slopes.

A diversity of conifers grows in the drainage. Large ponderosa pines line the Coast Ridge, and one of the most extensive stands of these pines in the range covers the summit of Pine Ridge. Elsewhere in the drainage, ponderosas are scattered amid hardwoods or form small stands in tributary canyons. Coulter pines grow throughout the drier parts of the drainage amid hardwoods and occasionally into chaparral. Santa Lucia firs grow mostly on upper north-facing slopes, but are also found at the bottom of the South Fork canyon and the lower canyon. The lowest elevation stand of Santa Lucia firs grows at Ventana Camp on the Big Sur River. Incense cedars also grow in the South Fork canyon.

PINE RIDGE TRAIL

The Pine Ridge Trail is the most heavily used trail in the wilderness, as each year hundreds of people make the trek to the 100°F hot spring at Sykes Camp. Away from this stretch of the trail, however, the watershed is not overused and offers some superb opportunities for wilderness solitude.

The trail begins in a redwood–mixed hardwood forest on the north-facing slope above the Pfeiffer–Big Sur State Park campgrounds. After an initial steep climb, the trail maintains a gentle grade up into the rugged landscape. In the first 3km (2 mi), it cuts through some sunny patches of coastal scrub with views down onto the open flats of the Big Sur Valley and the narrow defile of the Big Sur Gorge. Numerous buckeye trees add their fragrant flowers to the spring bloom here, which includes blue blossom, Indian paintbrush, sticky monkey flower, bush lupine, and many other coastal scrub flowers. The scrub openings seem to correlate with changes in slope exposure. Westerly and southerly exposures support coastal scrub, while live oaks and other hardwoods grow on northern exposures. Douglas' iris is plentiful near the margins of the oak and hardwood forests. Glimpses of Ventana Double Cone, towering high and rocky above the ridges to the northeast, come into view and give a hint of the grandeur of the upper canyon.

The trail stays on the cool, north-facing slope of the Big Sur canyon for most of the next 11 km (7 mi) to Sykes Camp. It contours through impressive forests of very large redwoods, tanoaks, and other hardwoods. Most of the forest along this stretch of trail shows evidence of fire. The redwood trunks are blackened, and some have been burned through at their bases and have toppled.

The trail crosses several ravines and small tributary creeks. There is a small stream of permanent water at Bad Gulch, and Logwood and Terrace creeks are larger tributary streams. A few Coulter pines are encountered along the trail just west of Terrace Creek. The Terrace Creek Trail to the Coast Ridge Road meets the main trail at Terrace Creek. There are few access routes down the steep slope to the Big Sur River along the trail. A steep spur trail to Ventana Camp branches off 6.9 km (4.3 mi) from the trailhead, and a shorter, gentler descent to Barlow Flat Camp diverges 4.2 km (2.6 mi) farther along.

Sykes Camp, 15.8 km (9.8 mi) from the trailhead, is heavily used by hot springs visitors. The springs are located on the south bank of the river about 0.4 km (0.25 mi) downstream from the point where the trail crosses the creek. Several small campsites are found upriver. The natural springs are dammed to form a small pool. Overcrowding, polluted water, and garbage are problems here.

From Sykes, the Pine Ridge Trail climbs up through some beautiful, grassy interior live oak groves and out into patches of chaparral. Many of the live oaks are resprouting, and the understory is open and lush in the wake of the Marble–Cone fire. Higher up, the south-facing slope is dry and very rocky and the chaparral is sparse. Our Lord's candle is plentiful here, and tree poppy, wooly blue-curls, wartleaf ceanothus, yerba santa, and other chaparral flowers bloom profusely in the spring. Just before reaching Redwood Creek, the trail cuts through outcrops of a reddish type of sandstone that crops out in only a few places in the Santa Lucias.

Redwood Creek is a small tributary that is an oasis of shade and cool water. There is a small campsite by the stream. These large redwoods are some of the most inland stands in the drainage, and their cool shade contrasts dramatically with the surrounding dry slopes. Native Americans apparently inhabited this canyon, as shown by the bedrock mortars on the hillside just west of the creek.

Beyond Redwood Creek, the trail climbs steeply through thick chaparral dominated by wartleaf ceanothus, chamise, and manzanitas. This climb can be tortuously hot on a summer day. The Big Sur Trail diverges from the main trail 1.4 km (0.9 mi) from Redwood Camp. Horned lizards are common in the sandy soil beneath the scrub. The remnants of an old telephone line that once went to a fire lookout on Ventana Cone can be seen roughly paralleling the trail.

The trail finally enters the burned pines and Pine Ridge Camp after a 600-m (2000-ft) climb from Redwood Creek. At nearly 1280 m (4200 ft), the campsite on the ridge is one of the highest elevation camps in the mountains. The cool, clear air makes for starry nights and clear sunrises, and snow has fallen on campers here as late as May. There are some excellent views of the Big Sur watershed from the camp, and the Pacific Ocean can be seen in the distance beyond the pine-silhouetted wall of the Coast Ridge. A short climb up the ridge behind the camp affords a better view to the east to the Carmel River drainage and north to Monterey Bay.

The ponderosa pine grove on the ridge burned in the Marble–Cone fire and is now a ghostly forest of dead, bleaching trunks. There is an abundance of new growth around the pines, including resprouts of manzanitas and madrone as well as *Ceanothus* spp. seedlings. There are few pine seedlings, however, and local ecologist James Griffin believes that the extent of the pine forest was markedly and perhaps permanently reduced by the fire (see chap. 5, Fire Ecology). The dead snags are good habitat for a number of birds. Purple martins and violet-green swallows nest in them, while olive-sided and ash-throated flycatchers and other birds use them as perches.

Scattered incense cedar seedlings can be found among the pines, and some Santa Lucia firs grow near the northeastern side of the ridge. The

Black Cone Trail leaves the pine Ridge Trail at the crest of the ridge, following the chaparral-covered ridge to the south. As of this writing, this trail is too overgrown to walk with a backpack, but it is being cleared. It eventually leads to Strawberry Camp in 13.8 km (8.6 mi). The Pine Ridge Trail continues eastward from Pine Ridge, dropping into the Carmel River watershed and reaching China Camp on the Tassajara Road in 12.6 km (7.8 mi).

BIG SUR TRAIL

The Big Sur Trail departs southward from the Pine Ridge Trail through open, rocky chaparral just east of Redwood Creek. After crossing a narrow saddle and entering the Cienega Creek drainage, the trail descends through an open woodland of ponderosa pines and interior live oaks. Resprouting redwoods appear on the lower slope, growing in close proximity to burned ponderosa pines. Cienega Camp is shaded by redwoods and sits on the banks of Cienega Creek. The trail follows the creek downstream a short distance and then begins contouring along the north-facing slope. Rounding the ridge, the trail enters the canyon of the North Fork of the Big Sur River.

The North Fork is a narrow creek overhung by a corridor of alders and surrounded by dense redwoods. Much of the upper canyon is shaded from the sun by a steep ridge to the south. The headwaters of this watercourse lie at the base of Black Cone, the southernmost of the Ventana Cones. The trail climbs from the North Fork up the steep, north-facing slope to a narrow saddle. It then descends down a south-facing slope, which supports a mosaic of interior live oak and hardwood forests in ravines, grasslands on ridges, and chaparral on exposed slopes.

The contrast in vegetation between the two slopes is dramatic. A nearly level bowl near the top of the slope is covered with interior live oak and Coulter pines in a picturesque, open woodland. The Big Sur Trail descends through this varied vegetation and crosses a small redwood-filled ravine to arrive at the South Fork of the Big Sur River at Rainbow Camp.

The South Fork is very different in character from the North Fork. Its canyon is open to the south and therefore less shaded, and it supports a diverse mixture of plant communities. The Big Sur Trail coincides with the South Fork Trail for about 1.6 km (1 mi) downstream to Mocho Camp. From there, it climbs steeply up toward the west out of the canyon. A large Cretaceous conglomerate boulder sits along the trail about 1.6 km (1 mi) up from Mocho Camp; it looks like a giant, cemented mass of coarse cobbles. Other boulders of conglomerates can be seen in the streambed.

The trail climbs out of the Mocho Creek drainage and crosses an unnamed creek to the northwest which supports a large grove of big redwoods amid dry, chaparral-covered terrain. The redwoods are severely fire scarred and black to a height of 18–30 m (60–100 ft), indicating the intensity of the fire they survived. They grow only a stone's throw from drought-resistant Coulter pines and chaparral. The trail winds among these giants and then continues its steep climb.

The trail ascends the southeast slope of Logwood Ridge, a long finger extending off the Coast Ridge. There are some striking cliffs of Sur Series metamorphic rocks visible across the canyon to the south. These light-colored rocks are strongly banded. The trail winds around Logwood Ridge and then traverses gently uphill through chaparral to reach Cold Springs Camp on the north face of the Coast Ridge. A road proceeds from the camp 0.4 km (0.25 mi) to the Coast Ridge Road.

SOUTH FORK TRAIL

This trail follows the South Fork of the Big Sur River downstream from the divide between the South Fork and the headwaters of Zigzag Creek in the Arroyo Seco drainage. There is a view from this divide down the length of the South Fork, which trends in a remarkably straight line to the northwest. The upper slopes of the South Fork canyon are dry, rocky, and covered with chaparral. Salt-and-pepper granitic rocks crop out in this area.

The creek drops steeply from the divide into shaded riparian vegetation. Alders and western sycamores follow the immediate creek, while the nearby slopes support bigleaf maple, interior live oak, and California bay. Looking down canyon, the sharp difference in vegetation between the north- and south-facing slopes of the canyon is apparent. The north face supports a lush mixed evergreen forest, while the upper south slope is drier and supports mostly chaparral. Coulter pines are scattered on both slopes at the upper reaches of the South Fork.

Although it drops quickly at first, the South Fork soon levels to a relatively gentle grade. Santa Lucia firs grow in the canyon bottom about 3 km (2 mi) down canyon from the saddle, just above the confluence of Pick Creek. South Fork Camp occupies a sunny, oak-shaded flat near the mouth of Pick Creek, which is a major tributary of the South

Fork. It is possible to follow Pick Creek upstream to some deep pools, a spectacular waterfall, and the beautiful Pick Valley.

The trail crosses the river several times as it traverses from one slope of the canyon to the other. Incense cedars grow alongside the creek just downstream from South Fork Camp, and there are more of these Sierran conifers farther downstream. All are charred at their bases with fire scars. Coulter pines bearing similar fire scars are also abundant in the canyon. Some were killed in the fire and subsequently toppled by the wind so that dead, broken trunks remain.

Rainbow Camp, at the junction with the Big Sur Trail, is about 5 km (3 mi) downstream from South Fork Camp. The first redwoods appear at about 550 m (1800 ft) in elevation along a small tributary entering from the east. This probably represents the deepest penetration of the summer fog, which is an important source of summer moisture to the redwoods. Large ponderosa pines also grow in the canyon near Rainbow Camp.

The South Fork is passable downstream from Rainbow Camp all the way to Sykes Camp. The stream grade is gentle, with only one major waterfall to climb around. There are many beautiful, deep pools in this 6.4 km (4 mi) stretch of river, and the waterfall is just 1.6 km (1 mi) downstream from Rainbow Camp. It is easiest to wear tennis shoes and simply walk in the creek, but the cliffs around the waterfall are extremely dangerous. It takes a leisurely four hours for the full hike to Sykes Camp.

The trail leaves the South Fork of the Big Sur River at Rainbow Camp and climbs up and over a ridge to Mocho Creek. This elevated part of the trail provides good views of the canyon and its diverse vegetation. Mocho Creek is a small year-round stream, and a small campsite is situated on its banks. The Big Sur Trail climbs from Mocho Camp up to the Coast Ridge.

COAST RIDGE ROAD

One of the best and most spectacular views of the Big Sur drainage and the Ventana Cones is available from the Coast Ridge Road. This road begins near the Ventana Inn and climbs to follow the crest of the 1200-m (4000-ft) Coast Ridge, which defines the western boundary of the Big Sur watershed. The road is accessible to the general public only by foot or bicycle. The initial climb from the Ventana Inn is steep and follows many switchbacks through open grasslands and redwood ravines. Once it reaches the top of the ridge, the road maintains a fairly even grade along the ridgecrest through mixed evergreen forest. Views of the ocean are spectacular from the road. Two trails drop off into the wilderness from the Coast Ridge Road—the Terrace Creek Trail and the Big Sur Trail at Cold Springs.

LITTLE SUR RIVER WATERSHED

ACCESS: The two main entry points into the Little Sur River watershed are along the Palo Colorado Road and the Old Coast Road. The Palo Colorado Road leaves Highway 1 18.1 km (11.3 mi) south of the Rio Road intersection in Carmel. It is 12.2 km (7.6 mi) along this road to Bottchers Gap. A dirt road, which is only open to foot traffic from here, continues 5.8 km (3.6 mi) down to the Boy Scout Camp; trails leading to Jackson Camp, Mount Manuel, and Pico Blanco Camp are located here. The Ventana Double Cone Train begins at the east end of the Bottchers Gap parking area, and connections to several other trails can be made from this route. The Pico Blanco Camp Trail can also be reached along the Old Coast Road. The trailhead is 6.1 km (3.8 mi) from the road's southern terminus with Highway 1, which is directly across from the main entrance to Andrew Molera State Park (see maps 1 and 2).

TOPOGRAPHY AND GEOLOGY

The Little Sur River watershed is shaped like a large, round bowl. The river flows straight west, unlike many of the other drainages in the Santa Lucia Range that trend to the northwest or southeast. In a clockwise direction from north to south, its main tributaries are Skinner Creek, Comings Creek, Puerto Suello Creek, the North Fork, Jackson Creek, and the South Fork.

These creeks have their headwaters near a curving series of peaks and ridges that include Devil's Peak (1267 m, 4158 ft), Uncle Sam Mountain (1453 m, 4766 ft), and Ventana Double Cone (1479 m, 4853 ft). The South Fork of the river, which has its headwaters on Ventana Double Cone, is separated from the North Fork by Dani Ridge, Pico Blanco (1130 m, 3709 ft), and Launtz Ridge. These two forks meet relatively close to the ocean at about 49 m (160 ft) in elevation. The river then reaches the sea a few miles north of Point Sur amidst the largest sand dunes on the Big Sur coast.

Several northwest-trending faults cut across the drainage: the Sur, the Palo Colorado, and the Church Creek faults. The river flows west for most of its course, but it makes a sharp northwestward turn near the Boy Scout Camp, where it meets the Palo Colorado fault. It then follows this fault for over a mile and then turns westward once again. The lower portion of the South Fork flows along the Sur fault zone on its way to the confluence with the North Fork. The Sur fault continues offshore near Hurricane Point, and west of the fault are some overlying sandstones, a few serpentine exposures, and Franciscan sedimentary rocks.

Most of the Little Sur drainage, however, lies east of the Sur fault and is therefore made up of granitic and metamorphic rocks of the Salinian block. The river has cut a deep canyon through these hard rocks, and there are narrow gorges, tall waterfalls, and large pools upstream from Jackson and Fox camps. The predominant rocks in these gorges are gneiss and mica schist, which are metamorphosed sedimentary rocks, and granodiorite, quart monzonite, and quartz diorite, which are all granitic rocks (see chap. 1, Big Sur Geology). The ridges and peaks above the Little Sur canyon are primarily made up of granitic rocks, while the Pico Blanco area is composed of crystalline marble.

VEGETATION

The vegetation of the Little Sur River watershed displays the same diversity that is characteristic of most of the coastal Santa Lucia Range. This river, like others along the coast, is lined with alder and willows that grow beneath redwoods and riparian hardwoods. The river mouth supports one of the more extensive willow thickets in Big Sur. The dry ridgetops are covered with grasses and open woodlands. Grasslands, scrub, redwoods, and hardwood—conifer forests all grow in close proximity to one another.

The vegetation of this drainage is also distinct from the other Big Sur watersheds. Large stands of very old redwoods grow along much of the lower rivercourse. Some groves were once logged, but others farther up the canyon remain intact and untouched. These virgin trees are some of the most impressive redwoods in Big Sur. The largest stands of Douglas fir trees in the mountain range are also found here. They grow along the canyon bottom with the redwoods, and some, at 46 m (150 ft) in height, are nearly as tall as the redwoods. There are also a few large ponderosa pines in the lower river canyon.

Redwoods often mark the lower elevational limit of the Santa Lucia firs since they are better adapted than the firs to growing in moist canyon bottoms. The lowermost Santa Lucia firs in the Little Sur drainage grow at 670 m (2200 ft) elevation along Jackson Creek. The largest Little Sur stands of the firs are on the steep slopes of Ventana Double Cone, and the northernmost Santa Lucia fir trees grow on Skinner Ridge.

The Santa Lucia fir is only one component of a large mixed evergreen forest. Extensive forests of tanoaks, bays, and live oaks grow above the redwood forest. Bay trees are especially common on the lime-rich soils in the Pico Blanco area. The ridgetops and wooded slopes of higher elevations are covered with drier evergreen forests that are dominated by madrone, ponderosa pine, and canyon live oak. Black oaks are common within the madrone forests, and coast live oak woodlands occur on south- and west-facing slopes. Ponderosa pines line the ridgetops surrounding the drainage and grow with manzanitas, canyon live oak, and grasses in many places. Coulter pines occur on ridgetops and high slopes as well.

The watershed also supports several types of chaparral and coastal scrub. Along the Pico Blanco Trail, for example, coyote bush and bush lupines representative of the northern coastal scrub mix with black sage and California sagebrush from the southern coastal scrub. Several plants of the chaparral, such as chamise, manzanita, and yerba santa, also grow nearby. The boulder-strewn area below Pico Blanco is covered with grassy meadows and a rocky scrub dominated by Our Lord's candle, while sandy areas near Devil's Peak support a very dry chaparral made up of tree poppy, manzanitas, chamise, and wartleaf ceanothus.

LITTLE SUR RIVER AREA

The river mouth area and lower Little Sur watershed are private property and are not open to the public. Most of the upper watershed, however, is part of the Los Padres National Forest and is accessible from a number of points. The easiest way to explore the canyon bottom is to hike from Bottcher's Gap to the Pico Blanco Boy Scout Camp and from there take the well-marked Jackson Camp Trail upstream. Jackson Camp is about 2.4 km (1.5 mi) upstream, and Fox Camp is about 3.2 km (2 mi) farther. Both campsites are located along the river beneath tall redwoods, Douglas firs, and streamside hardwoods.

An unmaintained trail continues for some distance upstream from Jackson Camp. Just past the camp are stands of virgin redwoods growing in a relatively open bowl on both sides of the river. Beneath these trees are some large bigleaf maple, tanoak, and western sycamore trees in sunny river flats, while thickets of alder, poison oak, and thimbleberry directly line the stream. A long, thin tributary waterfall cascades down the south canyon wall near here.

The canyon becomes narrow and steep walled past Fox Camp, and several more small falls spill into the river. Many falls and pools occur in the canyon and gorge ahead, and the area is passable in medium to low water. Patches of trail remain on both sides of the stream, and an old rope hangs near one fall to help hikers continue upstream. Some pools must be swum to avoid a dangerous climb up the canyon wall.

This entire area, which we call the upper Little Sur Gorge, is unusually sunny and open. The solid, sheer walls, which are made of granitic rocks, provide few areas where trees and shrubs can take hold. Scrubby live oaks grow on the south-facing wall, while the north-facing side of the gorge is usually covered with moss and ferns. Few trees can take root directly along the stream where floodwaters regularly scour the banks and lower walls. The result is a sunny gorge with warm rocks that is good for swimming.

The Little Sur is one of the Big Sur area's most pristine rivers. It has one of the best steelhead trout runs along the coast, and great blue herons and belted kingfishers hunt its pools and eddies. In recognition of its outstanding natural features, in 1973 the California State Legislature included the river in the California Protected Waterways System. In its Big Sur Coast Land Use Plan, Monterey Country is also encouraging the state to designate the Little Sur area as a "coastal resource of national significance." Such designations should help protect the area from future timber harvesting and mining.

PICO BLANCO AND SOUTH FORK AREA

The Pico Blanco area can be entered by three routes. The shortest and most frequently used path is along the Pico Blanco Camp Trail. This trail leaves from the Old Coast Road 6.1 km (3.8 mi) from the road's southern terminus with Highway 1. The other two routes are along the Launtz Creek Trail; one enters from the north from the Boy Scout Camp, and the other leads from the south and the Mount Manuel Trail.

It is about 9.2 km (5.7 mi) from the Old Coast Road to the Pico Blanco Camp. This route is a good day hike through a variety of plant communities. The trail first follows the South Fork of the Little Sur River upstream through a lush redwood–riparian forest. Many of the largest redwoods here were logged decades ago, but others have grown back to take their place. The understory is particularly vibrant in early spring when a profusion of flowers line the trail: forget-me-nots, redwood sorrel, redwood violets, woodland madia, Andrew's clintonia, thimbleberries, Pacific starflower, western wake robin, Douglas' iris, and western Solomon's seal. Many of these flowers continue blooming into early summer due to the moist microclimate beneath the canopy. The trilly songs of inconspicuous winter wrens are also heard near thickets.

Crossing the South Fork, the trail climbs out of the redwood forest and abruptly enters a scrub community made up of black sage, California sagebrush, bush lupine, poison oak, and coyote bush. Chamise, yerba santa, Our Lord's candle, and sticky monkey flower grow in some of the hotter, sunnier spots. This plant community appears to be a mix of northern and southern coastal scrub plants as well as a few chaparral species, and conditions favoring all three types occur here. The slope faces south and is inland enough to escape direct influence from the ocean. But fog is often channeled up this valley and provides moisture needed by northern scrub plants such as coyote bush.

The trail climbs around the south shoulder of Pico Blanco, and the scrub gives way to grassy slopes dotted with Our Lord's candle and lupines. Hardwoods and redwoods grow in the ravines. Outcrops of white and gray crystalline limestone and marble sparkle on the hot slopes, and many loose boulders along the trail have slid down from the slopes above. These limestone and marble outcrops are often more resistant to weathering and erosion than are the associated metamorphic rocks, and as a consequence they form ridgelines, knolls, and other elevated areas.

The Pico Blanco area holds one of the largest remaining deposits of pure limestone and marble on the west coast. The main deposit is more than 160 m (525 ft) thick and crops out over a distance of 4 km (2.5 mi). Limestone is a sedimentary rock composed of calcium carbonate, and marble is metamorphosed limestone. Limestone is most often formed from the skeletons of tiny marine invertebrates that are deposited upon the ocean floor. This particular deposit contains an estimated 640 million tons of limestone and is probably the largest mass of good quality limestone within 240 km (150 mi) of San Francisco. The mountain summit and much of the deposit is privately owned, and a court battle is currently underway to decide if the owners can indeed mine the limestone without having an adverse visual and environmental impact on parts of the adjacent national forest.

The trail continues between the limestone and marble outcrops and passes beneath a hardwood forest in the ravines. It then leads to more open meadows, and Pico Blanco Camp is located below the trail in one of these meadows. This area is one of the most picturesque campsites in Big Sur. Above the camp is an open oak woodland, dense hardwood forests, and wide meadows that are carpeted with flowers in spring. Below the camp is a dark redwood–riparian forest and a large waterfall and pool. Pairs of dippers regularly build nests of moss on the slick walls above the pool and within the spray of the waterfall.

The trail leads from the campsite up and around the south face of Pico Blanco. Our Lord's candle, Indian paintbrush, sticky monkey flower, and bush lupines are the primary plants in this rocky scrub. The trail then climbs through a tanoak–redwood forest to a saddle dividing the South and North forks of the Little Sur, and there are views across the North Fork to Uncle Sam Mountain and the Ventana Cones. The trail meets the Launtz Creek Trail on this divide; 2.4 km (1.5 mi) to the north is the North Fork and the Boy Scout Camp, and 12.8 km (8 mi) to the south is Mount Manuel.

Heading south on the Launtz Creek Trail, the path leads through a variety of microclimates and plant communities as it winds along the inland flank of the South Fork. There are good views across to the southeast side of Pico Blanco. A mixed evergreen forest grows along most of this ridge, but there are patches of live oaks where Douglas' iris, baby blue-eyes (*Nemophila menziesii*), and blue fiesta flowers (*Pholistoma auritum*) bloom in spring. The woodland suddenly gives way to chaparral dominated by wartleaf ceanothus, chamise, and manzanita; felt paintbrush (*Castilleja foliolosa*) grows in openings in the brush. The chaparral is gone just as quickly when the trail drops into the redwood–mixed hardwood forest of the Launtz Creek drainage.

The redwoods gain complete dominance at the bottom of the canyon. Launtz Creek Camp is located beneath the tall trees at the junction of this creek and the South Fork, while Vado Camp is a short distance farther along the trail. The trail leaves the redwoods and starts up the east face of the Cabezo Prieto, which is the ridge formed by Post Summit and Mount Manuel. Redwoods continue to grow in the side canyons, but much of the path is beneath live oaks, Coulter pines, and ponderosa pines growing in open woodlands. Some of the trail is overgrown with scrub oaks and blue blossom. The trail arrives at the Mount Manuel summit and can be followed to Pfeiffer–Big Sur State Park, which was discussed in the Big Sur River watershed section.

VENTANA DOUBLE CONE TRAIL

The Ventana Double Cone Trail leads around the entire perimeter of the Little Sur River watershed. It is a 24 km (15 mi) hike from the parking lot at Bottcher's Gap to the summit of the Double Cone, and several camps are located along the way. The initial ascent of Devil's Peak is steep, after which the trail levels off for a few miles before climbing again rather steeply up to Ventana Double Cone.

Bottcher's Gap is a notch formed by the Palo Colorado fault where it trends across this ridge. Such "gaps" occur elsewhere in the range where faults cross ridges. The east side of this fault is primarily an upthrown block of quartz diorite, while the west side of the fault is composed mostly of metamorphic rocks such as schist and gneiss. The fault-formed valley is visible to the southeast, and the Little Sur River flows along the fault for about 1.6 km (1 mi) before turning west again.

The vegetation is at first a mosaic of chaparral and hardwood trees. Chamise, manzanita, yerba santa, several species of *Ceanothus,* and bush lupine grow on hotter slopes, while tanoak, black oak, and madrone dominate the forest. Some of the largest madrones in Big Sur grow along parts of this trail, especially near its junction with the Turner Creek Trail. Stands of bracken fern grow in nearby grassy clearings.

The climb up Devil's Peak is a hot ascent through wartleaf ceanothus, manzanita, and tree poppy. Views around the rim of the Little Sur watershed are excellent from the summit. Pico Blanco, although about 90 m (300 ft) lower than Devil's Peak, is still quite impressive as a lonely pyramid of limestone that separates the North and South forks. The curvature of the coastline near Point Sur gives ocean views both to the west and the southwest. These views are even more impressive from Mount Carmel, a short detour to the north, where the Carmel and Salinas valleys, Monterey Bay, and the Santa Cruz Mountains are all in plain sight.

It is easy from such a vantage point to notice this watershed's intricate patterns of vegetation. The different colors and textures are quite clear: the velvety greens and browns of chaparral on the south-facing slopes; the golden knolls and ridges of grasses that are dotted with oaks and occasionally topped by pines; the dark green of the hardwood forests on the north-facing slopes; and the veins of redwood forest that are confined to the deepest valleys and streamcourses.

The hike from Devil's Peak follows the ridgeline north toward the Double Cone and contours the divide separating the Carmel River and Little Sur River watersheds. Dark forests of madrone and oak are recovering from recent fires in some areas, while in other places, open meadows are surrounded by old ponderosa pines. Canyon live oaks and manzanitas grow among the ponderosas. The vistas are excellent along the entire hike.

The trail along the ridge is punctuated by some well-placed campsites with water and is joined by several other trails. (A detailed topographic map should be consulted while reading the following description.) About 1.6 km (1 mi) from Devil's Peak, the trail reaches the short side trail to Comings Camp, which has water and several nice campsites. After another 1.9 km (1.2 mi), it arrives at the junction of the Big Pines Trail; this trail drops down into the Carmel River watershed and leads to the Los Padres Dam. Pat Spring Camp is 1.6 km (1 mi) farther, and the side trail to Little Pines Camp is another 3.2 km (2 mi). The Hiding Camp Trail, which drops down to Hiding Camp on the Carmel River, is 3.2 km (2 mi) from Little Pines. It is still another 6.4 km (4 mi) to the Ventana Double Cone summit, and Lone Pine Camp is located about halfway along this last stretch of trail.

The final part of the climb up Ventana Double Cone is well graded but overgrown with brush. The relative isolation and inaccessibility of the peak is in part responsible for its plant life being less explored than anywhere else in the Santa Lucia Range. Ecologist Jim Griffin, in a study of the plants on the five highest peaks in this range, found the smallest number of species on Ventana Double Cone. He hypothesized that this is due to the steep and rocky nature of the summit area and the general lack of a grassland community close to the peak.

Nonetheless, such isolated high peaks often support certain rare, disjunct, and endemic plants. Griffin points out that Ventana Double Cone has some floristic similarities to Cone Peak due to the many rocky outcrops and talus slopes. There are no well-developed forests up here such as on Cone and Junipero Serra peaks, but there are many scattered Santa Lucia firs growing around the summit. Other Santa Lucia endemics include Santa Lucia lupine, Santa Lucia bedstraw (*Galium clementis*), and a closely related subspecies of California bedstraw (*Galium californicum luciense*). The views from the summit are spectacular, and the peak was once used as a fire lookout.

CARMEL RIVER WATERSHED

ACCESS: The upper Carmel River watershed is accessible along several roads and trails. The Carmel Valley Road leaves Highway 1 just north of the Rio Road intersection. The Cachagua Road, located on the Carmel Valley Road 26 km (16 mi) from the Highway 1 junction, leads south and in 11 km (7 mi) arrives at the Los Padres Dam; the Big Pines and Carmel River trailheads are located southwest of the dam (see map 2).

The junction with the Jamesburg–Tassajara (or Chews Ridge) Road is 37.5 km (23.3 mi) from Highway 1. This unpaved road leads 29.4 km (18.3 mi) to Tassajara Hot Springs, and several camps and trailheads can be found along the way: Anastasia Canyon Trail at 11 km (7 mi), White Oaks Camp at 13 km (8 mi), and China Camp at 19 km (12 mi), where the Miller Canyon and Pine Ridge trailheads are found. The road continues over a divide and drops into the Tassajara Creek drainage; the Church Creek and Horse Pasture trails are located along this part of the road (see map 2).

Several other trails lead from the west into the Carmel River drainage. The Pine Ridge Trail leads from the Big Sur Valley to China Camp, and the Puerto Suello and Big Pines trails drop from the Ventana Double Cone Trail and connect with the Carmel River Trail. Many interesting loops and one-way hikes are possible by connecting some of these trails and roads, and the appropriate watershed maps should be consulted when reading the following descriptions.

TOPOGRAPHY AND GEOLOGY

The Carmel River drains most of the northern Santa Lucia Range, but we will only cover here that part of the watershed located within the Los Padres National Forest. This includes everything upstream from the Los Padres Dam to the headwaters in the Ventana Cones and Chews Ridge areas. The main fork begins on the north face of the ridge formed by the Church Creek Divide. Here the river is a small creek that flows down from the divide into Pine Valley, and it is joined by several other creeks that drain Pine Ridge and Ventana Cone. It is then joined by Ventana Mesa Creek from the west and Hiding Canyon Creek from the east, at which point the river's size and the depth of its canyon are greatly increased. Several large creeks flow down from Uncle Sam Mountain and Elephant Mountain and further swell the river.

The Miller Fork joins the Central River a few miles upstream from the Los Padres Reservoir and has its headwaters on Chews Ridge near China Camp. Danish Creek flows into the reservoir from the west where it drains Blue Rock Ridge and the north faces of Elephant and Uncle Sam mountains. The river is joined below the Los Padres Dam and outside the National Forest by several large tributaries, including Cachagua Creek and Tularcitos Creek. It flows from here through the town of Carmel Valley and out to the Pacific Ocean at Carmel Bay.

The topography of this drainage is as steep and rugged as that of Big Sur's other major watersheds. There are many high peaks and ridges, most of which trend northwest–southeast, and deep canyons, gorges, and falls occur along several of the larger streams. Chews Ridge is the longest and highest of these ridges. It reaches an elevation of 1537 m (5045 ft), and two other peaks along its spine are at 1498 m (4918 ft) and 1421 m (4662 ft). Miller Mountain, which has an elevation of 1323 m (4341 ft), is located on the divide that separates the Miller Fork from the Carmel River. Both Chews Ridge and Miller Mountain are composed of a mixture of granitic rocks and metasedimentary (metamorphosed sedimentary) rocks.

Elephant Mountain, at 1225 m (4020 ft), Uncle Sam Mountain, Ventana Double Cone, Ventana Cone, Pine Ridge, and South Ventana Cone form the southwest wall of the drainage. The latter four peaks are all over 1450 m (4750 ft) in elevation, and along with Chews Ridge, all are composed of highly resistant crystalline rocks of the Salinian block. These rocks include granitic quartz diorite and granodiorite as well as metasedimentary schist and gneiss. These hard rocks are well exposed on most of the peaks and in some of the canyons, such as near Hiding Canyon Camp along the Carmel River Trail.

The Salinian basement rock is overlain in places by several kinds of sedimentary rocks. In Pine Valley alone are sandstone, shale, and siltstone from four distinct formations. These sedimentary rocks weather in bizarre patterns and form picturesque outcrops along the Miller Canyon and Carmel River trails.

Most of the sedimentary rocks are found along the two major faults that cut through this area: the Church Creek and the Miller Creek faults. These faults are roughly parallel to one another and trend northwest–southeast. The Miller Creek fault runs the length of Miller Canyon and is located above the creek on the northeast wall of the canyon. The sandstone is also found above the creek adjacent to the fault.

The Church Creek fault has its southern end truncated by the Willow Creek fault in the Arroyo Seco drainage. It trends northwest from that point, cutting through Church Creek Valley and passing over Church Creek Divide and into Pine Valley and the Carmel River watershed. The river follows the fault briefly and then turns west out of Pine Valley. Over the course of a few miles, it turns north and then northeast and cuts straight across the fault near Hiding Canyon Camp. A narrow gorge and large falls occur near where the river crosses the fault.

VEGETATION

Most of Big Sur's major plant communities are well represented in the upper Carmel River watershed. Much of the area, especially south-facing slopes, is covered with dense chaparral dominated by chamise, scrub oak, and wartleaf ceanothus. North-facing, high elevation slopes support mixed evergreen forests rich in conifers, many of which are recovering from the Marble–Cone fire of 1977. Growing within these forested areas are some unusual valley oak woodlands and grassy openings. Santa Lucia firs grow on steep canyon slopes, while canyon bottoms are cloaked in a lush riparian woodland that belies the overall aridity of the region.

There are some special areas of botanical interest in the Carmel River drainage, particularly on Chews Ridge. Ecologist Jim Griffin has studied the plants growing on the five highest peaks in the Santa Lucia Range. He found that Chews Ridge has more species of plants than any of the other peaks. He attributed this phenomenon to the greater range of habitats on Chews Ridge, including hardwood forests, mixed oak–Coulter pine communities, a small stand of Jeffrey pines that were probably planted, open grasslands, and an unusual oak woodland with valley oaks.

These plant communities are all accessible along the Jamesburg–Tassajara Road. Hardwood and Coulter pine forests are the most common plant communities. The Jeffrey pine groves, which were discussed in chapter 4, are located on the summit both north and south of the old fire lookout. Valley oak savannas are also located near the summit, and these trees represent the highest elevation occurrence at 1545 m (5069 ft) of this species in the Santa Lucias. In a related observation, Griffin noted bedrock mortars located within these savannas. Such mortars were used by Native Americans to grind acorns, and Chews Ridge was the only one of Griffin's study peaks with definite signs of native activity on the summit.

CARMEL RIVER AREA

The Carmel River Trail winds through a great variety of terrain and habitats in a relatively short distance. A typical day's hike leads through burned forest and chaparral, over open ridgetops with pine-studded meadows, and along a deep river canyon rich in ferns and colorful hardwood trees. Many side trips and loops are possible along other trails.

The trail is reached from the Pine Ridge Trail, which starts just past China Camp on the west side of the Tassajara Road and is well marked. It climbs through a mixed evergreen forest of tanoak, live oak, and madrone trees that were severely ravaged by the Marble–Cone fire of 1977. The skeletal limbs of the burned parent trees stand out above the green, stump-sprouted shoots that grow from the charred stumps. Older forests of such trees are common throughout these mountains and denote areas that were burned decades ago.

The plentiful dead wood, much of it still standing, and the accompanying lush undergrowth create a two-tiered forest where birds are easily observed. Woodpeckers and western bluebirds look for nesting cavities in the dead trees. Band-tailed pigeons and cedar waxwings perch in large flocks on the dead limbs. Small songbirds—warblers, chickadees, and vireos—snatch insects from the leaves of the new growth.

The trail leaves the forest and drops over the ridgetop. It skirts the Church Creek watershed, offering excellent views of the valley below and the wilderness beyond. Hazy blue ridges line up one behind the other. In the foreground, a conspicuous spine of brown sandstone runs the length of Church Creek Valley. Part of The Rocks Sandstone, it rises in massive blocks west of the creek. Potholes, fissures, and small caves mar its grainy surface.

The trail soon reaches the Church Creek Divide, a low saddle separating the headwaters of Church Creek from those of the Carmel River. Several major trails intersect here. The Pine Ridge Trail continues straight ahead toward the southwest and eventually reaches the Big Sur River and Highway 1 (see section on the Big Sur River watershed). The Church Creek Trail heads southeast into Church Creek Valley and leads to sandstone exposures (see section on the Arroyo Seco watershed). The Carmel River Trail leads to the right toward the northwest and follows the upper Carmel River; it is the main route of this description.

The Carmel River Trail leads down from the divide and is an easy ramble through mixed evergreen and riparian forests. It soon enters the spacious, pine-studded meadows of Pine Valley. Towering ponderosa pines and steep sandstone cliffs lend a Sierran air to this elevated valley. These sandstones crop out along the Church Creek fault and are part of the same formations found in the Church Creek Valley. The four formations have been named by various geologists: Church Creek Formation, Junipero Formation, The Rocks Sandstone, and Lucia Shale. The relatively flat valley floor is composed of alluvium.

The sandstone buttes and cliffs rise above the pines and offer excellent vantages of the entire valley. Dusk is a good time to climb up and survey the area. The decaying crowns of ponderosas and their attendant woodpeckers are then at eye level. Deer often come to browse the meadows below, and an occasional bobcat pokes along the streamside rocks.

The route continues its descent from Pine Valley. The trail follows the fault rather than the Carmel River, and it leads into narrow Hiding Canyon and then onto a low open ridge. Uncle Sam Mountain and Ventana Double Cone form a massive granitic wall across the river canyon. Their swift runoff streams carve deep channels down to the Carmel River, and the sounds of rushing water echo up from the gorge below. The trail intersects a short side trail to the left that leads to the bottom of the gorge and beyond to Round Rock Camp.

The gorge can be approached during the low water season by following this side trail to where it crosses the river. Just downstream from this crossing, the river has cut a deep slice through the sandstone and into the underlying basement rock. William Fieldler, a geologist who surveyed this area in the early 1940s, noted that the western wall of this canyon exposes a long contact where overlying sandstone can be seen to rest on granitic and metasedimentary rocks. The convoluted twisting and turning of the chasm accentuates the already contorted bands in these basement rocks, and a waterfall cut through the rock prevents further hiking downstream. Huge boulders of the sandstone have fallen from the canyon walls, have been carried downstream by the current, and now litter the lower gorge.

The Carmel River Trail drops into the canyon below the gorge and crosses the river about two dozen times as it winds back and forth beneath a dense multilayered canopy. Bigleaf maple, black oak, western sycamore, and alder trees create a rich riparian woodland with a lush understory. Giant chain ferns over 2 m (6 ft) tall hide dark pools, and horsetail rushes grow in spongy clumps beneath elk clover and thimbleberry brambles.

The trail passes the Buckskin Flat and Sulphur Springs Camps before arriving at the Carmel River Camp and the junction with the Miller Canyon Trail. The Big Pines Trail junction and the Los Padres Reservoir are a few more kilometers downstream along the Carmel River Trail.

A loop trail back to China Camp can be made by leaving the Carmel River Trail at Miller Fork and following the Miller Canyon Trail upstream back into the high country. Miller Canyon is steeper and more narrow than the upper Carmel River. Its vegetation is typical riparian woodland. This canyon has fewer hikers, and its camps are small and secluded.

Clover Basin Camp is the first campsite along the Miller Canyon Trail. It is named for a marshy meadow on the slopes above the creek. A side trail just upstream from the camp climbs up a draw to the basin. Debris from an ancient downhill movement of earth has piled up at the end of the meadow, creating a holding area that remains moist for much of the year. Such marshy habitat, complete with cattails, is unusual in this type of terrain.

Several Esselen mortars can be found in low-lying boulders on the slope above the swamp, hidden beneath accumulated duff and soil. The mortars were worn deeper and deeper into the rock as Esselen women, using stone pestles, sat here and crushed seeds or ground acorns into flour. The acorn flour was prepared in several ways—as acorn mush soup, porridge, and bread—and it provided the staple of the family group's winter diet. Acorns are a remarkably nutritious and versatile food with a comparable nutrient level to that of wheat or barley. Human beings are not the only creatures to develop a lifestyle around this crop; birds, rodents, insects, deer, and grizzly bears once came to the oak groves each fall to feed.

The trail leaves Clover Basin Camp, climbs out of Miller Canyon, and contours along the upper canyon slopes. Riparian woodland gives way to a mixed evergreen forest that is broken up by grassy, oak-covered knolls. Deer are especially numerous on these slopes. Chews Ridge is directly above the trail, and Miller Mountain and some lesser peaks form the ridge to the southeast. As the trail continues to climb, the dry south-facing slopes support a patchy mix of Coulter pines and hardwoods. The trail soon reaches a large meadow and an artificial pond. It is joined here by a dirt road that leads through private property back to China Camp.

Autumn is the best time of year to hike the upper Carmel River. The river level stays low so it is easy to cross and explore. Yellow and red leaves fall from the trees, obscuring the trail and creating colorful skins on still pools. The days are warm and the nights are pleasant. Best of all, summer visitors have come and gone, and it is not unusual to see no other hikers for several days. The entire loop as we just described is 35.4 km (22 mi) long. It is rugged in spots, but it is mostly smooth and well graded. The combination of trails was chosen to give hikers a varied cross section of the upper Carmel River's natural and historical features, as well as to return them to their vehicles without having to backtrack.

DANISH CREEK AND BIG PINES AREA

The Big Pines Trail leads west from the Los Padres Reservoir to the Ventana Double Cone Trail, a distance of 14.8 km (9.2 mi). The trail follows Blue Rock Ridge and Danish Creek for most of the way through hardwood forest and chaparral. About 1.9 km (1.2 mi) from the reservoir, a side trail leads to the south to Danish Creek Camp and Rattlesnake Camp. Several unmaintained and overgrown trails lead from these camps to other trails and should only be followed by experienced hikers.

The main trail continues along Blue Rock Ridge. Much of this brushy vegetation was burned by the Marble–Cone fire in 1977, and a confusing network of bulldozed fire trails and old jeep roads scars the landscape. The trail continues climbing and eventually leads to a stream and stands of large ponderosa pines. Big Pines Camp is past the stream and down the slope on the south side of the trail. The junction with the Ventana Double Cone Trail is about 1.6 km (1 mi) farther. Many hikers continue on from here to Bottchers Gap, where they have arranged car shuttles enabling them to make the one-way 26 km (16 mi) hike.

Call the Carmel River Station (408-659-2612) or the Big Sur Guard Station (408-667-2556) before embarking on any of these hikes. Rangers there can provide current information on road, trail, and camp conditions, water availability, and fire regulations. They often have updated, hand-drawn copies of trail maps. These maps can come in handy because of the constantly changing trail conditions.

ARROYO SECO WATERSHED

ACCESS: There are two main access routes into the Arroyo Seco area. The first is along the Arroyo Seco Road, which leads 27 km (17 mi) from the town of Greenfield and Highway 101 in the Salinas Valley to the Arroyo Seco Camp and Guard Station. The Carmel Valley Road runs east from Highway 1 and Carmel through the Carmel Valley and intersects with the Arroyo Seco Road, a distance of 64 km (40 mi) (see map 4).

The Indians Road leads to the southern Arroyo Seco area. From King City, take the Jolon Road to Fort Hunter–Liggett headquarters; from Big Sur take the Nacimiento Road. Del Venturi Road runs from here to the Indians Guard Station, where the Indians Road begins. This road is steep, winding, and unpaved, and it is a distance of 29 km (18 mi) from the Indians Station to the Arroyo Seco Station. Several trailheads are found along this route and are discussed on the following pages.

TOPOGRAPHY AND GEOLOGY

The Arroyo Seco watershed includes some of Big Sur's most spectacular backcountry. *Arroyo Seco* is Spanish for "dry creek," a name that probably refers to this river's parched, sandy bed where it meets the Salinas River. Near its mountain source, however, the river is a rushing stream that slices through dry, brush-covered mountains. Narrow gorges hide cool, dark pools. Waterfalls spill down flumelike channels worn in sandstone. The tallest mountain in the range, Junipero Serra Peak (1787 m [5862 ft]), towers over the drainage and on good days affords views west to the ocean and east to the Sierra Nevada. Beneath this peak, massive layers of sandstone have been thrust up and tilted. This entire area, although extremely rugged, is accessible via a good network of trails and the Indians Road.

The Arroyo Seco drains much of the northeastern Santa Lucia Range before feeding into the Salinas River. The drainage is made up of several large tributaries and is shaped like a large fan. On its northern side, Paloma and Piney creeks drain the Sierra de Salinas and Chews Ridge. Farther west, moving along the fan counterclockwise, the Arroyo Seco is fed by Tassajara, Church, and Willow creeks. It is joined to the southwest by Lost Valley Creek, which includes Higgins and Zig-Zag creeks. Farther south, near the Indians Forest Service Station, the Arroyo Seco has its headwaters coming off the east face of the Coast Ridge and the north face of Cone Peak. Continuing around the fan, Roosevelt and Santa Lucia creeks flow down from Junipero Serra Peak. Several other large creeks join the Arroyo Seco from the south as it makes its way into the Salinas Valley outside the National Forest boundary.

The relief within many of these stream canyons is extreme. The change in elevation from Junipero Serra Peak to the Arroyo Seco canyon bottom is more than 1500 m (5000 ft), and changes in elevation of several thousand feet from ridge to creekbed are common throughout the area.

Like most of the Santa Lucia Range, the Arroyo Seco watershed has a fascinating but complex geological history. The swift streams have exposed a diversity of rock types: hard granitic rocks, limestone, schists, and other metamorphic rocks, and several kinds of sandstone, mudstone, and shale. Most of the creeks trend in a northwest direction and follow the general direction of the faults. Several large faults have been mapped here, such as the Church Creek and Willow Creek faults. A few of the fault zones are discernible by looking at the shape of the stream valleys. For example, Willow Creek Valley trends in a direct line west from its junction with the Arroyo Seco. Higgins Creek and upper Lost Valley Creek flow head-on into one another in a straight line, forming the long, flat Lost Valley. These and other faults are also discussed in chapter 1, Big Sur Geology.

VEGETATION

The Arroyo Seco watershed also has a great variety of vegetation. The climate is drier here than on the coastal slope, and chaparral covers more of the landscape than any other plant community. The east-facing slopes of the Coast Ridge above Lost Valley are dominated by stands of wartleaf ceanothus, scrub oak, and manzanita. Tree poppy, Santa Lucia sticky monkey flower, and scarlet bugler are some of the brighter flowers. On the east side of the drainage near the Indians Road, the brush is dominated by chamise with some black sage, yerba santa, California sagebrush, manzanita, and buckwheat.

A few areas of oak woodland are found here, especially near the Indians Station on the trail to Junipero Serra Peak, in Church Creek Valley, and along the lower part of Willow Creek. Some larger stands occur along the lower Arroyo Seco where it enters the Salinas Valley. But these areas are small compared to the expansive oak woodland just over the divide in the San Antonio and Nacimiento drainages.

Canyon live oaks grow adjacent to chaparral in many of the drier areas, while coast live oak, bay, and madrone form hardwood forests on the cooler slopes of most drainages. These trees are joined by some of the conifers at higher elevations. Coulter pines are the most widespread; they are found on drier, brush-covered slopes as well as within stands of mixed evergreen forest. They have grown quite large on the floor of Lost Valley. Sugar pines occupy the north slope of Junipero Serra Peak, and Santa Lucia firs are scattered on the watershed's steeper slopes. A few knobcone pines grow on the eastern side of the Coast Ridge, where they are restricted to sandy soils in open chaparral.

This dry vegetation contrasts sharply with that of the Arroyo Seco's lush riparian woodland. The woodland varies in density and makeup from creek to creek within the watershed, but it mainly consists of large western sycamores, bigleaf maples, black cottonwoods, several species of oaks, and a few incense cedars. Alders can grow quite large in the more open canyons, but they are usually part of a subcanopy along with several types of willows, which often grow in thickets along the stream-banks. Beneath these is an assortment of ferns, horsetail rushes, black-berry, poison oak, mugwort, and other riparian plants.

INDIANS ROAD

The Indians Road provides access at a number of points into the Arroyo Seco watershed. The road is a narrow, unpaved, circuitous car path that is impassable in the winter and extremely hot in the summer. It is not recommended for the faint of heart or those overprotective of their cars. But the road does offer some of the most spectacular views of the back-country, and for the nonbackpacker, it makes possible day hikes into the rugged gorges and surrounding ridges.

The south end of the road begins at the Indians Forest Service Station, about 32 km (20 mi) from the San Antonio Mission and Fort Hunter–Liggett headquarters. The road is about 29 km (18 mi) long, following the general path of the Arroyo Seco River in a northward direction. It stays on the east wall of the canyon until arriving at the Arroyo Seco Station and campground. It crosses the river here and heads east into the Salinas Valley.

The road leaves the river bed at the Indians Station and climbs steeply up the canyon past some sandstone exposures. After almost 5 km (3 mi) it arrives at Escondido Camp, a U.S. Forest Service car campground that is situated beneath large oaks. There are pay campsites, running water, and toilets. At the far end of the camp is the Lost Valley Trailhead, which crosses the Arroyo Seco River about 1.6 km (1 mi) below the camp and leads to Lost Valley.

The road continues climbing on its way north and enters Hanging

Valley. Some old campsites and fascinating outcrops of sedimentary rock can be seen along this unusually straight and level stretch of road. Leaving Hanging Valley, the road winds along steep canyon walls with expansive views of the Arroyo Seco gorge and beyond to the Coast Ridge. The vegetation is mostly chamise chaparral with some black sage and wartleaf ceanothus. Scattered within this chaparral is the Arroyo Seco bush mallow (*Malacothamnus palmeri* var. *lucianus*); this plant is quite rare and is known only from this site.

The road climbs a bit and then continues along at a level grade. The river is about 450 m (1500 ft) below and is hidden by steep, brush-covered slopes. A few green pools amid polished rocks are sometimes visible where the river takes a sharp turn. About 9.6 km (6 mi) from Hanging Valley is the trailhead to Last Chance Camp and the junction of the Arroyo Seco with Junipero Serra Peak Trail. This trail is confusing to follow, and hikers should inquire about conditions at the Indians or Arroyo Seco Guard Stations before using it. It is distinct from the Junipero Serra Peak Trail that is described later in this section. This latter trail leaves near the Indians Station, and the two trails join near the Junipero Serra Peak summit.

The road follows switchbacks downhill from here, and in 6 km (3.5 mi) reaches the Marble Peak Trailhead at the confluence of the Arroyo Seco and Tassajara Creek. Sedimentary rocks bounded by the Willow Creek fault are exposed here. An old metal and wood foot bridge, known as Horsebridge, crosses the river, and there are large pools both up and downstream from this point.

The road continues winding down along the east face of the canyon and becomes quite narrow at a few spots. It follows the course of the Arroyo Seco out of the canyon and reaches the Arroyo Seco Campground, picnic area, and guard station. There are pay campsites, pay picnic sites, and free day-use areas in this developed complex. This part of the Arroyo Seco receives heavy use by visitors from the Salinas Valley who come here to escape the blistering summer heat.

The road and the river leave the National Forest and turn east toward the Salinas Valley. It is worthwhile to drive this stretch and observe the lower canyon and terraces of the Arroyo Seco. Flat terraces occur on both sides of the river above the channel. These handsome terraces, covered with level hayfields and dotted with oaks, were formed by river alluvium. The terraces and steep canyon below them provide striking evidence of the recent period of uplift still taking place in this area. The river carried the rock, gravel, and sand down from the mountains, dropping much of it along the way to the Salinas River. Then came a sudden period of renewed uplift that elevated the wide river channel and forced the river to cut a new and deeper course into its raised terraces. This process is similar to that which forms the marine terraces found on the coast. From here the road passes a junction with the Carmel Valley Road and continues on into Greenfield.

ARROYO SECO RIVER

The Arroyo Seco Trail begins just north of the Indians Station and is well marked by signs. It is 5 mi (8 km) long and follows the river upstream from the Indians Station to the headwaters near the top of the Coast Ridge. This trail joins the North Coast Ridge Trail at the summit, which can then be followed south to the Cone Peak Road or north to Marble Peak and the Coast Ridge Road. Many connections and loops are possible from this junction, and readers should consult maps 3 and 4. Large boulders of sandstone loom over much of the trail, and the river spills over and around many others that have rolled down to the riverbed at some time. Many small pools and falls are scattered among these boulders.

The trail is a well-graded uphill climb through riparian and hardwood forests, and there are many incense cedars and Santa Lucia firs along the creek. It is about 2.4 km (1.5 mi) to Forks Camp and another 1.9 km (1.2 mi) to Madrone Camp. From this latter camp the trail leaves the river, which by now is a small stream, and switches up through open chaparral. There are stands of knobcone pine here, much of which burned in the Marble–Cone fire. Also, an old World War II era phone line lies along the trail that at one time probably connected with the fire lookout on Cone Peak. There are views eastward down canyon to the Arroyo Seco and across to Junipero Serra Peak.

There are no U.S. Forest Service trails that follow the middle and lower Arroyo Seco, but the channel is wide and dry enough that hikers can "boulder hop" and swim most of the river's course. Just downstream from the Indians Station, for example, large pools are cut into the sandstone canyon. Paths lead down to the river in many places along the length of Indian Road; these usually lead to nice swimming or fishing holes or to waterfalls.

The best way to find such sites is to walk up or down the river. Wear shorts and old sneakers and only bring things that can afford to get wet. Several waterfalls feed into the river, one of which is downstream from where the Lost Valley Trail crosses the river below Escondido Camp. Upstream from the Horsebridge is a series of gorges and pools, some of which have to be swum even in low water. A few miles farther upstream is probably the deepest, steepest, and longest gorge in the entire range; it is well worth the wet hike. Downstream from Horsebridge are more pools, sandy beaches, and some large bounders with Indian mortars worn into them.

The middle and lower Arroyo Seco, in contrast to most of the other rivers in the region, has an open and spacious riparian woodland. Many of the trees, including alders and even a few willows, get quite large and do not form the thickets characteristic of the Little Sur, Big Sur, and Carmel rivers.

WILLOW CREEK AND TASSAJARA CREEK

There are two major access routes to this area: along the Marble Peak Trail coming from either the Indians Road or the Coast Ridge Road, and along the Church Creek Trail and the Jamesburg–Tassajara Road (J-T Rd.). The J-T Rd. (see section on the Carmel River watershed) ends at the Tassajara Zen Center and Hot Springs, and reservations are needed for visitors planning to use the facilities there.

Hikers leaving the Tassajara Hot Springs for the Marble Peak Trail can proceed in two directions. The Tony Trail goes to the southwest over the divide separating Tassajara and Willow creeks and is for hikers heading toward the Coast Ridge along the Marble Peak Trail. Hikers headed to the Arroyo Seco should take the Tassajara Cut-off Trail. This route begins along Tassajara Creek just downstream from the hot springs. The trail is well marked and leads to the Horse Pasture Trail, which in turns meets the Marble Peak Trail. It is just a few miles east along this trail to the Arroyo Seco.

The most interesting geological feature of this area is the unusual sandstone exposures that crop out along the Church Creek and Horse Pasture trails. Actually two different types of sandstone are exposed side by side in thin strips running the length of Church Creek Valley and the ridges above Tassajara Hot Springs. The sandstone is found along the western edge of the Church Creek fault, which trends northwest–southeast through much of the upper Church Creek Valley. The sandstone and the fault also cross the divide to the north and extend into Pine Valley in the Carmel River watershed.

Rain and wind have eroded arches, caves, and curving channels into the rock walls. Cobbles and large stones made of harder rock are imbedded in the sandstone. As the softer sandstone erodes from around these round rocks, they are left perched on thin pedestals of sandstone and look something like golf balls on tees.

A different fault has helped form the Willow Creek Valley. Known as the Willow Creek fault, it is unusual in that it trends almost straight east from the Arroyo Seco to the Coast Ridge. Most other large faults in the range trend northwest–southeast. It truncates, or cuts off, the Church Creek fault near the Arroyo Seco. The Marble Peak Trail follows the fault almost its entire length from the Indians Road to the Coast Ridge. The trail winds through the dense alders and willows of Willow Creek, but it eventually reaches hardwood forest and brush at the higher elevations near the Coast Ridge. Along the trail are several floodplain areas strewn with large boulders and other debris, indicating that violent floods occasionally occur at the lower stretches of this creek.

Willow Creek joins Tassajara Creek 3 km (2 mi) upstream from the latter creek's confluence with the Arroyo Seco. A few miles up Tassajara Creek, just below the hot springs, a small gorge known as the Narrows has been cut through very hard crystalline rock. Some uplifted river terraces also occur along lower Tassajara Creek that are covered with spacious valley oaks and buckeye. This part of the trail is especially rich in riparian and woodland birds, including nesting acorn woodpeckers and colorful western tanagers (*Piranga ludoviciana*).

LOST VALLEY

There are three points of entry to Lost Valley: from the Indians Road and Escondido Camp along the Lost Valley Trail; along the same trail from its other end, at the Marble Peak Trail and Higgins Creek; and down from the North Coast Ridge Trail near the Cone Peak area.

Open meadows and tall Coulter pines make Lost Valley one of the most picturesque areas in the backcountry. It is a long, fault-formed valley that is drained by Higgins Creek to the northwest and upper Lost Valley Creek to the southeast. The two creeks flow along the fault zone in an almost straight line toward one another, joining and then flowing east through a narrow canyon toward the Arroyo Seco. The creek leaves the softer, more easily eroded sedimentary rocks of the valley (west of the fault) and enters the canyon, which is made up of the hard metamorphic rocks of the Salinian block (east of the fault). The presence of the fault explains the sudden change in landform from the gentle valley to the steep canyon.

The brown sedimentary rock forms the well-rounded knolls and knobs coming down off the Coast Ridge. The knolls at first glance look like ancient lava flows, but they are actually eroded shale and mudstone. They are composed of sediments that were deposited on the sea floor during the late Cretaceous period, 70 million years ago. The soil is very poorly developed here and the vegetation is sparse. Scrawny Coulters, many of them scorched by recent fires, grow mixed with yerba santa, Santa Lucia sticky monkey flower, wartleaf ceanothus, and tree poppy. The shrubs are often spaced well apart from one another, and running between them are coast horned lizards, western fence lizards, and western whiptails. Rattlesnakes and common kingsnakes are also seen here occasionally.

Although Lost Valley Camp is an ideal spot from which to spend a few days surveying the surrounding country, the heat and flies can be terrible during the summer. One long, wet, but interesting day loop can be made by hiking down Lost Valley Creek to the Arroyo Seco, then up the Arroyo Seco to the Lost Valley Trail, and then along this trail back to Lost Valley Camp. Several large pools and waterfalls occur along the way. Lower Lost Valley Creek is particularly rich in wildlife. We saw more western pond turtles in sandy pools here than in any other creek, and aquatic snakes, skunks, dippers, belted kingfishers, some ducks (wood ducks and mallards), and many songbirds live within the dense riparian woodland.

JUNIPERO SERRA PEAK

In almost every general category covered by this book—geology, climate, flora, fire ecology, history, and topography—the Junipero Serra Peak area is outstanding in some way. It is, at 1787 m (5862 ft), the tallest mountain in the Santa Lucia Range. The summit can be reached in 2–4 hours along the 9.6-km (6-mi) trail that leaves from the Indians Station. It is a hot, dry, steep climb but well worth the effort.

The mountaintop itself is composed mostly of hard granitic rock and metamorphic schist, but the lower surrounding area is geologically more diverse. The trail passes through different types of sandstone on its upward climb. These are exposed in long, layered ridges, rounded knolls, and steep cliffs that have eroded in interesting patterns.

Pines, blue oaks, and chaparral shrubs grow along fissures in the rock, and a blue oak woodland covers the more level areas between the outcrops. The rare butterworth eriogonum (*Eriogonum butterworthianum*), a type of buckwheat, is confined to sunny sandstone outcrops in this area only and is usually found growing alongside felt paintbrush.

The trail soon leaves the sandstone and climbs beneath oak wood-land and a mixed evergreen forest. Blue oaks and Coulter pines are on the drier knolls, valley oaks are in the moister low-lying areas, and live oaks appear on the higher, steeper slopes. The trail leaves the hard-woods and switches up through chaparral dominated by chamise, scrub oaks, scrubby canyon live oak, deer brush, and eastwood manzanita. Santa Lucia sticky monkey flower, scarlet bugler, and woolly blue-curls offer some bright colors when flowering in early summer.

The trail leaves the south slope of the peak and winds around to the forests of the north slope. The Marble–Cone fire burned through this area and destroyed much of the pine and hardwood forest. Ecologists Talley and Griffin, in a study on the fire ecology of the peak, found that fires occurred frequently in this forest before the turn of the century. By analyzing fire scars on older sugar pines, they conservatively estimate that fires burned here an average of every 21 years from 1640 to 1907. Aggressive five suppression began with the formation of the Monterey National Forest in 1907, and except for two small and short-lived light-ning fires, no other burns had occurred here until the Marble–Cone fire.

Small, recurrent fires, as this example illustrates, are important to the development and maintenance of montane pine forests. Such fires do not kill the mature pines, but instead thin out dead and dying trees and prevent the buildup of dangerous fuel levels. They also thin the under-story and provide a good seedbed. The absence of regular fires allows fuels to accumulate so that when a fire does occur, it burns very hot and destroys much of the forest. Also, this summit is drier than mountains closer to the coast and receives much of its precipitation as snow; the weight of the snow breaks many tree limbs and adds to the fuel load.

As a result of the burn, slopes that were once open sugar pine forest are now thick with deer brush. Blackened pine stumps burned to bizarre shapes protrude above the impenetrable shrubs. Canyon live oaks have stump sprouted, although much of the wood of the dead parent trees remains unburned. Coulter and sugar pine seedlings grow in dense thick-ets, where most of the seedlings will eventually die. Unless more fires occur here within the next 20 to 30 years, these shrubs and seedlings will accumulate to fuel levels that will again endanger the remaining old-growth pines.

Junipero Serra Peak, like other isolated mountains within the range, also supports several rare and threatened plants. The perennial Santa Lucia lupine, which is endemic to these mountains, actually expanded its population following the fire. It is a broadleafed lupine with light blue flowers that usually grows on the forest floor and along trails. Another endemic lupine, Abram's lupine, also expanded its range within this forest after the fire. Santa Lucia bedstraw is another rare endemic found on the summit.

The abandoned fire lookout tower stands to the southwest of the pine forest on the summit. Views from here are tremendous in all directions. To the west is the Arroyo Seco drainage, the Coast Ridge, and the Pacific Ocean. The oak-studded savannas of the Nacimiento and San Antonio valleys stretch to the south and southeast, and Lake San Antonio is visible near the horizon. The Ventana Cones and Pico Blanco rise to the north, and the hazy Salinas Valley runs along the eastern perimeter of the range. On clear days, the Sierra Nevada is visible beyond the Salinas and San Joaquin valleys.

ADDITIONAL COMMENTS

The popularity of sites within the Arroyo Seco area varies quite a bit. The easily accessible pools near both the Indians and Arroyo Seco Guard stations are often crowded in summer, but nearby pools a short walk or swim away are virtually untouched. The same goes for most of the backcountry trails. Certain spots are popular, such as Lost Valley, the Tassajara Hot Springs area, and the Marble Peak Trail, but spurs and offshoots from these spots are usually deserted.

The best seasons during which to visit depend on several factors. Summer is good for swimming and exploring the creeks, but the trails are hot and the insects intense. In contrast, winter has cool days with no flies, but the rivers are high and swift and can be dangerous. Flowers in spring and the turning of leaves in autumn make these the best seasons for color.

CONE PEAK AREA

ACCESS: Cone Peak is easily accessible via Cone Peak Road, which departs from the Nacimiento–Ferguson Road approximately 10.5 km (7.1 mi) from Highway 1 (see map 4). From this juncture, it is 6 km (3.7 mi) to the first of four trailheads in the Cone Peak area, the Vicente Flat trailhead. The Vicente Flat Trail joins the Kirk Creek Trail to eventually reach the coast. A little farther north along the Cone Peak Road, the San Antonio Trail drops to the east into the San Antonio drainage, coming to a dead end at San Antonio Camp. The Cone Peak Trail leaves the road about 8 km (5 mi) from Nacimiento–Ferguson Road and

climbs to the northwest to Cone Peak. Finally, at the end of the Cone
Peak Road near a small campsite and a picnic table, the North Coast
Ridge Trail departs northward.

INTRODUCTION

The terrain around Cone Peak is extremely steep and rugged. The
coastal slope, from the peak down to Limekiln Creek, is the steepest
coastal slope anywhere in the continental United States. This makes for
both spectacular views and difficult hiking. The peak is a central hub to
diverse drainages: the steep, lime-white canyons of the Limekiln Creek
drainage to the southwest are the most extensive, while the deep gorge
of Devil's Creek dominates the peak's northwestward drainage. The San
Antonio watershed drains the east side of the peak. The summit, a bare
and jagged point of metamorphic rocks, towers over this precipitous
landscape and commands a view over many square kilometers. The
peak's neighbor to the west, Twin Peak, is about 100 m (300 ft) lower,
and its summit is blanketed with a dense cover of stately sugar pines.

The Cone Peak area has probably received more attention from botanists than any other area in the range. This is largely because an extensive stand of Santa Lucia fir grows on the northwest slope of the peak
and down into the south fork of Devil's Canyon. This fir was first described here by David Douglas in 1831. It was most accessible here
because a trail, long used by natives as a trade route to the coast, passed
through the area. (The existing Gamboa trail is a remnant of this route.)
The inhabitants of San Antonio Mission, about 19 km (12 mi) to the
east, obtained pitch from the trees for use as incense, and they directed
early botanists to the peak. Thomas Coulter discovered the Coulter pine
in the vicinity of Cone Peak in 1832, bringing more botanical attention
to the area.

The first sugar pines to be described in California were also found in
the Cone Peak area. This population is isolated from Sierran stands,
and later botanists continued to catalogue a number of disjunct plants
on this and other high summits in the Santa Lucias. Ornithologists were
also attracted to the area and noted the mountain chickadee, a disjunct
montane forest bird, on the slopes of Cone Peak around the turn of the
century.

Recognition of this area's ecological uniqueness has continued to
grow since these early days. Perhaps of most interest from an ecological
viewpoint is the number of different habitat types found within this

relatively small area. While habitat diversity is characteristic of the Santa Lucia Range, in this region the habitats are particularly diverse. The sudden change in elevation contributes to this because plants accustomed to different altitudinal climates are literally stacked on top of one another. The variety of soil types in the area—from limestone-derived soils to harsh serpentine to granitic and metamorphic rocks—also contribute to this diversity.

Primarily because of its great diversity of habitats and this combination of unusual plants, the Cone Peak area has been designated a Research Natural Area (RNA) by the U.S. Forest Service. This designation restricts activities that might compromise its ecological values while encouraging research use of the area. The land to the northwest of the peak adjacent to the RNA, including the lower reaches of Devil's Creek and Big Creek, is owned and managed as a Natural Reserve (Landels–Hill Big Creek Reserve) by the University of California for the same reasons. The entire Devil's Creek–Big Creek–Limekiln Creek area makes up one of the United Nation's Man and the Biosphere Reserves.All of these designations are an indication of the biological richness of this part of the Santa Lucias.

GEOLOGY

Metamorphic rocks of the Salinian block dominate the entire landscape around Cone Peak. The upper Limekiln Creek drainages to the southeast of Cone Peak are the best areas in the range to see the oldest rocks in central coastal California. The rocks, composed mainly of gneiss and amphibolite, are often strikingly banded and form spectacular cliffs around the peak.

Marbled limestone also outcrops extensively in the area and is the reason why a large limekiln operation was once located in lower Limekiln Creek. These are the largest limestone deposits in the Santa Lucias outside of the Pico Blanco area about 32 km (20 mi) to the north. Sedimentary and metamorphic rocks of the Nacimiento block make up the lower areas of the coastal drainages. The Sur–Nacimiento fault separates these two distinct rock assemblages as it cuts across lower Limekiln Creek from south to north. The lower elevation rocks are obscured by much vegetation, but more exposed Franciscan greenstone, sandstone, and shale form the coastline.

The area is well traversed with trails and roads despite the steepness of the terrain. The Cone Peak Road reaches to the base of Cone Peak's summit, and a network of trails winds from the coast up the Limekiln Creek drainage to the peak. Other trails allow access into upper San Antonio Creek and Devil's Canyon.

CONE PEAK ROAD

The Cone Peak Road diverges from the Nacimiento Road at the Nacimiento summit 7.1 miles from Highway 1, and penetrates northward into the Ventana Wilderness. It is well traveled but is sometimes closed by a gate at Nacimiento Road. It follows the top of the Coast Ridge for most of its length, hugging the east side of the ridge and providing a good vantage down into the San Antonio watershed and Fort Hunter–Liggett. In several spots it crosses saddles with views to the west where the blue Pacific sparkles far below forested and grassy slopes.

A canopy of mixed evergreen forest of madrones, tanoaks, interior live oaks, Coulter pines, and ponderosa pines dominates along most of the 10.5 km (6.6 mi) to the road's end at the base of Cone Peak. Most of the road is above 1000 m (3200 ft) in elevation, and snow occasionally covers it in winter. The Rat Creek fire of 1985 burned much of the terrain north and east of the road, and it is interesting to watch the vegetation recovering. As of this writing, the chaparral and mixed evergreen forests to the east are open and green with new understory plants. The striking metamorphic rocks of the area have been exposed by the fire.

VICENTE FLAT TRAIL

The Vicente Flat Trail climbs briefly to the southwest as it leaves the Cone Peak Road, then descends steeply northwestward through mixed evergreen forest. The forest was lightly burned and heavily reseeded following the Rat Creek fire. Resprouting oaks and abundant Italian ryegrass are common here as of this writing. A typical mixed evergreen forest understory is developing and filling up the open ground left by the fire. The trail switches back to the northeast and descends more gradually to reach redwoods along an upper fork of Hare Creek. Like all the canyons in this area, even this small tributary canyon is steep and forms a small, deep gorge. A beautiful cross section of banded gneiss and other Salinian metamorphic rocks form the canyon's north wall. The spire of Cone Peak rises behind the steep cliff faces.

The trail reaches the other fork of Hare Creek in about 0.5 km

(0.3 mi). The Rat Creek fire left scorch marks about 7–10 m (20–30 ft) high on the trees, and many of these trees have *cat eyes*—triangular, hollowed-out scars from numerous fires. The dramatic transition into the redwood forest microclimate is marked by the appearance of western Solomon's seal, redwood sorrel, wood ferns, and many other humidity-loving plants. But the understory in these higher elevation redwoods is not as rich as it is nearer the coast. Arid climate canyon wrens sing their descending scales from surrounding dry cliffs, while dippers bob along the cool creek.

The trail winds downstream for a short distance, crossing it several times to reach the upper Vicente Flat campsites beneath streamside redwoods. The level, grassy glade of Vicente Flat opens up a little farther on. More campsites are situated on the edge of the clearing, which lies at about 520 m (1700 ft) elevation.

The large clearing is one of several nearly level benches, or terraces, that border the creek. These terraces are indicators of the recent uplift of the mountain range. Each terrace represents a streamcourse that has been lifted up and left high and dry, and there are few places in the range where the results of this process are so clear. Very large redwoods grow in this little valley, some of them as large as 10 m (30 ft) in circumference. Alders, maples, and large old sycamores lean over the stream, while canyon live oaks, California bays, and madrones shade the flat streamside terraces and clearings. The Stone Ridge Trail, described later, branches off the Vicente Flat Trail at the lower end of the large clearing.

Parts of the stream dry up in the summer months, and the creek disappears into sand only to reappear several hundred meters downstream. This happens in other high streams in the Santa Lucias as well. Floods periodically sweep down this small creek, as evidenced by deep deposits of gravel and mud. The extremely steep, chaparral-covered slopes above feed these floods in the wake of fires. In some places, logs are wedged high in streamside redwoods, while others protrude from gravel banks.

From Vicente Flat Camp it is possible to continue on down to the coast via the Kirk Creek Trail or to climb up to the north on the Stone Ridge Trail.

KIRK CREEK TRAIL

The Kirk Creek Trail climbs at first to the southwest, winding in and out of ravines on the north flank of Hare Canyon. This cool slope is covered with tanoaks and live oaks and passes through redwood groves in the ravines. Banded gneiss has been exposed by the floodwaters in some of the ravines. An occasional Douglas fir appears in the mixed evergreen forest. The steep slopes of lower Limekiln Creek frame a view of the Pacific Ocean down the canyon.

After about 3 km (2 mi) of gradual climbing through this forest, the trail rounds a ridge and breaks out onto the ocean-facing slopes with spectacular views at about 600 m (2000 ft) elevation. It enters grassland and rocky scrub dominated by deerweed and Our Lord's candle. Broken outcrops of white limestone dot the terrain.

The trail descends gradually, curving in and out of ravines. These ravines are cooler and shadier than the open slopes, and they shelter redwoods, sword ferns, maidenhair ferns, western hounds tongue, and other redwood forest plants. Other ravines are filled with live oaks and madrones and are also cool relative to the open slopes. An understory of bracken ferns, milkmaids, baby blue-eyes, and Douglas' iris borders the trail here. Ponderosa pines are visible on ridgecrests above but are lacking along the trail. Although typical for these mountains, the abrupt change in microclimate between ravine and slope seems especially dramatic on this stretch of the Kirk Creek Trail.

The lower parts of the Kirk Creek Trail pass through coastal scrub and grassland. Down within reach of the fog, deerweed and Our Lord's candle are replaced by California sagebrush, blue blossom, and coyote bush. It is a good area to see coastal scrub in several phases. The typical birds of the coastal scrub are plentiful and relatively easy to see because of the common grassland openings.

The trail eventually reaches Kirk Creek Campground at Highway 1, completing a dramatic transition from dry scrubby slopes to cool, foggy coastline. The rocky shore intertidal habitat along the cliffs below Kirk Creek Campground is the antithesis of the arid, yucca-dotted slopes above. Although inaccessible from Kirk Creek Campground, the rocky shore can be reached a short distance to the south at Mill Creek picnic area.

STONE RIDGE TRAIL

The Stone Ridge Trail connects Vicente Flat Camp to Goat Camp, crossing two rocky, limestone-backed ridges in the process. It begins by climbing up a rocky, south-facing slope covered with deerweed and other shrubs. There is a good perspective up and down Hare Canyon from this slope, and you can see the descent of the Vicente Flat Trail from the Coast Ridge. At about 600 m (2000 ft) elevation, the trail crosses Stone Ridge, turns to the north, and descends into Limekiln Creek Canyon.

Cone Peak is once again the dominant landscape feature visible from this ridge, capping an extremely steep terrain of metamorphic rocks and diverse vegetation. Groves of large redwoods line the bottom of Limekiln Creek Canyon and its tributaries, while a patchwork of scrub and grassland covers the south-facing slopes. Mixed evergreen forest follows the ravines. It is easy to see the complex patterns of vegetation in Limekiln Creek from this vantage.

In about 1.6 km (1 mi), the trail reaches Limekiln Creek, a perennial stream and an oasis on summer days. Trout live in this creek, probably the descendants of fish stocked here by homesteaders long ago. The trail crosses the stream and begins climbing up an east-facing slope through mixed evergreen forest. The path cuts into a small drainage and follows it upstream a short distance, reaching a quiet, open flat where large tanoaks and canyon live oaks grow. A small spring here has been trampled to a mire by cattle.

Leaving this small ravine, the trail steeply follows a narrow ridgeline upward, crosses another small ravine, then follows a contour along the slope and abruptly enters grassland near the ridgecrest. A promontory of limestone on a high shoulder of the ridge stands a short distance west of the trail. A walk over to the promontory is rewarded by a magnificent view of the coastline and Hare and Limekiln creek canyons. The trail then begins to drop downhill along the north-facing slope through mixed evergreen forest where some Coulter and ponderosa pines grow. It passes another small, cattle-trampled spring as it enters a redwood grove in one ravine.

The trail begins to angle up the slope above the West Fork of Limekiln Creek, crossing ravines and open south-facing slopes. The heavily forested, east-facing areas of the watershed are clearly visible from here. The redwoods here were once slated to be logged but were spared in a last-ditch effort by environmentalists. The trail frequently disappears in this stretch and remains obscure for much of the remaining stretch to Goat Camp. We strongly recommend checking with the U.S. Forest Service on the condition of the remainder of this trail before attempting to hike it.

Once found, the trail can be followed along the slope passing from scrub to forest and back. It crosses a small tributary ravine of the West Fork and reaches Goat Camp on a small, nearly level bench on a ridge.

Water is available from a spring in a ravine just beyond the camp. The single table and firepit of Goat Camp sits beneath madrones and has a good view down the West Fork.

The trail continues with a tortuous climb up out of the West Fork Canyon, heading straight uphill in a few switchbacks to a saddle on the ridge above. Heavy regrowth after the Rat Creek fire has obscured the trail. If the trail is lost, it is relatively easy to find the saddle, which is situated between Twin Peak and an unnamed peak to the northwest. This is the only reasonable place to cross the ridge, and so it has been the location of a trail to the coast ever since the Esselen and Salinan natives lived in these mountains.

The Stone Ridge Trail meets the Gamboa Trail at the saddle, and a short, very steep spur trail descends to the north to the South Fork of Devil's Creek and Ojito Camp. This shady little camp is on the banks of the creek which, like Hare Creek, is sometimes dry in sections at this high elevation.

GAMBOA TRAIL

The main Gamboa Trail turns to the east from the Stone Ridge Trail at the previously mentioned saddle and follows a rough contour along the slope up Devil's Canyon. Shaded and with a few views, the trail is an enjoyable route through quiet mixed evergreen forests. This is a good place to see Santa Lucia firs on both sides of the trail amid canyon live oaks, madrones, and tanoaks. Large sugar pines accompany the firs a bit farther along the trail and soon dominate. The slopes are very steep and rocky and the understory is very sparse, which is typical of Santa Lucia fir habitat. The slope also faces north, giving the firs and the pines needed relief from the summer drought.

The forest is unusual habitat and is one of the unique ecological corners of the Santa Lucia Range. The rare Santa Lucia lupine and the Abram's lupine grow amid the sugar pines, and the forest floor was carpeted with blooming Abram's lupines for two springs after the Rat Creek fire. The rare Santa Lucia bedstraw and California bedstraw are also found here.

This is a quiet forest. The dry wind and the rustle of squirrels in the oak litter are often the only sounds to be heard. We have seen roadrunners in clearings, and ornithologists have spotted mountain chickadees in the sugar pines—far from their haunts in the Sierra Nevada.

The Gamboa Trail continues up the South Fork of Devil's Canyon and curves into several dry ravines. Cone Peak comes into view. The South Fork of Devil's Creek, frequently dry, is in one of these ravines. Trail Springs Camp is situated at the headwaters of the creek just below the junction with the Cone Peak Trail. The camp is shady and water is available downstream if the creek is dry at the camp.

The trail climbs steeply from Trail Springs Camp through a mixed evergreen forest to join the Coast Ridge Trail in about 2 km (1.3 mi). Near the top of the climb it enters a woodland of large ponderosa pines. There are spectacular views down the deep and wild Devil's Canyon. The Coast Ridge Trail runs north along the Coast Ridge, while to the south it drops over the east side of the ridge and reaches the Cone Peak Road in 2.4 km (1.5 mi).

CONE PEAK TRAIL

This route is the shortest way to get to the top of the Santa Lucia Range. It is just 3.5 km (2.3 mi) from the Cone Peak Road to the 1571-m (5155-ft) summit and some of the most spectacular views in the range. Although the vertical climb is about 427 m (1400 ft), the walk is relatively easy.

The trail leaves the Cone Peak Road 8 km (5 mi) from the Nacimiento–Ferguson Road. Most of the first half of the trail climbs at an easy grade up a southwest-facing slope that has excellent views of the coastline. The slope was burned in the Rat Creek fire, which enhanced the spectacular views. The burned chaparral is recovering and resprouting quickly and should encourage magnificent wildflower blooms for several years until the chamise thickens again.

The trail cuts through outcrops of white marble and the characteristic banded metamorphic gneiss of the Salinian block. Garnets are prominent in some of these rocks. After about 1.6 km (1 mi) of gentle climbing, the trail begins to switch back more steeply up a rocky ridge. It skirts the foot of a 21-m- (70-ft-) high cliff of banded gneiss. Canyon live oaks, bays, and madrones overshadow the trail, and Coulter pines appear a short distance farther.

Soon after the appearance of the Coulter pines, a spur trail diverges upward to the left, leading shortly to an overlook with spectacular views down Limekiln Creek to the coast. Cone Peak is visible high above to the northeast. The trail then climbs gradually again to meet the junction with the short spur trail to the summit of Cone Peak. The main trail continues down into Devil's Canyon and Trail

Springs. The summit trail climbs steeply through a rocky terrain where Santa Lucia firs lean from rocky ledges and canyon live oaks cling to the slopes. The trail reaches the top of the spire of the Cone Peak about 100 m (320 ft.) higher, where a lookout tower perches with a commanding view of a vast landscape.

To the east, the rolling oak woodlands of Fort Hunter–Liggett sprawl toward the Salinas Valley. Although a thick haze over this and other inland valleys usually blocks the view farther east, it is occasionally possible to see the Sierra Nevadas from the summit. The jagged edge of the Ventana Cones defines the northern horizon, with Pico Blanco visible just to their west. Chews Ridge and upper Carmel Valley are visible to the northeast, and the massive hulk of Junipero Serra and Pinon Peak, the only two mountains higher than Cone Peak in the range, lie to the east.

The Big Sur coastline is laid out like a map from this vantage point. Pfeiffer Point and the points southward clear to Cape San Martin are easily picked out. Mount Mars is discernible as a slight bump in the Coast Ridge far to the southeast, above the Salmon Creek drainage. Few sights can compare with the endless blue, sparkling Pacific as seen from the summit of Cone Peak. The waves on the ocean look like ripples in a giant pond. Foggy days are rewarding too, as the blue ocean is replaced by a white ocean of clouds that is just as vast.

The summit is a good spot to sit and study the patterns of vegetation and topography. The grasslands stripe the ridgetops and south-facing slopes of the coastal ridges. Pines line the ridgetops, redwoods blanket north-facing slopes, and chaparral stands out like patches of dark carpet on south faces. The general trend in the topography of the Santa Lucia Range, from the rugged peaks in the north to a gentler terrain in the south, is also quite clear from Cone Peak.

The summit itself is composed of metamorphic rocks that are rich in garnets—small purplish crystals imbedded in the rocks. These are low grade garnets and not gem quality. They erode from the rocks of the high summits in the Santa Lucias to make the purple "garnet sands" that are especially common at the beaches in Andrew Molera State Park to the north.

The lookout tower is occupied during the fire season from April or May to October or November. It is the fire lookout's home, and it is best to announce your presence as you near the summit to avoid startling him or her.

The main Cone Peak Trail descends from the summit trail junction into the South Fork of Devil's Canyon. It takes several long switchbacks through an extensive grove of giant old sugar pines to reach a junction with the Gamboa Trail at Trail Springs Camp. This grove is the largest in the range and is truly grand and worth visiting. Unfortunately, fire management practices of the past several decades may be threatening this and other high elevation conifer stands in the range. The hot fires that have resulted from fire suppression kill more of the trees than would smaller, more frequent fires. The pines seem to have fared well in the Rat Creek fire, although scars are visible far up the trunks. Several of the giants toppled when burned through at their bases.

To avoid backtracking, a loop hike can be made from the Cone Peak Trail, up the Gamboa Trail to the northeast toward the Coast Ridge Trail, and back to the Cone Peak Road. A short 2-km (1.3-mi) walk on the Cone Peak Road brings you back to the Cone Peak Trailhead for an overall loop length of 9.6 km (6 mi). This loop will bring you a short distance along the Coast Ridge Trail as it descends from the Gamboa Trail to the Coast Ridge Road. This short section of the trail cuts downhill at a fairly steep grade with a few switchbacks. It crosses several talus slopes and goes through stands of sugar pines and Santa Lucia firs.

SALMON CREEK–VILLA CREEK AREA

ACCESS: The most popular routes into this area are the Salmon Creek and Cruikshank trails, located on Highway 1 about 112 km (70 mi) and 105 km (66 mi), respectively, south of Rio Road in Carmel (see map 5).

TOPOGRAPHY AND GEOLOGY

Salmon Creek, Villa Creek, and San Carpoforo Creek are the most southern of Big Sur's coastal drainages. South of these watersheds, the coastal ridge of the Santa Lucia Range swings sharply inland and the steep coastal cliffs give way to broad marine terraces around Point Piedras Blancas. The South Coast Ridge defines the eastern boundary of the watersheds. Each drainage is remarkably different from the others, in spite of their close proximity.

The ridges and mountain peaks are much more gentle here than farther north in the range, although the coastal slope is no less steep. The gentleness results from the fact that the land here is underlain by rocks of the Franciscan complex, which erode more easily than the rocks of the Salinian block in the northern mountains. The highest points in the area are Silver Peak (1094 m, or 3590 ft) and Lion Peak (1067 m, or 3499 ft). The ridgetops are remarkably uniform in height, suggesting that at one time they formed a low, rolling landscape that has since been uplifted. The steep lower slopes are an indication of the recent uplift of this old topography, and nowhere is this ancient erosional surface more apparent than here in the southern part of the Big Sur area.

This region has a simpler geology than most areas in northern Big Sur. The area is composed almost entirely of Franciscan sedimentary rocks, and the complex faulting characteristic of much of Big Sur is absent here. A single major fault, a portion of the Sur–Nacimiento fault, traverses the area trending southeast–northwest. The most outstanding geological feature is the abundance of *ultramafic rocks*—rocks rich in magnesium and iron—including numerous serpentine outcrops. There is more serpentine in this region than anywhere else in Big Sur. Soils derived from these rocks support an unusual flora, including a number of plants that grow only on serpentine.

Mining activity has been greater in this area than anywhere else in the range because of the presence of rare minerals such as chromium, silver, gold, and mercury. None of these mines is currently active, but at one time gold supported the boom town of Manchester in the Los Burros area. Nephrite jade is mined locally and collected along some beaches.

VEGETATION

This area is noticeably drier than the northern coastal Santa Lucias, and chaparral covers a larger area than any other plant community. The chaparral is comprised mostly of chamise in this part of the range. Cool riparian corridors of maples and alders wind through the dry, dense vegetation. The variety of conifers in the area is remarkable and includes Coulter pines, bull pines, Sargent cypress groves, extensive stands of Santa Lucia firs, Douglas firs, and redwoods.

Redwood trees reach their southern distributional limit just north of the Salmon Creek drainage, where Douglas firs are the dominant conifers. A number of plants associated with redwoods, such as redwood sorrel, also reach their southern limit here. Paradoxically, Villa Creek, only a few miles farther north, supports extensive groves of large redwoods.

Serpentine soils, which are found on the Franciscan Complex throughout California, are the dominant botanical attraction in this area. Although more than 1036 km² (400 m²) are covered with serpentine soils in the Santa Lucias, most of this is south of the Big Sur area. The largest areas of serpentine in Big Sur occur in the Salmon Creek–Villa Creek area and in lower Los Burros Creek on the east side of the mountains.

Serpentine soils have been of interest to botanists for a long time because they contain a very unusual mixture of minerals that many plants cannot tolerate. They are typically high in iron and magnesium and low in such crucial plant nutrients as calcium, potassium, phosphorus, and nitrate nitrogen, although the composition of serpentine varies widely. Serpentine soils are also shallow and become highly saturated with water in winter and extremely dry in summer because of their porosity, making them even more difficult for plants to tolerate.

A number of plants known as *serpentine endemics* have adapted to these harsh conditions and do not grow elsewhere. Other dry climate plants that can survive the unusual drought stress of the serpentine also occupy these soils. Serpentine vegetation usually includes fewer plant species than surrounding vegetation, however, and may be dramatically different. Serpentine barrens, where all but a few hardy serpentine endemics are excluded, represent the extreme situation. Both barrens and less obvious serpentine areas can be found in the Salmon Creek--Villa Creek area.

The most obvious serpentine endemic in this area is the Sargent cypress. Sargent cypresses are found on serpentine soils from Mendocino County in northern California to the San Rafael Mountains of Santa Barbara County. The species grows on serpentine soils that are damp and in some cases boggy, and for those groves that occupy drier sites, fog may be the crucial factor for survival. A number of northern California water-loving plants accompany the cypresses on wet sites in the Santa Lucias. Both the mineral content of the soil and the high moisture are probably important to the Sargent cypress.

According to botanist Clare Hardham, the groves in the Santa Lucias are generally found along the Pine Mountain fault, an area of numerous springs, and near the heads of permanent or semipermanent streams at about 760 m (2500 ft) elevation. In the Los Burros drainage, however, Sargent cypresses grow on sandstone nearly 1.6 km (1 mi) away from serpentine. Hardham speculates that ions leached from serpentine infiltrate the groundwater in this area, favoring serpentine endemics.

There are two groves of Sargent cypresses at the head of Villa Creek, just north and south of Lions Den Spring. The northern grove burned severely in the Gorda fire in 1985. As of this writing, the dead remains of 9-m- (30-ft-) tall cypresses stand over a lush understory of new growth that includes many cypress seedlings. The most northern grove of Sargent cypress in the Santa Lucias is on a small tributary of Alder Creek. The South Coast Ridge Road passes directly through this grove, which consists of dwarfed trees huddled in a low basin.

SALMON CREEK—VILLA CREEK AREA

The Salmon Creek—Villa Creek area is covered by a network of good trails. The most popular trail is the Salmon Creek Trail. The waterfalls on Salmon Creek, visible from Highway 1, are the most visited spot in the drainage. Other waterfalls 3 km (2 mi) up the creek are also well known. Salmon Creek is one of the most heavily used areas in Big Sur, second only to the Pine Ridge Trail into Sykes Camp. However, there are miles of trails in the area that are less visited and include a great deal of wild backcountry.

A long loop hike that passes through a variety of plant communities can be taken by following the Salmon Creek Trail up to the South Coast Ridge and the Cruikshank Trail back down the Villa Creek canyon to the coast. This is an interesting loop hike because it leads through two parallel drainages that are quite different in character. While Villa Creek is filled with redwoods and Santa Lucia firs, Salmon Creek lacks redwoods but harbors Douglas firs and Coulter and bull pines. Furthermore, the Villa Creek drainage was severely burned in the Gorda fire in 1985, while the Salmon Creek drainage has remained relatively unburned since the 1970 Buckeye fire. This makes for dramatic differences in vegetation and a good comparison of fire's effects on two parallel watersheds.

The Salmon Creek Trail follows Salmon Creek Canyon up on its north-facing slope, remaining 30–60 m (100–200 ft) above the creek most of its length from the highway to the South Coast Ridge Road. The trail begins in a shady grove of coast live oak and bay trees with a lush understory of thimbleberry, blackberry, and other shrubs. Chain ferns grow in moist seeps, and a small spring flows down the hillside.

The trail soon enters a clearing dominated by grasses and dry climate plants. The soil is crumbly and loose, and the nearby slopes and outcrops of gray-green serpentine rock are devoid of plant life. The plants in this clearing include succulents such as dudleyas and sedums, grasses,

Our Lord's candle, and a number of serpentine endemics. A promontory from the edge of the clearing affords excellent views of the ocean and the highway winding into Salmon Creek Canyon. Above the grassland is a true serpentine barren where almost no plants grow.

The trail switches back through the serpentine area and then turns up into the canyon and follows a gentle uphill grade. Outcrops of hard metamorphosed sandstone tower over the trail in places. A short distance up the canyon, a large grove of Douglas firs grows from the canyon bottom and up the north-facing slope. The Douglas firs are large, old-growth trees and grow amid tanoaks. This is one of the few extensive stands of Douglas firs in the Santa Lucias; other stands are in the Los Burros drainage, along Willow Creek, and in the Little Sur drainage about 80 km (50 mi) north of here.

The trail intersects with the Spruce Creek Trail 3 km (2 mi) from the trailhead and soon after descends to the confluence of Spruce and Salmon creeks, both of which are perennial streams. The trail leaves the creeks and continues to climb along the north-facing slope of the canyon, which becomes noticeably drier above this confluence. Bull pines and Coulter pines grow on the flat area where Estrella Creek meets Salmon Creek, and Estrella Camp sits beneath oaks near the confluence.

The canyon becomes broader and more open, and the whole upper basin is dominated by chamise chaparral. Oaks and bays grow in the ravines, along the canyon bottom, and on the north-facing slopes. Bull pines and Coulter pines are scattered throughout the chaparral, especially in ravines and at higher elevations near the ridgetops.

The chaparral is dense and homogeneous and shows little evidence of recent fire. It burned in the 1970 Buckeye fire, and charred pine trunks remain from this fire. Several elongate, barren areas of pale serpentine outcrops lie in the upper watershed. Western whiptail lizards are common on the open soils surrounding the serpentine areas. Bull pines often grow on the serpentine soils, accompanied by manzanita, toyon, California coffeeberry, and chamise.

After a 4-km (2.5-mi) climb, the trail reaches the South Coast Ridge Road just north of Lion Peak, 9.1 km (5.7 mi) from its start at Highway 1. Spectacular views spread out in every direction: west down Salmon Creek Canyon to the ocean, north to Cone Peak and Junipero Serra Park, east to the valleys and ridges of Ford Hunter–Liggett and the Central Valley beyond, and south to the Dutra Creek drainage, Mount Mars, and Point Piedras Blancas. The Sierra Nevadas may be visible on a clear day. The entire landscape above 760–900 m (2500–3000 ft) is dominated by chaparral, and the openness of the vegetation adds to the expansiveness of the view.

Lions Den Camp is a short distance north of the Salmon Creek Trail and Coast Ridge Road junction on a spur off the Coast Ridge Road. A stand of Sargent cypresses grows just south of the camp in serpentine soils that are almost white in color.

CRUIKSHANK TRAIL

The Cruikshank Trail goes from Lions Den down Villa Creek to the coast, initially following a bulldozer swath cut during the Gorda fire. The fire was apparently stopped by this fire line, as everything to the north of it is severely burned, while the landscape to the south remains unburned.

The Cruikshank Trail drops from the fire line down into the Villa Creek drainage and passes through a grove of burned Sargent cypresses. Numerous cypress seedlings dot the area, indicating that the cypress seeds were able to withstand the heat of the fire. These cypresses do not sprout from their roots or trunks as do redwoods. A number of fire-following plants were in flower here two years after the fire. These included golden ear drops (*Dicentra chrysantha*), whispering bells (*Emmenanthe penduliflora*), and short-lobed phacelia (*Phacelia brachyloba*).

Live oaks are resprouting and songbirds are in abundance in the burned area. This is in stark contrast to the dense chaparral in upper Salmon Creek, which is quiet and lacks the wildflowers and new growth of the burned area. Deer sign is also plentiful in the burned areas of Villa Creek drainage and almost totally lacking in Salmon Creek, confirming that the new growth attracts these browsing mammals.

The trail descends along the north-facing slope of Villa Creek Canyon. Santa Lucia firs appear in the canyon bottom where the trickle of Villa Creek begins a short distance below the cypress grove. This extensive stand continues down canyon for more than 1.6 km (1 mi). Most of the firs were killed in the Gorda fire since the habitat here is not ideal for them. It is neither steep nor rocky and affords little protection from fire, and the firs probably spread here in the long fire-free period that ensued when the U.S. Forest Service began controlling fires.

The trail continues its gradual descent, coming to Silver Camp in the shade of oaks near a small creek. Large, burned ponderosas stand in the grasslands nearby. The trail drops from Silver Camp, continuing down through a burned mixed hardwood forest to a junction with the Buckeye Trail, which leads southward to Buckeye Camp. Upper Cruikshank Camp is just below this junction on the edge of a clearing.

Uphill to the northeast of the camp is a large fenced clearing that was once the Cruikshank homestead. It occupies a midden site, probably a Salinan Indian campsite. Lower Cruikshank Camp is just below the upper camp, in the redwoods by a small creek. The Buckeye Trail to Alder Creek Camp branches off just upstream from this camp, while the Cruikshank Trail continues down canyon. A short distance from Cruikshank Camp, a few gum trees (*Eucalyptus* spp.) are growing in the forest and were probably planted by homesteaders. The redwoods throughout the canyon are resprouting profusely following the Gorda fire and form dense thickets. Near the campsite, they are impenetrable in places, but create a cool, shady atmosphere.

The trail continues down canyon from lower Cruikshank Camp, winding through redwoods and hardwoods and a postfire understory of vetch, hedge nettle, rye grass, and resprouting oaks. In about 2.4 km (1.5 mi), it breaks out to coastal scrub and swings onto the coastal slope. It heads southward at the canyon mouth and descends steeply down switchbacks to its Highway 1 trailhead. It is about 6.4 km (4 mi) back along the highway to the Salmon Creek trailhead from this trailhead.

BUCKEYE TRAIL

The Buckeye Trail begins on Highway 1 just north of the abandoned ranger station at Salmon Creek. It contours along the coastal slope of ridges between Salmon Creek to Villa Creek and on up into the Alder Creek drainage. Spectacular views down to the coastline are available along the way from Salmon Creek to Villa Creek, where the trail winds in and out of ravines and across grasslands.

The small patches of coastal scrub in this area are different from the scrub farther north in the mountains. This scrub seems to be more closely related to southern California's sage scrub, and plants such as black sage, deerweed, and redberry are much more common here. These southern plants are also found at high elevations farther north in the Santa Lucias, but are uncommon near the coast.

Water remains year-round in the first major ravine that the trail enters. Bull pines grow along the upper slopes, and redwoods are visible below the trail in some ravines. Everywhere on the Buckeye Trail evidence of the Gorda fire is plain, and many of the big pines are charred and dead. Buckeye Camp is on a flat area beside a tributary spring of Redwood Gulch about 4.8 km (3 mi) from the trailhead. True to the name, buckeye trees grow amid the sparse hardwoods on the grassy flat. The buckeyes have resprouted since the fire, like most of the coast live oaks around them. Planted gum trees shade the campsite, which occupies the corner of a huge midden. Ponderosa and Coulter pines grow on the flat and add to its parklike quality. A small spring at a trough provides water for the camp.

Beyond Buckeye Camp, the trail climbs out of Redwood Gulch onto the flank of the ridges again. A house comes into view far below toward Highway 1 just before the trail crosses a ridge and drops into the Villa Creek drainage. This is a good viewpoint up Villa Creek Canyon. Villa Creek is a broad, open drainage and looks very austere in the wake of the Gorda fire. The south-facing slope appears almost barren. Extensive stands of redwoods grow in the canyon bottom and up tributary ravines on the north-facing slope. The north-facing slope is also covered with dead and live ponderosa pines, live oaks, bay trees, and a lush growth of herbs that have sprung up since the fire. The south-facing slope is much more sparsely vegetated and is covered mostly with grassland. Very little scrub occurs on either slope.

The trail follows switchbacks down the north-facing slope and enters resprouting redwoods before coming to the Cruikshank Trail and Upper Cruikshank Camp. Beyond the campsite, the trail departs from the Cruikshank Trail, crosses Villa Creek, and follows it downstream a short distance before climbing up the south-facing slope toward Alder Creek. The trail on this exposed south-facing slope is very hot and dry until it enters some sparse shade in a stand of burned ponderosa pines and crosses into the Alder Creek drainage. Alder Creek Camp, at the terminus of the Buckeye Trail, is also accessible by car from South Coast Ridge Road.

SPRUCE CREEK TRAIL

The San Carpoforo Creek watershed is accessible via the Spruce Creek Trail, which departs from the Salmon Creek Trail 3 km (2 mi) from its trailhead at Highway 1. This trail climbs up along the northeast-facing slope of Spruce Creek, a perennial stream, through hardwoods and conifers. Douglas firs grow in the canyon bottom for a distance, but soon dwindle as the canyon becomes drier. In about 3 km (2 mi), the trail crosses a fenced saddle and enters the upper Dutra Creek watershed.

The vegetation here is much different than that in the Salmon Creek drainage. The upper south-facing slopes are dominated by grassland. Bull pines huddle with the hardwoods in the ravines and also grow on several flat benches that interrupt this slope of the drainage. The north-facing slopes of the Dutra Creek watershed are mantled with a forest of mixed hardwoods that includes occasional Coulter pines. The trail weaves in and out of the ravines on the south-facing slope. There are some very large black oaks on some of the flats traversed by the trail.

Little obvious evidence of fire can be seen in this drainage, and the most apparent disturbance here has been grazing. The slopes are terraced with cow trails, the grass is cropped short, and cowpies litter the landscape. At springs or stream crossings, the earth is a mire from hoof prints. Some of the ravines are deeply gutted down to bedrock, and the watercourses in the lower drainages show evidence of extreme fluctuations in water level, which is often a consequence of overgrazing.

Dutra Flat Camp is situated on one of the larger flats notched into the south-facing slope. Four planted Monterey cypresses shade the camp, which is fenced to keep cattle out and is surrounded by an extensive grassy clearing. A trough and a spring uphill are also fenced. At the southern end of the flat, several fruit trees grow, the only evidence that remains of the homestead that once occupied this flat. Large ponderosa pines are scattered around this and the other level areas on the slope. A trail sign near camp marks the junction with a trail to the Coast Ridge. This trail was widened into a fireline during the Gorda fire.

The main trail continues to descend, leaving the grassland slopes and entering mixed hardwood forest. Along the descent, an occupied ranch house, the Baldwin Ranch, comes into view to the southeast. Turkey Springs Camp is located a short distance down the trail near a small stream in the forest, about 1.1 km (0.7 mi) from Dutra Flat Camp. Shortly beyond the camp, the trail intersects the Baldwin Ranch Road. The Dutra and San Carpoforo creeks merge just down the canyon.

The lower parts of these watersheds are remarkably level and broad with many open grassland clearings surrounding the well-developed riparian corridor. The trail follows the road east and then branches off toward San Carpoforo Camp, crossing a broad, cobbled, intermittent streambed and San Carpoforo Creek. It then follows the shaded riparian vegetation of willows, maple, and alders down to the broad, shady flat occupied by San Carpoforo Camp. Nearby, the creek flows on a nearly level grade through slow pools, an unusual occurrence in the steep Santa Lucias.

It is possible to climb up to the Coast Ridge Road from a trail that branches off the Baldwin Ranch Road, although the trail is poorly maintained and cuts through the dense chaparral. The Baldwin Ranch Road leads westward back to Highway 1 but is not open to the public. This means that the trail to San Carpoforo is usually a one-way walk, and the easiest way out is back to Salmon Creek. However, the trail up from Dutra Flat Camp to the Coast Ridge Road makes an alternate return route possible.

Big Sur Area

California

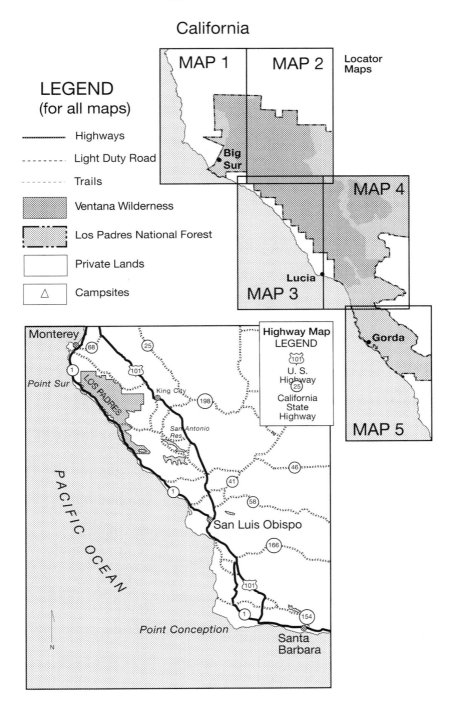

MAP 1

MAP 2

Locator Maps

Big Sur

MAP 4

Lucia

MAP 3

LEGEND
(for all maps)

Highways

Light Duty Road

Trails

Ventana Wilderness

Los Padres National Forest

Private Lands

△ Campsites

Gorda

MAP 5

Monterey

68

25

1

101

King City

198

Point Sur

LOS PADRES

San Antonio Res.

46

41

1

58

San Luis Obispo

166

PACIFIC OCEAN

101

1

154

Point Conception

Santa Barbara

N

Highway Map
LEGEND

101
U. S. Highway

25
California State Highway

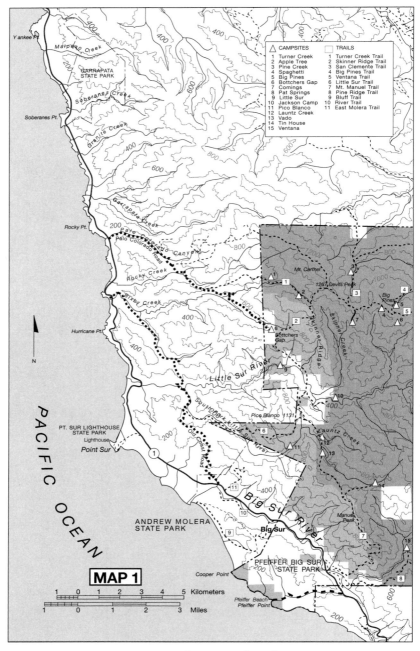

Map 1.   Northern coastal Big Sur area

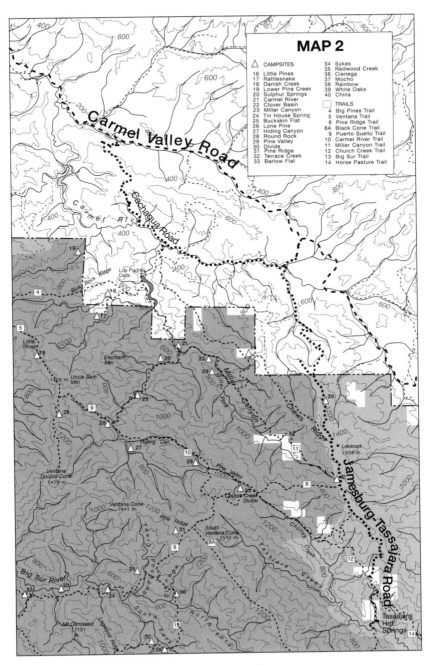

Map 2.   Northern inland Big Sur area

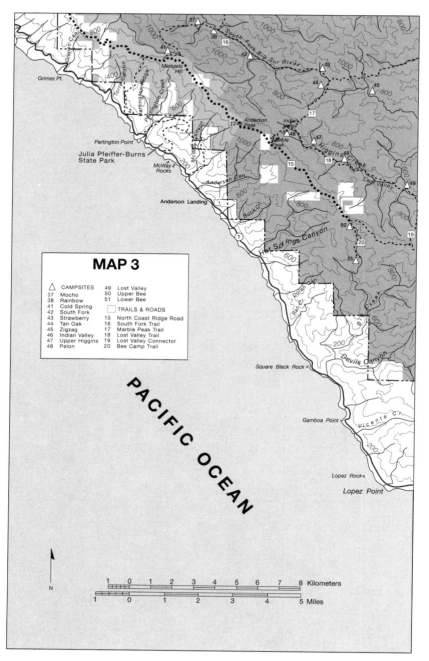

Map 3. Central coastal Big Sur area

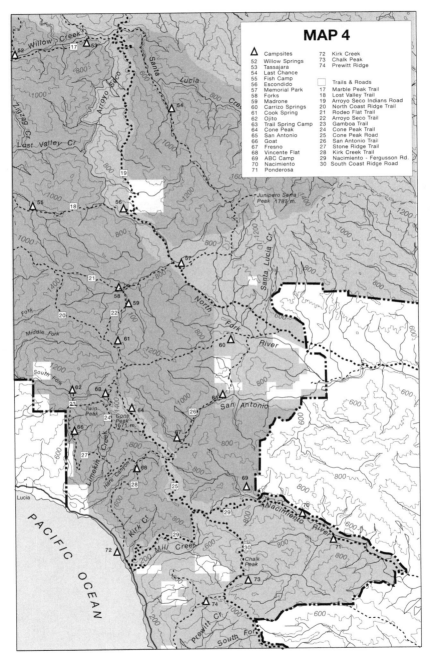

MAP 4

△	Campsites	72	Kirk Creek
	52 Willow Springs	73	Chalk Peak
	53 Tassajara	74	Prewitt Ridge
	54 Last Chance		
	55 Fish Camp		
	56 Escondido	☐	Trails & Roads
	57 Memorial Park	17	Marble Peak Trail
	58 Forks	18	Lost Valley Trail
	59 Madrone	19	Arroyo Seco Indians Road
	60 Carrizo Springs	20	North Coast Ridge Trail
	61 Cook Spring	21	Rodeo Flat Trail
	62 Ojito	22	Arroyo Seco Trail
	63 Trail Spring Camp	23	Gamboa Trail
	64 Cone Peak	24	Cone Peak Trail
	65 San Antonio	25	Cone Peak Road
	66 Goat	26	San Antonio Trail
	67 Fresno	27	Stone Ridge Trail
	68 Vincente Flat	28	Kirk Creek Trail
	69 ABC Camp	29	Nacimiento - Fergusson Rd.
	70 Nacimiento	30	South Coast Ridge Road
	71 Ponderosa		

Map 4.   Central inland Big Sur area

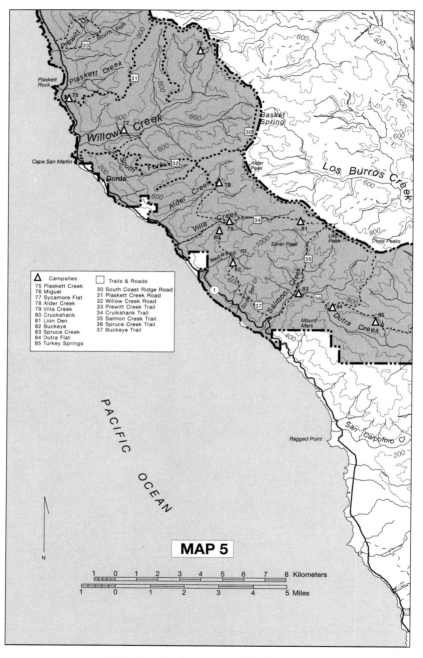

Map 5.   Southern coastal Big Sur area

Index

Designer: U.C. Press Staff
Compositor: G & S Typesetters, Inc.
Text: 10/13 Sabon
Display: Sabon
Printer: BookCrafters
Binder: BookCrafters